WITHDRAWN

A MESSAGE
TO THE CHARNWOOD READER
FROM THE PUBLISHER

Since the introduction of Ulverscroft Large Print Books, countless readers around the world have confirmed that the larger and clearer print has brought back the pleasure of reading to an ever-widening audience, thus enabling readers to once again enjoy the companionship of books which had previously been denied to them due to their inability to read normal small print.

It is obvious that to cater for this ever-widening audience of readers a new series was necessary. The Charnwood Series embraces the widest possible variety of literature from the traditional classics to the most recently published bestsellers, and includes many authors considered too contemporary both in subject and style to be suitable for the many elderly readers for whom the original Ulverscroft Large Print Books were designed.

The newly developed typeface of the Charnwood Series has been subjected to extensive and exhaustive tests amongst the international family of large print readers, and unanimously acclaimed and preferred as a smoother and easier read. Another benefit of this new typeface is that it allows the publication in one volume of longer novels which previously could only be published in two large print volumes: a constant source of frustration for readers when one volume is not available for one reason or another.

The Charnwood Series is designed to increase the titles available to those readers in this ever-widening audience who are unable to read and enjoy the range of popular titles at present only available in normal small print.

FOUR GENERATIONS

The fourth in the Gollantz saga. Emmanuel, the central character of this book, is no less lovable than his Grandfather, who bore the same name. Immediately after his marriage he is forced to take a place in a world he neither likes nor understands. The story tells of his attempt to find happiness, to make his own career, apart from the one offered to him as his father's son, and his final goal. It differs from the one he had planned, but it is one which will yield him a greater measure of contentment than he has previously known.

Books by Naomi Jacob
in the Charnwood Library Series:

THE FOUNDER OF THE HOUSE
THAT WILD LIE . . .
YOUNG EMMANUEL
FOUR GENERATIONS

NAOMI JACOB

—◆—

FOUR
GENERATIONS

Complete and Unabridged

CHARNWOOD
Leicester

MAY 28 1985

First published in 1934

First Charnwood Edition
published April 1985
by arrangement with
Judy Piatkus (Publishers) Ltd,
London

British Library CIP Data

Jacob, Naomi
    Four generations.—Large print ed.—
Charnwood library series
    I. Title
823'.912[F]   PR6019.A29

ISBN 0-7089-8255-7

Published by
F. A. Thorpe (Publishing) Ltd.
Anstey, Leicestershire
Set by Rowland Phototypesetting Ltd.
Bury St. Edmunds, Suffolk
Printed and bound in Great Britain by
T. J. Press (Padstow) Ltd., Padstow, Cornwall

To
LAURA
(Mrs. Walter Ashmore)
with my love
MICKIE

Book One

1

VIVA wasn't attending to the service. She never felt that weddings in fashionable churches were really services at all; they were necessary, and they gave one an opportunity of seeing one's friends en masse. In this case it enabled her to review the whole of her family and Emmanuel's as well.

She glanced at her husband, then her eyes travelled up to the altar where Julian stood, then to the broad back of Bill Gollantz, who was standing at the other end of the pew in front of her.

"You none of you ever look frightfully at home in an English church," she had once said to Bill after one of the Heriot weddings.

"Perhaps because we aren't," Bill said. "Perhaps the faith of our fathers is too strong for us. Angela says that when she married the Guv'nor, he gave a most ghastly exhibition of funk."

She had shrugged her shoulders. "That's rubbish, Bill, and you know it. None of you have ever been inside a synagogue in your lives. You all went to English schools and you all look absolutely English. That's a pose, that stressing 'Here have we no abiding city'."

The grin had faded from Bill's face as he

3

answered: "Is it? I wonder. I don't know. Somehow I believe that it crops up once in a way, and all the Heriots and Wilmots and the rest of 'em count for nothing. P'raps not so much in me, I'm all Heriot, but in Julian and—certainly—in Emmanuel."

She had felt a queer annoyance, almost a sense of distress, and had repeated that he talked nonsense, and that it was only a faint echo of the romanticism which had been so strong in old Emmanuel.

"You're all romantics at heart," she said, "and it's so damned out of date!"

Looking at Julian now, she had to admit that he looked modern enough and self-controlled and all the other things which she felt romantics ought not to look. He stood there, very slim, very straight, far too handsome, his face expressionless, the light catching his fair hair. The sight of him irritated Viva a little.

She thought: "He's far too good-looking, too successful, too—everything. It's only two—no, three years ago since he allowed Emmanuel to shoulder his nasty little sins and cut himself off from us all for a year! Now, it's all forgotten, and —apparently forgiven. He's making a success in the Party, he's marrying a frightfully rich wife— I don't wonder she's glad to change a name like Van der Hoyt—and I suppose one day he'll be Prime Minister! I believe that he is different from Emmanuel and Bill. He's a sort of intellec-

4

tual pirate, is Julian. He'll make anyone 'walk the plank'—and yet I like him. He's stimulating."

The organ began to play, and she realized that the service was over, and that Julian and his little American wife were turning away from the altar. Emmanuel leant down and said that he didn't think they wanted to go and join them in the vestry, and Viva shook her head. She certainly didn't want to. She remembered at her own wedding it had been rather fun, but she had played "lead" that day. She didn't want particularly to play second fiddle to Mrs. Julian Gollantz.

Emmanuel said: "I suppose we can sit down now, can we?"

"Why not? Tired, Emmanuel?"

"A little . . ." Then very quickly, "Not really, no, I'm not really tired. This place is so hot, isn't it?"

She looked at him as he sat at her side, and thought that he did look tired, his shoulders stooped a little, and once or twice he blinked his eyes as if they felt heavy.

"Max leaves too much to him," she thought. "Ever since he came back he's done nothing but work, work, work. It's all right for Max to say that he can trust Emmanuel with everything, and for Angela to tell everyone what a marvellous flair he has, but none of them think about me. I scarcely see him, and when I do he's too tired to talk. Taking them all round, they're a self-centred lot, the Gollantz family!"

Charming, all of them, but they "used" people. Angela had used that wretched old Bill Master for years just because she knew that he adored her. Max and she used Emmanuel and even Bill very often. Angela might laugh and say: "Darling Bill, he's like his godfather—dependable." They had a sort of tribal spirit, they gathered a crowd of people round them and never let them go. There were the Davises, old Meyer Bernstein, the Bermans, to say nothing of the whole collection of people who were distantly "family"—the Hirschs, Ludwig Bruch, and the Jaffes. All of them "relied on" to do this and that and the other. Angela had caught it from the Gollantz family when she married into it and it had become part of her, Viva thought. Julian always admitted that he used anyone who could be of the slightest use to him.

She let her thoughts run on, back to old Emmanuel.

"They've made him a sort of legend," she thought. "They've built up a whole series of stories and recollections about him. His manners, his methods, his dignity—everything about him. The huge picture that hangs in the dining-room at Ordingly pervades the whole house. It's not Max's house, it's only a home where the cult of old Emmanuel Gollantz is practised."

Bill moved down the pew and leant back whispering that they were coming, and the organ

6

blared out and everyone looked towards the door of the vestry.

Viva said: "The last bit of church atmosphere has gone. From now on it's only a social function. Nice little turned-up nose the bride has, hasn't she?"

Bill said stolidly: "I like her, she's a dear little girl."

Emmanuel said nothing. He was staring straight in front of him, and Viva wondered if he didn't want to meet Julian's eyes. They spoke when they met, Emmanuel was always perfectly friendly and courteous, but he never went out of his way to talk to his brother. Viva remembered that she had never seen them shake hands.

Julian was making a sort of royal progress down the aisle, he was turning this way and that, his smile varying, Viva thought, according to the importance of the person to whom he directed it. Emmanuel still stared straight before him, and, leaning a little sideways so that her arm touched his, Viva felt that his muscles had tightened. She watched Julian and saw him catch Bill's eye, and nod in a friendly elder-brother sort of fashion; then he saw Emmanuel, and for an instant his eyes widened. He moved a little from the direct path and drew nearer to his brother.

Scarcely checking his walk, he said: "Emmanuel . . ."

Viva watched, fascinated, wondering if Emmanuel was going to forget the Gollantz tradition so far as to make an even miniature scene. She nudged him, and he seemed to force his eyes to meet those of his brother.

Julian bent his smooth fair head towards his wife, and Viva caught the whispered words; she felt that Julian wished that she and everyone else should do so.

"Emmanuel—my best friend . . ." Then he raised his head, met Emmanuel's eyes, and put out his hand. It was all done so quickly that the procession never halted. It was characteristic of Julian to do things swiftly, neatly, without fumbling.

She felt, rather than noticed, the pause before Emmanuel put out his hand and took his brother's. The clasp lasted the merest fraction of a second, and possibly only Viva noticed that the pressure came from Julian; Emmanuel only gave his hand.

The bridesmaids passed, and Angela with Hervey Van der Hoyt, Max with Mrs. Van der Hoyt. They slipped out of their pew and made their way towards the door. Emmanuel never spoke, and she listened to Bill, who walked on her other side, talking all the time. As they stood waiting to get into the cars, Angela turned and smiled at them over her shoulder. Emmanuel made an almost imperceptible movement towards her, then drew back and said:

"Hello, darling. Nice you look!"

Bill's voice, younger and more gruff, said:

"She is always the best-dressed woman wherever she is."

Angela turned away and disappeared into a car with Van der Hoyt. Viva felt another moment of irritation. This was a demonstration of the Gollantz tradition. Angela must always be praised, treated as if she were the only good-looking woman in the world. Max did it, Bill had learnt to be quite good at it, and Emmanuel had done it ever since she could remember.

"This is ours," Bill said. "Come along."

Emmanuel's hand was under her elbow to help her in, and as she turned to him she smiled and said:

"Oh, Emmanuel, cheer up, my angel! It's a wedding, not a funeral. I shall begin to think that you were in love with the bride yourself!"

"No one would know so well as you," Emmanuel said, "what a foolish thought that would be. No, no, I'm all right."

Bill grumbled: "I hate this reception in Town; wish it could have been at Ordingly. After all, that's our own place. This beastly Town house that old Van der Hoyt's taken has nothing to do with us."

There it was again!—Us—Ordingly. Viva moved restlessly. The whole thing was getting on her nerves, and the reception would be terribly hot and boring, with high-pitched American voices as well as the soft lisping of the Gollantz Foreign Contingent.

In the entrance hall they met her mother. Lady Heriot had been a Gaiety girl in the days when the ladies of the chorus of that theatre invariably married into the peerage, or at least into the titled classes. She still talked as she had done when, as Miss Beatrice Grantley, she captured the heart of Walter Heriot, Fifth Baronet.

"My dear, what a crowd! Hello, Billee—Little Billee, eh? Manny darling, how are you? Going to look after your unfortunate mother-in-law? That's right. Take me round and let me meet all the tribes of Judah, some of them look too charming for words."

She walked away with Emmanuel, and Viva stood watching them for a moment, thinking how queer it was that Emmanuel, of all the three brothers, got on best with her mother.

"Let's go and congratulate old Julian," Bill said.

"None of you would ever congratulate Julian," Viva said. "You would only tell his wife what supreme good fortune is hers in marrying into the family."

Bill lifted his eyebrows, half whimsically. "Well, there might be something in that," he said. "Anyway, let's go and do it."

Julian seemed to possess the gift of talking to a dozen people at once, saying the right thing to each one, and apparently giving the person to whom he spoke his undivided attention. He came forward to meet them. Bill shook hands and said:

"Good luck, old man," then turned to speak to his sister-in-law. Viva could hear her rather metallic voice chattering away to him, and she waited for Julian to speak.

"Well," he said, "that's done!"

"I hope you'll both be very happy."

"That's kind of you, Viva. She's very charming."

She shrugged her shoulders. "More Gollantz patronage! I'm disliking you all very much today."

"But you always do dislike me!" he laughed.

"Haven't I every right to?"

"Oh—right! That implies that you feel it your duty to dislike me."

She said very quickly: "Believe me, it's a pleasure as well."

"You didn't always—feel like this."

"I didn't know you so well."

He said very softly: "Doesn't it ever strike you that perhaps you knew me much better? I wanted to marry you so much that I embarked on my career of unscrupulousness, and lost!"

"But felt your aptitude for it and won on your next venture—with Emmanuel."

For the first time she saw him flush, and for a moment he hesitated, turning quickly to shake hands with some tall man whom Viva didn't know, saying: "Thanks awfully—and I can't tell you how delighted we are with the goblets. Beautiful—thanks so much, Charlie." Then he turned back to her and said very quietly: "My dear, you're rapidly developing into that most objectionable of mortals—the female cad."

She held out her hand, smiling. "I had a good master, Julian. Good-bye, I must find Emmanuel."

She didn't search very long, for she caught sight of him in the distance talking to old Simeon Jaffe, who had come all the way from Vienna. She saw Jaffe, with his parchment skin and beautiful white hair, take Emmanuel's face in his hands and kiss him on each cheek. She thought: "I know that expression on the faces of the Foreign Contingent so well. Old Jaffe is telling him how like old Emmanuel he is. Oh, Lord, here's Walter!"

Her brother limped towards her, leaning on his stick more heavily than usual. His white, fat face always repulsed her. She had very little belief in the affection of families for each other, and never made any bones about disliking Walter cordially.

"W'arrer show!" he said. "God, how ever you came to marry into this mob beats me, Viva."

She said: "You'd better go home, Walter. This mob never understands that getting tight is a necessity to a gentleman."

"Tight!" he said. "I li' that. Have you seen our respected father? He's helpless." Walter chuckled.

Viva's mouth twisted as if she tasted something unpleasant.

12

"Oh, go away, Walter! I hate everyone today, particularly my own people. You may not like the mob, but they can behave decently."

It was pleasant to find Max and listen to his voice, watch his deft movements as he brought her champagne and minute sandwiches, and stood listening with grave attention when she talked, as if she was the only concern he had in the world.

"Max," she said, "I've been horrid to you all today, and I'm beginning to be rather ashamed of myself. I've been railing—inwardly—against the Gollantz tradition."

"Is there one?" Max said. "I didn't know."

"Haven't you one in your business?"

"Oh, that—yes. We had it handed down to us from my father."

"And you've evolved another for home consumption, haven't you?"

The smile reached his eyes—nice kind eyes, Viva thought. He looked younger, as if he had thrown off some of the weight which he usually carried.

"Have we? You know so much about us, my dear. Tell me."

"You all stick together so—you're so tribal. Look at them here today. They've come from Vienna, Berlin, Paris, even Madrid, to make a show! You all admire each other so strenuously. You all flatter Angela, you all praise Emmanuel,

13

talk of Bill's solid worth—it's just a little tedious for a mere Gentile, Max."

He said nothing, only continued to smile, as if he laughed at some secret piece of knowledge.

"You've even forgiven Julian," Viva said, and would have given a great deal to have unsaid the words after she had spoken them.

Max's smile died, and she thought that his eyes were reproachful.

"I'm sorry, Max, forgive me. I didn't mean to say that."

He laid his hand on hers. "But, my dear, you did mean to say it," he said. "You wanted to jolt me out of some of my smug self-satisfaction, didn't you? I understand. I know how boring we must be to you, and that's why I like you so much —you generally hide your boredom so well. We are tribal, but after all that's not to be wondered at. We were developed in that way, we were tribal from our inception as a nation. Everyone is, Viva, more or less. Even you have your cousins, second cousins, ramifications that even after all these years I cannot follow. Angela astonishes me when she says that young Rowsley, who is going to marry Trent's daughter, is a connection of hers. I never knew what that word meant until I married Angela. We don't have connections, we have relations. And this adulation of each other—it's honest enough. We don't flatter Angela, we only pay tribute to her. We're very grateful to her, my sons and myself. She and I are very proud of our

14

sons—" He stopped and then said again. "Very proud of our sons. They are successes, and"—he laughed—"they're ours. You see, we're really rather a simple race, in spite of all our accredited trickery and 'slimness'. We say what we feel about the things that matter. Old Jaffe kisses Emmanuel because he loves him as Emmanuel, because he respects him as a clever fellow, and because he sees in him something of the first Emmanuel whom he loved."

Viva sipped her champagne and nodded.

Max went on: "As for forgiving—"

She said quickly: "No, Max, never mind—leave that!"

"No, no," he said, "I want to explain. You knew all that there was to know, we're still grateful to you for making us bring Emmanuel home, and you have a right to know. Julian is our son, and we love him. You can't, you don't, stop loving people for what they do. You hate them possibly for that one individual thing—but the love remains. Then we are very proud, and it would be terrible for us to let the world know that once—once—we had something occur which lowered that pride. So we forgive Julian, we have taken him back, and I don't think that he will ever betray us again."

"And Emmanuel paid!" she said softly.

"Emmanuel paid," Max said. "If he paid Julian's debt—as it were—didn't he wipe out what Julian had incurred? If we demand payment again, don't we perhaps dim a little the brightness of Emmanuel's sacrifice?"

"It sounds a little like sophistry to me, Max."

"And perhaps it is, just a little," he admitted, "but Angela loves her sons and her family, and so do I, and by loving Julian, yes, in spite of everything, we don't love Emmanuel less. You may discover some day, Viva, though I hope that you never will, that it's very hard to harbour anger against your own flesh and blood. You see, women like Angela don't only see their sons as what they are, they see them as they once were, and they can never quite dissociate the little boy from the man. Emmanuel feels no resentment towards us for—taking Julian back."

She rose, put down her glass, and, taking a little mirror from her bag, examined her face in it attentively.

"I wonder sometimes if Emmanuel feels anything these days," she said. "Good-bye, Max. Thank you for talking to me, you've charmed away some of my bad temper."

"What did you mean about Emmanuel?" Max asked.

"Nothing—I don't know why I said it."

She moved away, and stayed talking first to one person, then to another. Once her mother met her and said:

"My angel, those Austrian Jews are too delicious. Such pets. Did you see Wally? Dreadful boy he is! I hope that he's gone home.

16

And your father! Told the most frightful story to old Hirsch—that old fellow with the dyed beard. Thank the Lord, he didn't understand it. You look a bit stuffy, Vi. Tired?"

"I don't think so."

"You rush about too damn much. You ought to settle down and have a couple of babies. Do you all the good in the world."

"A couple of confinements as a tonic don't appeal to me, darling."

Lady Heriot considered the reply, then said: "Oh, I dunno. Lots of worse things, and men like their wives to have babies. I've always heard that Jews are frightfully keen on families, it's a Sheenie trait."

"Your knowledge of the family lore of the Jews, mother dear, is marvellous. I'll speak to Emmanuel about it."

Her mother retorted: "Don't be so coarse, Vi. He looks as if he could do with something to cheer him up. He's been kissed by all the old tribal chiefs, and that little French fellow de Lara, and it's put him off his stroke by the look of him."

Emmanuel was standing near Bill Masters, who, leaning on his stick, was talking to the bride's father. Emmanuel scarcely listened to what they said, his mind was going back to his own wedding nearly two years ago. His mother had said then: "It's the beginning of things, do believe that," and he had thought that she was

17

right. Only lately it had been different. Viva was wonderful. It wasn't Viva's fault, she hadn't changed. Only it was as if all his old dreams asserted themselves and insisted that he should remember them.

Nothing very definite at first, only snatches of memories. A garden very hot under the sun; someone playing, Gilly saying, "It's called a canna, they grow in India"; and someone else saying, "They grow here, too, Gilly." Then that same voice, "What shall I sing, Saul?"

It was the recurrence of that voice which made him work so hard, which made him insist that his father left more and more of the work of the firm to him. It drove him early to the office, it sent him flying to obscure salerooms where the sound of the auctioneer's hammer only beat it out more plainly for him. Viva said that he was getting moody, stuffy, that he never wanted to go out, that he had lost his love of the theatre, of music. . . . Oh, it wasn't Viva's fault. From today he'd be different. He wouldn't hear those voices, remember that hot sun, those suffocating Saturdays in Milan, when he had looked forward to twelve o'clock, knowing that it meant the car, the road to Como, and Juliet.

He loved Viva. Once again he said to himself that she was wonderful. It was his own fault, he was working too hard, trying to do too much. Antiques, pictures, old wood-carving, china, designs for furniture, materials for upholstery—

a hundred things! Too much. He'd leave some of it to other people in future. He'd go out more with Viva, he'd dance, hear music—no, perhaps not hear very much music—see plays. . . .

Van der Hoyt's slightly nasal voice cut across his thoughts.

"I hev always maintained that we hev a far more adequate sense of appreciation over home, Mr. Masters, and here is the proof of it. There is not a man in the Philadelphia Orchestra who does not receive remuneration which is in every way commensurate with his ability as an artist. In other words—we are ready to pay."

Bill Masters scratched his chin and said: "Ye-e-es, I see that."

"Now," Van der Hoyt continued, "I heppen to know something about singers. I mean that I know many of the world's greatest artists in-tim-ately. That is, my wife and I keep open house in Noo Yark. When Juliet Forbes was over with us —you know her, Mr. Masters?"

"Very well indeed."

Emmanuel said: "Forgive me, sir, but would you excuse me? My wife is signalling to me that she wants to be off."

Van der Hoyt said: "Why, yes, sure. If she was my wife I know that I'd not keep her waiting ten seconds! Hope we'll see you again before we leave."

"Perhaps you'd dine with my wife and me one evening?"

19

"I'd like it."

"I'll ask my wife to arrange it. Good-bye, sir. Good-bye, Bill."

They watched his tall figure move over to where Viva stood, then Van der Hoyt said: "Funny stiff way these Englishmen hev of always talking about—my wife, my wife, my wife, eh?"

Bill said: "Have they? I never noticed it."

The American laughed. "Almost as if they didn't wanter forget it. Well, to get back to my story about Miss Juliet Forbes . . ."

2

VIVA said: "Hello, darling. When are those two people going to start on their honeymoon? I'm bored and want to get home. We've got to change and be back at the Carlton by half past eight. It's going to be the most unholy rush."

"They've gone to change now," he said, and, watching Viva's face, told himself again how pretty she was, and how vital, and what a lucky fellow he was to be married to her. They moved about, meeting sallow-faced members of the Gollantz family, and rubicund-faced members of the Heriot, the Harris, and the Wilmot families, each expressing their approval of Julian's marriage in their own terms and their own phraseology. For the gathering was composed not only of the Jews—English, French, German and Austrian—who belonged to old Emmanuel Gollantz' family, but of the English who were the relations of Angela Drew who had married old Emmanuel's son, Max. The friends and relatives of the American bride were only a very small percentage of the people who thronged to Hervey Van der Hoyt's rented house in Berkeley Square.

Once when Viva stopped to speak to one of the

family up from Gloucestershire, little Louis Lara touched Emmanuel's arm.

"I go back to Paris tonight," he said. "I have scarcely seen you. I want to talk to you very much."

Emmanuel, with the queer sense of being pulled back into the past, said: "I'd like to talk to you, Louis." Then, still living in that time nearly three years ago, he added: "Your clothes are beautiful, Louis."

Louis preened himself and smiled. "They are very good taste, I think. I have looked all day but have not seen another cravat like mine. Have you?"

Emmanuel said: "No, and I don't suppose I ever shall. Try calling it a tie, not a cravat; and I don't care for the watch-chain."

"No? Olympia gave it to me after her first night at the Odeon. It is platinum and pearls."

"I don't doubt it, but we don't wear 'em any more."

Louis frowned. "But it is typically English. The late Prince Albert always wore one."

"I know, but he's been dead some years now. Fashions change."

Then Viva turned round and said: "Oh, Mr. Lara! How nice! Come home with us and have some tea before we come back for dinner."

There was a sudden stir, and Julian came back, and then the bride, ready to go off to the station. Everyone crowded round, and Bill entered, rather hot and dusty, having wrestled with a white satin shoe and yards of string at the back of the car.

They gathered on the top of the steps, and Julian's best man, a rising Member of Parliament, did his best to get them into the car quickly and failed, because Julian had to stand with Angela and whisper something to her which made her laugh immoderately, and Emmanuel heard the Press cameras snapping, and cursed himself for a jealous, small-minded fool. "Mr. Julian Gollantz shares a last joke with his mother." What did it matter, anyway? Who cared?

Driving back in the car, Viva talked French very fast and very incorrectly with Louis, and Emmanuel sat back and wished that his head didn't ache so damnably, and that he didn't keep hearing a nasal voice saying, "When Juliet Forbes was with us," over and over again.

Louis adored the house, praised it immoderately, and it seemed hours before they got into the drawing-room and Viva poured out tea. She drank a scalding cup very quickly, jumped up and said: "I must go to repair the ravages for tonight."

"Ravages!" Louis exclaimed with at least twenty "r's" in the word. "I see none! You look like something that is very fresh—per'aps new-mown hay, what?"

"Stay and talk to Emmanuel," she said, "and don't tell English women that they look—fresh!"

Left alone, the little Frenchman changed. He

became older and more human. He looked at Emmanuel gravely, then said:

"And now, my more than cousin, tell me, how is everything with you? I tell you that I myself do not find it all beer and jam. It is not possible to find life a bed without thorns when one is the lover of Olympia! She is too beautiful, too great-hearted! But there are compensations, and so life goes on. Tell me, with you it is one long dream of beautifulness, no?"

Emmanuel poured out a second cup of tea. His head still ached and he hoped it might do it good.

"Life is very good," he said firmly. "It is very full; I have a great deal of work, and—as you see —I have a very charming wife."

Louis nodded. "I know, it must be all wonderful. Then why do you look so many years older, my dear?"

"I don't; it's only that you always remain so very young. You make other people looked damned old, that's all!"

His cousin sighed, and taking out an elaborate cigarette-case, on which his initials blazed in rubies and diamonds, he extracted a cigarette and lit it with care.

"I hev found," he said, "that when one speaks openly, when one ventures to mention the affairs of the heart, Englishmen think one a cad. But because I love you, my brave cousin, because when life was ended for me you offered me

24

sympathy and kindness, I will dare very much. You are not, I believe, very happy."

"I think that I have everything to make me happy."

Louis nodded. "Perhaps. But does it"—he paused—"do the trick? I don't know. I only know that one day you left us, Guido and me, very happy, and we knew why. The next thing we know is that you have been torn from us, and we are left alone. But—the rest is darkness, and perhaps in my so warm heart for you is still a little pain because you hev not spoken freely to me."

Emmanuel rose and walked to the window, standing for a moment staring out into Gloucester Place. He was very fond of this queer, over-dressed little Frenchman who had helped him in the days when he found himself wandering about Paris, unable to decide where to go and what to do. Together they had worked in Milan, and when Juliet had come into his life, Louis had been kind and sympathetic. Emmanuel remembered the day when Louis had said that Guido had compared Juliet to Juno, and how annoyed he had been. Then he had returned to England, and here was Louis wondering a little what had happened, and he—Emmanuel—wondering how on earth he could tell him, without inflicting unbearable pain on himself. He turned and walked back to where Louis sat and began to speak in his most matter-of-fact voice.

"It's rather difficult, Louis," he said, "but what happened was briefly this. When I was in Milan I became engaged—"

"I know that part," Louis said. "She was beautiful, a Juno, Guido said!"

"We were going to be married, and she decided that she wouldn't have me. I came back to England, met my wife, and—well, you know the rest."

"That is very well said, like English gentlemen in plays," his cousin said. "I saw her—the lady you were engaged to—in Paris."

Emmanuel sat down in the low chair near the table and began to fumble with the sugar-tongs, saying nothing, but with his face suddenly rather white and drawn. Louis's lisping voice continued: "We went together, Olympia and I. When it was over, she asked me, did I know her? I said that I had neither the honour nor the pleasure. 'If you did,' Olympia said, 'I would forgive you if you left me, for she is a rare bird.' I replied—"

The silver tongs clattered down and the hand which had held them clenched suddenly. Emmanuel, speaking in a voice which held no expression except violence, said: "Louis, for God's sake, don't! I can't bear it! I don't want to hear. I'm happy, d'you hear? Happy. Viva is adorable, she's all I want. I don't want even to remember that time—it's over, over, over. I went away because there was a ghastly mistake. Letters were planted on to me that I never wrote. Then

26

one mistake followed another, and—that—my engagement was one of them. Anyway, she threw me over! It's done, finished."

Louis picked up the tongs and replaced them, saying as he did so: "Dear Emmanuel, I am so sorry. I am taking off my hat to you always. Your wife is delicious. One day you will be a baronet, and very, very rich. If indeed you hev all that you want, I am very glad; but no mistake is so bad that it cannot be restored—I mean repaired. The people who love you most will understand you best. I, Louis Lara, understand you very well. Good-bye, my dear: I must go and get ready for the festivities."

Emmanuel looked up and nodded. "See you tonight. Don't talk, there's a good chap, Louis. Sorry I got rattled."

"I talk to you," Louis said, "never of you —except to offer tributes. Good-bye."

Emmanuel sat for a time, his chin propped on his hands, staring into space, thinking, thinking, thinking. He glanced round the room, thought how successful the scheme of decoration had been. The whole house was charming. His knowledge and Viva's taste had produced something very satisfactory. What a fool he had been to allow things which were over and done with to tear him to pieces! He repeated the phrase again, very softly, "Over and done with." He had gone away three years ago because he wanted to safeguard Julian from a scandal, not for his own sake,

27

but because he knew what such a scandal would mean to Angela. Even then, as he remembered it, his fine mouth twisted a little. Angela had always loved Julian best of them all. He had met Louis in Paris; together they had opened an antique-shop in Milan. What a one-horse affair it had been compared with Gollantz and Son! A little place in a back street where he had worked with Louis and later with Guido, who looked like an Italian cherub. He had been desperately lonely, and Juliet had come in to buy brocade. They had fallen in love—his thoughts halted for a second. Had she loved him? She had promised to marry him, they had been very happy, he had loved her. Then Max had found out that the letters were not Emmanuel's but Julian's, and Angela had come to take him home again.

Even now the recollection of that last morning made his face twist with pain. She had said, "It's over, Emmanuel," and had told him that she couldn't marry him. He remembered how he had begged, how he had tried to bargain, begged her to take him as her lover if she didn't want to marry him. He had implored, entreated, had poured out his heart to her, and she had remained firm. "No. Emmanuel, no."

England and Ordingly. Angela being wonderful, trying to heal all the scars; Max very kind, begging his pardon: Bill—who had never known the full facts of the letters, and who never should, please God—glad to have him home, inclined to make a hero of him. And Viva very clear-cut, just a little hard, but oh, so good to talk to again. Viva with her funny modern trick of swearing, and meaning nothing by it, with her slang, and her clear brain. He had loved her before—had loved her until Juliet had come and he had forgotten everything in his worship of her —and he loved her again. They had been married nearly two years. Good years, fun, laughter, splendid times; and now, lately, old things had begun to tug at his heart and hurt again. The old longing, the old sense of loss, had swept over him and ruined everything.

"Old unhappy things"—he pressed his finger-tips against his eyes as if to blot out something which he saw. Old things . . . He laughed suddenly.

"I deal too much in old things," he said, "my mind turns too often to them. I won't deal in them out of work hours. I'll have what's new and fresh and young. Let Como be as blue as it may, let the sun blaze down on that marble faun I found and put in the garden to surprise her, let her be a great singer, a beautiful woman, it's nothing to do with me. My life there ended. I'm making my own life here! I can't, I won't live in dreams, I'll make a grand reality."

He opened the big tortoiseshell box, took out a cigarette and realized that his hands were shaking. Impatiently he lit the cigarette and threw the match away, then, turning, walked from the room and ran upstairs.

The door between his room and Viva's was open, and he could see her, seated at the dressing-table, polishing her nails with a huge buffer.

"Can I come in?"

She looked up, said, "Oh, it's you! Yes, you've got plenty of time. Where's the little Frenchman?"

"Gone to prepare for the festivities. You didn't expect me to bring him up, did you?"

"Little oddity. Is he really Olympia's lover? Seems impossible."

"I believe so. He's a bit of a Don Juan in his way."

"A bit," Viva said, "pretty small bit!" She picked up some small steel instrument and concentrated on her first fingernail, then said: "You were mother's little ray of sunshine this afternoon, weren't you?"

Emmanuel dabbed his cigarette out in one of her ridiculous little ash-trays before he answered.

"I came up to tell you about that," he said slowly. "I'm sorry. I've been a bit gloomy lately, Viva. I'm sorry."

"Gloomy, darling." she said, "that's putting it mildly."

"I know," he agreed. "I think I might let up on the work for a little. We'll go out more, see more people, do a lot of shows."

She laid down the buffer and twisted round in

her seat so that she faced him. Her vivid face
with its slightly impertinent nose and bright eyes
was very serious. She looked at Emmanuel, tall,
and grave, with his dark hair that would one
day be the same pure, dead white that old
Emmanuel's had been. She met his dark, almost
melancholy eyes, saw his well-cut sensitive
mouth, with its trace of fullness about the lower
lip. She noticed his whole air of distinction—
rather elaborate distinction, with little signs of
what ought to have been affectation, and yet in
Emmanuel never seemed to be—and thought
what a good-looking man he was, and how much
she liked him.

"That will be nice," she said, then added
abruptly: "I like being with you better than
anyone. Still love me, Emmanuel?"

"Yes, you know that I do. You don't need to
ask."

She sighed contentedly and resumed her work
with the nail buffer.

"My mother thinks that we ought to start a
family," she said, her eyes still on her work. "She
says that it's a Jewish trait to want children. She
advises a couple—quickly."

Without turning towards him, she glanced in
the looking-glass and caught sight of his reflection, saw that his pale face flushed suddenly.

"Oh," he said, "did she?"

"Do you want children, Emmanuel?"

"I—I don't know," he stammered a little; "I haven't thought about it. Do you, Vi?"

"Me? I should hate having them! I might like them when they were here. I'm not terribly keen, I only felt it my duty to—offer!"

He said gravely: "I should loathe you to do anything from a sense of duty."

She turned and made a face at him. "Angel, don't get all serious and sanctimonious about it. I'd hate the title to go to Julian and his brats! If there was only Bill, I wouldn't bother. Well, we'll leave it at that, shall we? Only if mother begins to talk to you about the joys of family life, don't let her own—I mean father and Walter—put you off. There, cut along, my sweet, and get dressed. I'm streets ahead of you!"

He came a little nearer, slipped his hand under her chin and turned her face up to his. Looking down, he smiled at her and watched her mouth curve into an answering smile.

"Kiss me!" she ordered.

"I was just going to."

"Kiss me and promise to be good in future and not gloom!"

"I promise."

That night Emmanuel made a supreme effort to be gay. He danced and tried to forget how tired he was, he accepted invitations to go here, there, and everywhere with Viva, and made himself charming to both the Foreign Contingent and the Americans.

32

Gradually he began to feel that he had awakened from a dream, that in truth he had been allowing something which was past and over to terrify him. Life was a good business, he had everything a man could wish for, and at twenty-nine already held a position which made him financially sound. His work interested him, he was known to be one of the rising men in his special line, and already the old dealers, Marcus Arbuthnot, Jacob Lane, and Augustus Morris, declared that his methods, his knowledge and his determination were legacies from his grandfather, old Emmanuel.

Once, dancing with Viva, he asked, "Happy, darling?"

"Frightfully! You?"

"Astonishingly—no, not astonishingly. Naturally! I'm married to you."

She laughed softly. "I adore you when you put three 'r's' where Englishmen put one! Will you rob and murder your great grand-aunt Carolina Jaffe and give me her pearls?"

"Poof!" he said. "They'd take years to get the colour right. Wait until next year, I'll give you better ones."

Later, when he stood talking to his mother, he kept repeating silently that everything was all right. It had been good to talk to Louis—Louis, who was looking magnificent and slightly reminiscent of the Rue de la Paix; it had laid the ghosts, it had established him again.

33

Angela said: "You're looking better, Emmanuel. Nice evening?"

"Lovely, darling. You and Max have excelled yourselves."

She said: "I wonder if you could tear yourself away and take me down for something to eat—sandwiches or something?"

"My dear, I'll cut any young thing's dance to do that!"

Angela sipped soda-water and pretended to nibble a diminutive sandwich. Emmanuel thought, "She didn't want to eat or drink. She wanted to talk to me alone. I wonder what it is?"

He smiled at her. "Now," he said, "finish acting, and tell me what it's all about. I'm curious."

She drummed with her fingers on the table for a moment, then said, "It's about you, Emmanuel."

"What have I done? Offended one of the Hirsch clan?"

"No, darling, you're always charming to them —and why not? It's—it's about a letter I've had, from"—she broke off and her eyes, distressed and worried, met his—"from Juliet."

A voice that did not seem to belong to Emmanuel Gollantz said, "Yes?"

"It's a very nice letter," his mother went on. "I don't think she could write a letter that wasn't nice—"

Emmanuel said sharply: "We'll take that as read, shall we? What's it about. Tell me."

34

"She's coming to London. She wouldn't come last year, and now she says that it's impossible to avoid doing so—or practically impossible. She's singing twice at the Albert Hall, once at the Queen's and once for the Claytons in Belgrave Square."

"When? What are the dates?"

She fumbled in her bag and produced a card on which four dates were scrawled in pencil, and handed it to him, saying: "The tenth, the twelfth, the fourteenth, and the fifteenth."

"Next month?"

"Yes."

"Did she mention me?"

"She wanted you to know in plenty of time, in case you didn't want to meet her by accident. You know how one runs into people."

Emmanuel held the card in his long, sensitive fingers, then tore it carefully into very small pieces, dropping them into the glass which had held his champagne.

"Then she doesn't want to meet me?" he said. "She needn't worry. She wants to see me no less than I want to see her, believe me. If you write, say that I shall be in Paris on those days—with Viva. We're going for a holiday." Then, changing his tone: "Shall we go back, dearest? Viva'll wonder where I've got to."

35

3

"LIKE to go to Paris with me?" Emmanuel said. "I thought of going over on the eighth."

Viva looked up from the letters which she was opening, strewing the envelopes all over the bed, to where he stood at the foot of it. Viva never ate breakfast; she drank a tumblerful of orange juice. Emmanuel broke his dry toast and drank his coffee alone in the ultra-modern dining-room that his taste and Viva's had only just saved from banality. He had come up to say good morning to her, and found her immersed in her letters. Emmanuel always wondered why so many people wrote to Viva. She never seemed to write letters herself, seldom sent telegrams, and never answered the telephone if she could avoid doing so.

"I don't want to go to Paris," she said, "if it means trailing curious people who have a table to sell round with us."

"It doesn't. I'm going for a holiday."

"In November! It's going to be damned cold, angel."

"I'll buy you a new fur coat."

"I'd rather have jade, if it's all the same to you."

36

"Jade," he repeated reflectively. "I believe that old—"

Viva stopped him. "Emmanuel, don't! Don't tell me that old Something-or-Other has a lovely string that belonged to the Dowager What's-her-name, because I can't bear it. I want modern jade, not some that Noah gave his wife when they sailed. I hate old things."

"You shall have the most modern and horrible jade Paris can produce. Now—are you coming with me?"

"On the eighth? Yes—oh, wait, we've got the Claytons' party on the fifteenth. We shall have to be back for it."

With an air of slightly overdone unconcern, Emmanuel said: "I don't want particularly to go. Their parties are pretty dull."

"Frightfully exclusive. I've had to imperil my immortal soul to get asked to this one. It's taken me months of civility to old Mother Clayton. I had to talk about Bach for half an hour. I never know a thing about Bach except that he wrote a thing called a Toccata and a fugue on his own name, called G-sharp H"

Emmanuel laughed. "Why go, then? You don't like music much."

"Idiot, everyone likes music. Especially if it's expensive. It's like caviare and truffles and things. If you don't like them, it argues that you can't afford them, and they're just sour grapes. Well, if we're back, we'll go, and if we aren't back we'll

37

send a frightfully costly telegram, beginning, 'Dear Mrs. Clayton', to say that you've found a Rubens in a back street and have been laid out with shock. All right, Emmanuel, the eighth. Lovely."

He walked to Bond Street, congratulating himself that it was arranged, and that when Juliet Forbes arrived in London he would be on his way to Paris with Viva. He'd been a fool to get worried over it. "What's Hecuba to me?" It was over and done with, and he was having a devil of a good time. Viva and he were going everywhere. He was dancing a lot, and jolly good exercise it was too. Only in the mornings he felt fagged. Three and four in the morning, and the office at ten, didn't give one a lot of time for sleep. Not that he did sleep awfully well. After dancing a lot, he found that the tunes went on and on in his head. Such damned silly tunes too, as silly as most of the songs one listened to. People said, "How divine! It's the most wonderful tune!" and all the time it was just a stupid reiteration of a phrase from some half-forgotten negro melody. He never heard any music now—and quickly he added, mentally, that he didn't want to. It was too drugging, a dangerous narcotic. Music and scents were terrible things for dragging you back. Violets always took him automatically to Ordingly in the spring, brown Windsor soap to the change room at school, a bean-field to the road which led to Juliet's villa at Como. . . .

He blinked his eyes, as if to close the shutter of his mental camera and make it impossible for more pictures to be made. He didn't want to remember the villa or anything to do with it. Italy was an over-rated country anyhow. Colour, sunshine, and people thought that made up for the dust and the heat. He'd never go back there, never!

Hannah Rosenfelt came into his office with his letters. Max never arrived until late, and Emmanuel only reserved special and highly important letters for him.

"Anything important?" Emmanuel asked.

"I don't think so. The usual half-dozen people enclosing amateur photographs of bits of furniture and asking what you would be prepared to offer for them. It's only a way of getting a cheap valuation. Do you remember how at first you used to spend hours trying to find out what they were worth? Now I just send back a form saying that it looks very interesting, but that we are overstocked in that particular line."

"Horrible expressions!" Emmanuel said. "Nothing else?"

"The catalogue of the Earl of Howark's pictures and furniture on the fourteenth," she said. "There's some wonderful stuff, Mr. Emmanuel. I suppose Sir Max will go. Arbuthnot's manager told me that they're after the Reynolds for Glassons of New York."

Emmanuel smiled. "I think they'll find that

Gollantz' are after it for England," he said. "My father's determined to have it."

She flicked over the pages with her well-kept, square-tipped fingers. Emmanuel liked Hannah Rosenfelt. She had been first employed by his grandfather, when she left school. She had kept the stamp book, then had been raised to a clerk's status, and now for some years had been secretary to his father and himself. She was a handsome woman in a very pronounced Semitic style, growing a little heavy as she grew older, but her vitality was as unimpaired, and her keenness in her work and the interests of the firm were as great as ever.

Emmanuel watched her in silence, his eyes heavy for want of sleep. She stopped turning over the thick, beautifully printed pages and looked at him.

"You're doing too much," she said. "You're tired out."

"Only a headache. Got an aspirin, Hannah?"

She nodded. "I'll get one—two. I should think you could take two? I'll send out for a cup of strong coffee."

"No, no. I don't want coffee."

But she had gone, and he sat idly turning over the letters, reading them mechanically, making pencil notes at the bottom of each. It all seemed deadly uninteresting, and not even a packet of sketches which had come up from the Camden Hill studios held any real interest for him. Letters from Beaumont, who was travelling in Spain and had discovered, so he said, marvels of old brocade. "Too lovely," he wrote, "like sunsets, spilt wine, and half-dead roses." Emmanuel grinned. Beaumont always wrote in that style. How Max hated it! He scrawled on the bottom, "Say that his prices are all right, but that his language is too expensive." Craddock wrote from somewhere in Albania that he could buy in small quantities some special wood which he had never seen before. "Appears to be excellent. Suggest whole quantity. Admirable for inlay. Polish high. Consider worth money asked. Wire reply." Craddock always wrote letters in telegraphese, and telegrams like three-volume novels.

It struck Emmanuel as he sat there, with the letter from Albania before him, what a lot of them there were in the firm. Old Emmanuel had come from Vienna bringing with him all the stock he possessed. He had started with one house on Camden Hill. His grandson doubted if he even employed a single man regularly in those days. Now, after sixty years, Gollantz and Sons employed an army of men. Carpenters, designers, painters, men who knew how to restore and restore beautifully, upholsterers, polishers, and packers. Experts in wood like Craddock, experts in materials like Beaumont, accountants like Davis, book-keepers, clerks, commissionaires, office boys, cleaners, to say nothing of the minor specialists like Brown, who could find door-handles and keyhole mounts in old rubbish shops, and knew at a glance their age and worth. And over them all, the greatest specialist of them all, Max Gollantz himself. Max, who carried on the tradition of the house and had never descended to any business which was not honest and above-board. If Max said, "Genuine", that was sufficient, but where the slightest doubt existed, Max set his face against either insinuation or doubtful dealing.

"Don't you neffer advertise, Mex?" old Jacob Lane asked.

"Every day of my life," Max said. "Every time we sell anything."

Arbuthnot, who always talked like an Englishman of the 'nineties, said:

"By Jove, Max is the good boy of the trade. The day that I can get my people to make a fake piece and persuade Max to sell it as genuine, I shall retire. I shall have earned a rest."

But they none of them resented it, and they liked Max as they had liked his father. He was less spectacular, he was not in the least flamboyant, he was sound as the English oak which he had made so popular, and they knew it.

Hannah returned with the coffee and set it down at Emmanuel's elbow with a scrap of paper on which reposed two white tablets.

"There, drink that, take those and you'll feel better."

"Nice kind person you are, Hannah."

42

"Oh, I don't know, Mr. Emmanuel," she said with a faint hint of confusion, "one only does what one can. Now sip it, it's very hot." She watched him gravely, and then gathered up the letters and turned to go. Emmanuel set down the cup and said:

"I've not been through them all. Wait a minute. Sit down. Take five minutes' rest yourself. How's the house?"

Her rather heavy face brightened. "Delightful. Takes no time to get to Northwood by train, you know. Why, last night I didn't leave the Queen's Hall until nearly half past ten."

Idly sipping his coffee, subconsciously wishing that his head would stop aching, Emmanuel asked whom she had heard at the Queen's Hall.

"This new woman, Eleanora Pettrachi," Hannah said. "Not very good. Showy, but no feeling. Like an expensive gramophone record only not so good. I waited, always believing that I should hear something worth hearing—but it never came. Over-advertised and over-trained. There, you've finished the coffee, the head will be better soon. Could you look at the rest of the letters now?"

They had just finished the letters when a knock came to the door, and when Emmanuel called, "Come in," one of the junior clerks entered with the news that Sir Max had arrived. Emmanuel got up, pushed the letters over to Hannah Rosenfelt and said:

43

"That's good, we'd just finished. I'll go and see my father, and we'll ring through for you when he's ready."

Max sat in his own huge office, his foot resting on a footstool, his face rather haggard and yellow. It was one of fate's jokes that Max Gollantz, who had never abused any of the good things of life, should periodically be smitten with gout. Emmanuel knew the signs and prepared to be sympathetic.

"Good morning, sir. Not so well. Foot again?"

Max drummed with his finger-tips on the big desk which had once belonged to Benjamin Disraeli and nodded.

"No sleep. It's—well, it's fairly bad, Emmanuel. Angela wants to carry me off to Aix for a cure. It's intolerable, cuts into one's work so badly."

"I should say get away, nothing does you so much good."

Max moved impatiently in his big chair. "How can I get away? It's impossible at the moment. Howark's sale on the fourteenth, and we want the Reynolds too much to let it go to America. No, no, I can't go yet."

With a feeling that his tone was half-hearted, Emmanuel said that he could bid for the Reynolds. Max looked at him, under heavy lids, and smiled.

"Good fellow you are," he said, "but it's scarcely fair. Too much responsibility. We work

44

you too hard as it is, my boy. No, I shall be all right. Nothing to worry about."

Then a sudden twinge of pain caught him and he sat rigid, his face very white, and when the paroxysm was over, wiped away the sweat from his forehead. Emmanuel reflected that his father never cursed as most men did; rather, he seemed to offer an apology for even allowing his pain to be manifest.

"Anything in the post?"

"Mine was dull enough in all conscience," Emmanuel said. "Hannah may have some plums for you. Shall I ring for her?"

Max nodded, and when Hannah entered, Emmanuel went back to his own office.

Angela came in just before one, and came direct to his office. She was obviously worried, and Emmanuel, who loved his mother with a queer unobtrusive devotion, noticed it at once. She sat down, obviously prepared to talk to him.

He stood by her chair, looking down at her, wondering how at fifty she still managed to remain one of the most attractive women in London.

She sighed. "Emmanuel, I'm worried about Max. I want to get him away. This gout is more serious than it seems. Bernstein has tried everything, and he himself told me that he gets alarmed. You see, Max never tells anyone the whole truth. He pretends, he says what he thinks will please me. Max's heart isn't what it might be."

Emmanuel laid his hand on her shoulder. "Then take him away, darling. Aix always does him good."

"I know, but—but you wanted to go to Paris, didn't you?"

Taken off his guard, Emmanuel gave a short exclamation of dismay. He had forgotten Paris, and Juliet Forbes. But this was Angela who was worried, and it had become a habit with him to push everything aside, to throw over all his personal inclinations if they affected his mother adversely. Emmanuel might be weak, he might vacillate, his stability might be questioned, but his love for his mother remained the unchangeable thing in his life.

"Paris?" he said. "What's Paris compared with your peace of mind about Max! Nothing!"

After all, London was big enough. Surely he need see nothing more of Juliet than her name on the bills.

His mother looked up at him, then suddenly caught his hand and pressed it against her cheek. For a moment they remained very still, Emmanuel feeling nothing except delight that he had pleased her, lightened her worry a little.

"Oh, my dear," she said, "people count me a happy woman, and yet I seem to myself to do nothing but sacrifice you for other people. It's not fair, and yet what can I do? I can't let Max get worse and worse when I know, and Isadore Bernstein knows, that Aix will do him good. I wonder that you don't begin to hate me, Emmanuel."

He bent down and kissed her. "Angel," he said, "you're getting everything distorted. I can very well stay in London. It's sufficiently big to hold—Juliet and myself. I've grown more sensible lately. Viva and I are having a glorious time, and nothing can touch me!"

She laughed, rather miserably. "I ought to have called you Ajax, I think. Oh, my dear, don't be worried, don't be afraid. If you are really happy, cling on to it, conserve it. It's so much of it my fault. I ought to have let you stay and marry her. Only my courage failed me, I was weak and conventional."

Emmanuel laid his finger-tips on her mouth, very gently, the touch was a caress in itself.

"S-sh," he said, "I won't have you speak so. I tell you it's over, that I'm very happy, and that I shall go on being happy. Forget it all, take Max to Aix. I'll buy the Reynolds, and we shall all be happy ever after."

So that afternoon it was arranged that Max should go to Aix for a month, and that Emmanuel was empowered to bid an enormous figure for Sir Joshua's painting of "Persis, Lady Granton".

When he told Viva, she shrugged her shoulders and said that she expected it.

"You are all bound to that family machine,"

she said, "and it's a juggernaut that crushes you all. You can't even go to Paris for a holiday but the machinery catches you up and whirls you off to sale-rooms. Oh, I don't really care. London is sufficiently amusing at the moment."

"I could manage from the eighth until the thirteenth—no, with Max away, I should have to be back on the eleventh. Oh, damn!"

Viva said, "Quite—that's what I often say—'Oh, damn', but it never cuts any ice."

Emmanuel's nerves snapped. He was tired. Max had left for Ordingly immediately after luncheon. Reuben Davis had been quibbling about some wretched account of three pounds seven and eightpence which the upholstery claimed ought to be met by the polishing department. Hannah had defended the polishers, and Reuben had argued about principles and precedents until they had nearly driven Emmanuel crazy. Then Julian had blown in and demanded a loan from petty cash of a couple of pounds, because he had left home with no money, and Hannah had looked frosty, and Julian had been slightly impertinent, and finally Emmanuel had said, "Damn the petty cash—here you are, Julian!"

He swung round on Viva, and for once let his temper get the better of him.

"Confound it," he said, "do you suppose that I don't want a holiday? I've had my nose to the grindstone for over two years. Ten to six day after day, and then this damned silly round of parties where I meet people even duller than those I meet in the office."

Viva laughed, and blew a smoke-ring with care, then said:

"You'd better go to Aix with Max. I should think your liver is out of order, my child. Go and dress; we're dining with the Morrisons."

When he met her again just before they started she was quite unruffled and behaved as though there had been no slight storm. She talked about anything and everything, told him a very smart and slightly improper story about a mutual friend, and was evidently prepared to enjoy her evening.

Emmanuel decided that here lay one of the main differences between himself and Viva. He remembered things, she forgot—or apparently forgot—them. He allowed things to sting and hurt, she assumed an armour of indifference and was protected. Her father and brother, because they both led lives which she regarded as unworthy, were simply erased from her mind. She never spoke of Sir Walter, except to express her contempt of him, and all her brother's bouts of illness—brought on, Emmanuel had to admit, by his own idiocy—never roused any spark of compassion in her.

She disliked them both, despised them both, and never wished to speak to or meet either of them. It was not that she lacked kindliness, nor

49

that she was devoid of sympathy, but simply that she looked facts in the face and refused to allow sentiment to rule her. The fact that poor, stupid, white-faced Walter Heriot was her brother made him no more to her—because of her disapproval —than the casual drunkard in the streets.

Not that there was any narrow-mindedness, or excess of conventionality, in her make-up, Emmanuel reflected. She cared nothing for public opinion, and when Nina Westernhouse had run away with Giles Kently, and had returned to London and taken a house in Chelsea, Viva had been the first person to call and behave perfectly charmingly to Giles.

People had raised their eyebrows, and Viva had laughed.

"I like Nina," she said, "and the fact that she ran away with Giles can't make me like her less. Westernhouse was always dull, and she couldn't stand it. I only ticket sins those nasty little failings that come out of bottles and hypodermic syringes. If I realized that I hated Emmanuel, I should leave him, and very quickly. Westernhouse was limiting Nina horribly, with his perpetual religious congresses and mothers' meetings. It wasn't her line."

Emmanuel put out his hand and laid it on hers, as they drove to the Morrisons'. "Sorry I lost my temper and got rattled."

She turned and smiled. "Darling, I didn't care

a hoot. Only I wish you wouldn't repent—verbally—it makes me hot under the collar. It's all right."

4

THE evening started very well. Emmanuel felt that it was going to be less boring than usual. He sat next to Georgina Hardman, the actress, at dinner, and found her amusing and interesting. She was plain; she said that in her plainness lay her real success, because it titillated the palates of an audience to see a plain woman playing passionate love scenes. But her intelligence was unmistakable, and a rather tired Emmanuel found it pleasant to listen to her delightful voice uttering opinions which were neither commonplace nor unbearably advanced.

It was later, when the dance began, that he hated the evening. Everything conspired to irritate him. Viva began by saying: "My poor darling, having to sit next to that hideous Georgina Hardman."

"I liked her," Emmanuel said. "Her voice is lovely."

Viva laughed and said, "Kind lad you are!" and suddenly he felt a prig.

Then Julian arrived, and his pretty little American wife began to talk about Eleanora Pettrachi. She talked intelligently enough, but she seemed to believe that the world had produced only one method of singing, and that the Italian.

52

Emmanuel, trained from the time he was a child by his grandather, and later by Angela, hated what old Emmanuel used to call "firevorks", and said so.

Julian said, "Have you heard this particular Brock's Benefit?"

"No," Emmanuel said, "I haven't. I don't like Italian singers much. I did hear that she wasn't very good."

Amanda Gollantz said, "Well, now, that's too bad, because I thought she was just too lovely."

With a lazy indifference, which ought to have warned Emmanuel, Julian asked, "Who told you that she was not very good?"

Taken off his guard, Emmanuel said that Hannah Rosenfelt had told him.

Julian's smile widened and he turned to his wife.

"Hannah Rosenfelt, darling," he said, "is not a leading musical critic, but the firm's tame Yidd-isher woman. She acts as secretary to Emmanuel and my father in her spare time, the rest of the day she spends in exchanging musical and artistic chit-chat with them both. Oh, a rare bird, Hannah Rosenfelt."

Amanda looked at her husband doubtfully for a second, then turned to Emmanuel with a smile that was essentially kindly. It was evident that she felt the small chill which had descended on the group.

"I think that's lovely," she said. "That's what

I call real democracy. I reckon that she's been with you for years, Mr. Gollantz?"

"A long time, ever since she left school."

"Now—look at that! And she'll be quite an old woman now?"

"Not a bit of it," Julian said, "Gollantz' never employ old people. They are pensioned magnificently as soon as they grow old enough to know anything about the business. That's why you and I are relatively paupers. The firm's profits all go in pensions."

Viva looked at Julian as if she was mentally adding up the cost of his admirable clothes.

"'Relatively' is good," she said. "That's a lovely new Bentley of yours."

Nothing disturbed Julian. "My wife's wedding present to me," he said. "Knowing the generous Jewish proclivities of the house, I married a rich wife. That she happened to be beautiful, utterly adorable and super-intelligent were secondary reasons."

He turned and, slipping his arm round Amanda, began to dance. Viva watched them both in silence. Emmanuel stood feeling that he wanted nothing so much as to go home and leave them all.

"I loathe your brother," Viva said, "almost as much as I dislike my own, and yet he is stimulating. I don't wonder they like him in the House. His speeches must brighten things considerably."

"Don't talk to him," Emmanuel said. "He only annoys you."

"I never want to."

Yet later in the evening, when Amanda was talking to some friends and he stood talking to Bill Masters, he saw Viva dancing with Julian, her face all alight, and heard her laughter as she passed them. Bill Masters said in his slightly heavy manner:

"I'd give a devil of a lot to dance with a woman as pretty as your wife, Emmanuel. I'm not so damned old that I couldn't still enjoy it."

Emmanuel said, "She's the best dancer in Town."

Then Viva's laugh reached them again, and he felt a rush of dislike for his brother and wondered how it was that, though Viva said she hated him, he could always amuse her. He wasn't jealous, only he felt "odd man out", and remembered that so often when he danced with her they moved in dead silence. His own thoughts went on and on in a sort of miserable circle, while Masters talked and he said "Yes" and "No" and "Really" at the proper intervals. Suddenly, Bill's words reached him distinct and clear, and he switched his thoughts away from himself and decided that he was only indulging in self-pity, and that was the lowest of all indulgences—worse than Viva's detested "little sins out of bottles and hypodermic syringes".

". . . The nicest women always have the most worries," Bill said.

Bill believed that all women were saints, and took their worries dreadfully to heart. Viva said, "Bill Masters is a mental midwife to every woman he likes. He's always telling them to set their teeth and it will be over soon."

". . . Take your mother. She's miserable about Max. Going to take him to Aix. I might pop over myself and try to cheer them both up a little."

Bill's cheering up, Emmanuel remembered, took the form of very good champagne and dry biscuits at eleven in the morning. He thought people rather cads who drank fizz at any other time.

". . . Aix isn't what it was once, but there's still a certain amount of fun to be found there. Pretty women, good fellows, and so on. They'll be there for a month. I'm going to try to get Juliet to join them there. The four of us might make up a very jolly party, eh?"

Juliet at Aix with Max and Angela. Juliet making a "jolly party" with his mother and father and old Bill Masters. It didn't fit somehow. It seemed to put Juliet among the last generation. To ticket her as middle-aged.

Emmanuel said, "Awfully jolly."

". . . When she's finished this London business, she's free for nearly a month. Said that she wanted a holiday, and so did Gillie. So she does —Australia, America, half Europe, and London.

She works too hard. God knows why—she's got plenty of money. Hast left her everything he had in the world, poor chap."

Leon Hast, Juliet's lover—Emmanuel felt that he had been her only lover—who had left her all his fortune, his collections, his pictures—everything. His mother had once said that Leon Hast was the only person she had ever hated. Hast and Bill and a man called Seyre, whom Juliet had married, went through the war together. That was how Bill got his lame leg, and Hast and this chap Seyre had gone out and got him off the wire. The war . . . Emmanuel thought that it seemed like the Dark Ages. Abruptly, Emmanuel said to Bill:

"Did you know Juliet when she was very young?"

Bill blinked and considered for a moment, then said: "I'd put her at twenty when I first saw her. In Verona, it was. The three of us were there on holiday. My God, how hot it was!"

Throwing caution to the winds, forgetting the subsequent pain it might cause him, Emmanuel asked questions recklessly. He suddenly felt hungry, felt that he must talk to someone about her or die of starvation. It wasn't possible to go on day after day, week after week, year after year, avoiding all mention of her, never hearing of her. He'd fought too hard and too long, and now for a time he would lay down his arms and listen, and if later it all hurt desperately, well, he would set his teeth and bear it. He glanced round the room. Viva and Julian were standing near the door. Viva was serious, but Julian, his fair head bent towards her, was laughing. A moment later they turned and went out together. Emmanuel, feeling in one moment desperately tired, almost weak, sat down by Bill Masters.

Bill looked at him, his round face with the thousand little lines round the eyes concerned and anxious.

"Feeling all right?" he asked. "Look a bit white. It's hot here, isn't it?"

Emmanuel said, "I'm all right." He was almost impatient. He wanted to ask Bill a great many questions, and he didn't want to waste any time. It was terribly important that he should talk about Juliet at once. At any moment he might realize how stupid it all was, might gather together the remnants of his determination and change the subject. He was two people. One weak, tired, hungry for the sound of her name, for news of her, the other sensible, and refusing to give way to what was at best only a very foolish impulse.

He said, "I expect that she was very lovely, eh?"

Bill nodded. "Very—though I don't believe any of us knew just how lovely, except Leon." Then he added very quickly, as if he had been guilty of disloyalty, "Mind, I never thought her, never shall think her, as charming as your dear mother."

58

"You've seen her lately?"

"Your mother? Oh, Juliet. Yes, I saw her—where was it last? In Nice this summer. June or July, just after she got back from America. I have to see her periodically, y'know. I'm executor for Hast's will." He chuckled. "The first real job of work I've ever done! But it's a pleasure, a great pleasure. Dear Juliet. How your grandfather loved her!"

"Did he?" The grandson of old Emmanuel Gollantz sat with his hands clasping his knees, his eyes intent on Bill's face, his whole attitude expressive of intense interest. An interest so deep, so keen, that had Bill looked at his face at that moment it would have told him that it was wiser to tell this young Emmanuel nothing more of Juliet Forbes. But Bill was looking back and seeing his own pictures, seeing a very handsome old man with white hair and skin like old, smooth ivory, his beautiful hands clasped on the handle of his stick, his fine eyes half regretful, half humorous.

"Indeed he did! I remember sitting with him one night at Ordingly. He used to talk almost confidentially to me sometimes. I'd known him since I was a youngster, and he was always very kind to me. We were talking about the way she gathered up her life after Hast died, and how pluckily she started work again, and didn't let her unhappiness break her as it might have done. He said, 'Beel'—he never quite lost his accent,

59

y'know—'I haven't loved many vimmen. Not nearly so many as people have believed. The woman I merrit, and Anchela. You t'ink that —even at seventy-nine, I'm in love with Juliet Forbes. You're wrong.' As a matter of fact, I did think that he was—well, a bit sentimental over her, and I'm damned if I blamed him either. He went on to say that only his dislike of looking foolish prevented him asking her to marry him. I said, 'Why foolish?' He said, first—if he asked her and she turned him down, he'd look foolish in his own eyes. He was half laughing, pulling my leg a bit; if she accepted him, he'd look foolish in the eyes of everyone who knew that he was nearly eighty.

"I said that was he certain that he wasn't a bit in love? He shook his head and said, 'No, Beel, no. But I like lovely vimmen, like them too well —partly from an artistic point of view—to like to see them knocking about the world with no one to look efther them.' I said that the modern woman didn't need looking after. He said, 'You're right, but they want it just the same, and vimmen ought to have everyt'ing they want. Alvays remember that, Beel. It's a duty and a pleasure.' He said she'd never had anyone to look after her—I say, isn't this very boring for you, Emmanuel?"

"No, go on, go on."

"He said that Seyre—the chap she married— smothered her in cotton wool heavily scented with

60

lavender water. He always disliked both Seyre and his work. He said Hast made a velvet-lined case for her and scented it with patchouli." Bill broke off and looked suddenly distressed. "I say, I ought not to have said that. It was unforgivable. Forget it, Emmanuel."

Emmanuel said, "What is patchouli, anyway?"

Bill's face cleared. "I forgot that you wouldn't know. I don't suppose that any of your generation have ever heard of it. It's a rather beastly heavy scent. Gad, how time flies! Do I seem a frightfully back number to you, Emmanuel?"

The younger man shook his head. "I don't think I ever thought much about it. You are older, of course, than I am, but it doesn't matter, does it?" He added, more insistently, "It doesn't matter people being older if they think and feel as you do, or if you think and feel as they do, does it? I mean—" His voice trailed off, and Bill was too absorbed in reaching for his stick to notice that he had left his sentence unfinished.

"Going, Bill?" Emmanuel's voice seemed to have lost its colour.

"I think so. I'm too old to hang around until the not-too-small hours. Good night."

Emmanuel rose, pushed back his chair and said with sudden sharpness, "How you harp on about being old, Bill! It's idiotic. You're not old. Anyway, it's no great catch being young! Good night, Bill."

"Going to dance until they deliver the milk for the morning coffee?"

"If I can."

He made his way over to where Viva stood leaning against the wall, with a cigarette in a very long holder, talking to his brother Bill.

"Hello, Bill. Come and dance, Viva?

She shook her head. "This is half over, and I've promised Julian the next."

"Very well. The one after that?"

"If you like. Where have you been? I looked for you weeks ago, and you were listening to old Masters with your soul in your eyes. I looked again and you were still listening. Was he telling you stories of the Naughty 'Nineties?"

"More or less."

"Lovely hectic stories of Merode and Otera, eh? Oh, these old warriors fighting their battles over again for the benefit of the rising generation. I don't suppose they ever did anything very thrilling, do you, Bill?"

"Might easily be more thrilling than the things the rising generation do. They're a dull lot. The go-ier they think they are, the duller they get."

She laughed. "You're a serious-minded young feller, and I expect all serious-minded young fellers have talked like that since Cleopatra gave parties on the banks of the Nile. Here's Julian—come on, Julian, don't let's waste a minute of this heavenly tune."

62

Bill came a little nearer to his brother. "How's things?"

Emmanuel nodded, his eyes following Viva and Julian. "All right."

"Good. Viva tells me that it's decided that the Guv'nor goes to Aix."

"Yes."

"Lot of work for you, eh? Well, if there's anything I can do, let me know, won't you?"

"Thanks, Bill."

Bill pulled down his immaculate waistcoat. "I'm off. Say good night to Viva for me. I meant that, Emmanuel—anything. Good night."

Later Viva came back to him and Julian went off to find his wife. As they danced, she said, "Depressed, old thing?"

He laughed. "No, loving dancing with you."

"Better than discussing the charms of Cora Pearl with old Masters?"

"Bill didn't mention the lady—but much better."

Very softly she said, "We're not sort of—slipping away, are we, Emmanuel?"

For a moment a kind of panic gripped him and he wondered what he could say. His throat seemed stiff, disobedient, unwilling to obey him.

"Slipping away," he said at last. "No, of course we're not. What made you say that? You're happy, aren't you?"

"I think so—I'm never very certain of anything. At this minute I'm terribly happy. The floor's good, the band is marvellous, and you do dance divinely. But in five minutes from now—I might be miserable. You can never be certain of anything except the minute you're living in. Don't you agree?"

"I don't know—it's not a very cheerful doctrine."

"Well, life isn't really one long round of gaiety and fun. That's why we've all got to be so busy about nothing in particular. You sell and buy pictures; I dance; Walter drinks; Julian goes and talks at Westminster. None of it matters a hoot."

They danced on in silence, and as the music died with a long wail from the saxophone Viva slipped her arm into his and they walked slowly over to one of the long windows. She stood looking out over the quiet square where a little group of loafers stood watching the guests leave the house. She looked at her best, and Emmanuel felt a thrill of satisfaction in her smooth well-groomed head and her general air of attention to detail. But his thrill was disturbingly impersonal, and he knew it. He was watching a very attractive young woman, a young woman he liked—dimly he wondered if he had ever loved her. He wanted to make her happy, he wanted to behave decently towards her, to conform to the code which he believed was part and parcel of all men who were not unspeakable; but it was all for her happiness, not for his own pleasure or satisfaction.

She said, turning to him and looking back over

her shoulder: "Don't stand so far away. I can't talk to you when you're standing somewhere over in Hampstead."

He came a little nearer and together they stood in the bay of the window, the curtains cutting them off from the rest of the room. The wailing music reached them, smothered and dulled.

"If ever I fell in love with someone else," Viva said, "or you fell in love with someone else, could we both be sufficiently decent to tell each other and go away and get it over, do you think?"

Emmanuel felt that queer sense of panic again, and despised himself for answering, "Is it very likely?"

"Very likely," Viva returned. "More than likely—almost certain I should think. We're both young, we're both attractive, we're quite, quite different in lots of things which we believe matter terribly. Probably they don't, but at the moment we think they do. I'm talking in this way because I realized this evening how damned easy it would be to fall in love with Julian. Oh, I'm not in love with him. I actually dislike him and quite definitely distrust him. But it would be easy— comparatively—to fall in love with him. I don't say to love him, remember. I love you, I believe that you love me—but we might easily stop being 'in love' at any moment."

Emmanuel said, "I rather hate to hear you talk in this way."

"I'm sure you do, that's because you hate

facing facts. You think it's frightful bad taste for me to have chosen Julian—your brother—as an example. You feel I'm being just a little incestuous. Oh, face facts, Emmanuel, and tell me that if ever you fell in love you'd come to me and not pretend, not manufacture a sort of faked fidelity, when all the time you ached and longed to be unfaithful to me."

He said, "Would you?"

"Come and tell you? Yes, I should. You see, I should feel that it might only be transitory. You and I may not have a lot in common. I loathe your stuffy antiques, I hate this family fetich, I detest your rather stupid pride, but there is something about you—fundamentally—that I like, that I really love quite a lot. That's what will last, if we neither of us lie about it and try to pretend that it's what is going to keep us 'faithful'—mentally or physically. If or when the day—or night—comes when I feel that I want to go off with some other man, to sleep with him, live with him, I'll come and tell you quite frankly. And if you are wise, you'll do the same to me."

Very slowly, almost painfully, he said: "I don't know. I should hate it, whether it was you or me."

She moved impatiently, and, leaning forward, flung her cigarette out so that it fell beyond the little crowd of loafers and lay like a gleaming red eye on the dark roadway.

"But can't you see that I want you to live freely

66

and allow me the same privilege? I don't want either of us to go looking for lovers, but I do want us to be able to develop without a lot of imitation trappings and worn-out conventional ideas trailing behind us, hampering us. If something really big exists between us, then that will last and nothing can really affect it. You believe that?"

He stood watching her, his face very pale, his eyes narrowed as if he tried to see very clearly. Then he said: "I don't know. I'm not quick, as you are, Viva. I need time to think things over. It's difficult for me because of that lack of quickness. I do believe that there is something very big, very lasting between us, but what I don't know is if it would survive so big a test as the one you suggest."

She laughed. Viva always laughed at him when he was very serious.

"Let's leave it," she said. "It was stupid of me. I was trying to be so desperately honest. Let's go home."

5

IT seemed to Emmanuel that suddenly
London was covered with placards bearing
her name, and that wherever he looked the
two words "Juliet Forbes" met his eyes. The
tenth, the twelfth, and the fourteenth. Those
were the days when, by paying money, he might
go and see her, listen to her, and renew all his
memories, which two years' separation seemed to
have made almost impossibly vivid.

The ninth—and he wondered all day what time
she would arrive, where she would stay, and if
he might not run into her when he either went to
lunch or left the office in the evening. He felt
that Hannah Rosenfelt was something of a saviour
when she brought in the letters and pointed out
that the Dowager Countess of Carlington was
selling off her superfluous pictures, books, and
silver at Carlington Manor in Dorsetshire.

"Did you think of sending anyone down, Mr.
Emmanuel?"

He glanced through the very thin catalogue;
then, with a simulated show of interest, said that
he believed he'd better go himself. Hannah
looked down the pages as he turned them, and
remarked that there didn't seem anything very
good, and it was a pity to give himself extra work.

68

Emmanuel, hiding his anxiety to get away, persisted that you never knew in these country sales, and that he didn't want to let anything slip. Wasn't it the Carlingtons, he asked, who had a lot of letters written by Charles the First to the Earl of that date? Hannah didn't know, and her lack of knowledge appeared to deepen Emmanuel's conviction concerning the letters.

He left home very early on the morning of the tenth and got back to London very late, his purchases consisting of two prints and a very small and exceedingly dubious Morland. One of the local dealers had spoken to him during the luncheon interval, when they had all eaten under-done roast beef in the village inn.

"Mr. Emmanuel Gollantz?" he asked, and when Emmanuel nodded, said: "Very like your esteemed grandfather, if I might say so. You can't expect us to welcome you here, Mr. Gollantz. It's got round, and every parson and doctor, every retired colonel and half-pay Navy man is believing that you've come down for something special. It's going to run the prices up for old Lady Carlington!"

Emmanuel laughed, and said something about it being an ill wind that blew no one any good. The local man came a little nearer and dropped his voice to a confidential whisper.

"In strict confidence, Mr. Gollantz, was there anything you was after, particularly? Because if

69

so the boys here would stand by you and keep it in the ring."

"That's more than kind of you," Emmanuel said, "but candidly, I am here for a little holiday as it were, and we—my father and I—never work with the ring, you know."

Another man, who had halted near the table to listen, interjected: "Leave it alone, Harry. We all know about the splendid isolation of Gollantz and Son! When you're baronets and live in the West End, you don't need the ring."

Emmanuel smiled very pleasantly. "We're not all baronets," he said, "only my father, at the moment; and none of us lives in the West End. Would you all allow me to finish my luncheon in peace?" He dined at his club and got home only just before Viva entered.

"Find any treasures?" she asked.

"Nothing much. A couple of amusing prints, and a doubtful Morland. Where have you been —you're home early?"

Viva sat down on the arm of his chair and, picking up his glass, sipped his whisky-and-soda appreciatively. She handed it back to him and remarked that it was a topping drink and beat any cocktail hollow.

"Have a whole one all to yourself?"

She considered the suggestion gravely, then said: "D'you know, I believe I will. Not too yellow, angel, my head's rather weak."

He mixed the drink and brought it back to her,

thinking that it was very pleasant to be home, and that Viva was the nicest person in the world and quite the prettiest. He settled himself in his chair again and prepared to be amused by her comments on the evening.

"Tell me where you've been," he said. "I thought this was an off evening for you."

"It was, and I decided that I'd be dutiful and go home and dine with the family. Walter's away. He and father have indulged in one of their periodic rows, and father ordered him out of the house for being tight! At the moment father is recovering from an attack of what the doctor—a diplomatic feller—calls acute gastritis, and is drinking nothing but soda-water and a little diluted white wine. Old Masters was there, and he and mother talked about how lovely Gertie Millar was in 'Our Miss Gibbs' and what a marvel Hayden Coffin was in 'Dorothy'. They got all technical about some song called 'Queen of the Something or Other', and who wrote it, and mother offered to bet Bill seven to two that it wasn't put in until the second night, and Bill said, 'Make it six to four, because you're bound to lose.' Oh, it was thrilling! Bill was all dolled up, gardenia and tails and an ultra-modern white waistcoat, and when I asked him why, he said that he was going to the Queen's Hall. He said that if I liked he'd take me, as he'd got a seat for Angela, not knowing that she'd be away. Darling —going to have another whisky? You'll never be able to cope with the dealers tomorrow. No, I'm only in fun. Have it—have ten if you want to."

With his back to her, his hands very busy with bottles and siphons, Emmanuel asked, "And did you go?"

"Having nothing better to do, I went. Oh, my dear, what a marvellous woman! Lovely, lovely, lovely! Wild horses won't keep me from the Claytons' on the fifteenth. I didn't understand one word in ten—all German stuff—and I don't know much about voices. Bill listened as if he was in church. I wanted Bill to take me round and introduce me, but he pulled down the corners of his mouth and said that he didn't know, she'd had a long journey, and never talked much after a concert, and generally was rather sniffy. You know her, don't you?"

"I used to."

"Could we ask her to dine here—before the Albert Hall Show?"

"I don't think she'd come. She doesn't—I imagine—have much in the way of dinner before a concert."

"Then I must meet her at the Claytons'. She's heavenly. Oh, you know her, I forgot. Is she nice?"

"She was when I knew her. I met her first when I was about seventeen, I think." He stopped speaking because he felt that he was being disloyal to Viva, and yet he could not bring himself to tell her the whole story. Angela had said before they married that it was foolish even to mention it. That it was over, that there had been no—she hesitated and then found the word she wanted—complications. He had been happy and excited about his engagement; it had seemed a solution of everything which was difficult; he had believed that once he was married all memory of Juliet would sink into the limbo of forgotten things—and had agreed.

Now he would have given a great deal to sit and talk to Viva quite frankly and openly. To have told her how much he liked her, what a good friend she was and always would be, but that his love belonged—as it had done in reality for years—to Juliet. Once he almost mustered sufficient courage to speak, because Viva herself had talked only a few nights ago about courage, and trusting each other, but as he tried to find words, his courage dwindled and died. After all, what was there to say? Simply that he loved her, and was fighting against his inclination to go and see her. If Viva asked, "Does she love you? Does she want to see you?" he could only answer that she had thrown him over two years ago, and that apparently she wanted to avoid seeing him. All very nebulous, tinged with romanticism and sentimentality, reeking of "hopeless passion" and "unrequited love". Slightly ridiculous!

Viva swung herself off the arm of the big chair and said that she was going to bed.

"I believe that I'm more tired after an early

evening than I am after an early morning," she said. "Good night, Emmanuel, and if you think of making an early start hunting the wily Georgian silver, don't wake me, there's a lamb. I'm getting old, and I need my full nine hours." She stooped and kissed his hair lightly. He caught her hand and held it.

"What is it?" she asked, smiling down at him.

"Nothing—just—oh, I don't know. You're terribly nice, Viva."

"I am, aren't I? So are you. I'm not as fundamentally kind as Angela, I'm not as attractive as Amanda, and I'm nothing at all so far as looks go compared with your Forbes woman, but—I am nice." She caught his face and held it between her cool palms, turning it up to her. "Remember, Emmanuel, my sober-sides, I am distinctly intelligent. Not intellectual, but damned intelligent. Good night, my sweet, sleep well. If I'm awake in the morning, I'll tell Caroline to let you know."

He closed the door behind her, and went back to his chair. There he sat, his hands clasped, trying to fight down the sudden sense of longing for a sight, a sound of Juliet. It seemed that in all London he was the one person who must be denied the right to see and hear her. Bill Masters, Viva, everyone except Emmanuel Gollantz might crowd into the concert halls and listen to her. Then, possibly because it was late, because he was tired, and because he was carrying a weight too heavy for him in the sole management of one

74

of the greatest firms in England, his will weakened and he began to wonder how he might at any rate hear news of her. He couldn't wait for the morning papers. He wanted to know then and there how she had sung, how good her reception had been, how she looked—anything and everything that appertained to her.

He looked at his watch; it was only a quarter past eleven. He might quite reasonably telephone to Bill and ask him all he wanted to know. Bill was always ready to talk about Juliet. He might say that Angela wanted to send her flowers, or that he knew that Angela would want to send flowers had she been in England. He might ask where she was staying, might ask a hundred things, and ease this horrible hungry aching to know something of Juliet.

A quarter past eleven. Talking to Bill on the telephone would certainly only take five minutes at the outside. He couldn't contemplate going to bed; he almost feared the silence of his room, the sense of loneliness which he knew would possess him. He might walk round to Bill's flat in Park Crescent, and talk to him for an hour or so. Bill never went to bed until the small hours. Angela always said that the whole family automatically took their worries to Bill Masters.

He found Watson locking the front door when he went into the hall.

"Leave it," he said, "I've got to go out for half

an hour. Don't any of you wait up for me. I've got my key."

"Very good, sir. Good night."

"Good night, Watson."

The night was very still, the sky cloudless and full of stars. There was more than a touch of frost in the air, and his feet seemed to ring on the pavements as he walked. He kept assuring himself that he was a fool, and then added mentally that he couldn't help himself. After all, his mother would want to send flowers. She would like to know that anything that could make Juliet's stay in London more pleasant should be done through one of the Gollantzes. It was so easy, so terribly easy, to justify what he was doing; so dangerously easy. He clenched his hands suddenly and threw back his head as if for the first time he faced things clearly.

What did he care for what Angela wished? How much did he care about her problematic little kindnesses? Nothing, less than nothing. He wanted news of Juliet and he was going to get it. He'd lost his nerve and given way to an impulse which seemed irresistible. He'd face it, and not try to hide behind excuses and imagined reasons. He might be a fool, he might be all kinds of unworthy things, but he'd at least be honest with himself.

He turned into the hall of the block of flats where Bill Masters lived. The porter opened the lift and said: "Good evening, sir; cold night, isn't it?" The lift seemed to whirl him out of the world in which he lived into some other sphere. He caught sight of his face in the little strip of mirror and noticed that his eyes had lost their look of weariness. Involuntarily he smiled at his reflection.

Bill's servant, Judson, opened the door to him. Judson was a privileged person, a little stocky ex-soldier who still retained a mania for spit and polish.

"Ah, Mr. Emmanuel!" he said.

"Hello, Judson. Not too late, am I?"

Judson grinned. "Trifle on the late side, sir, but better late than never." He took Emmanuel's coat and said, "Been working overtime sir?"

Emmanuel nodded. "Just a little. Really too lazy to change, Judson."

"We should worry about that, Mr. Emmanuel," Judson said soothingly. "My contention being that a gentleman can be a gentleman even without a tail coat and a white shirt. Mr. Masters is in the drawing-room. I'm afraid supper's over, but if you fancied anything, I don't doubt as I could fix it."

"No, that's all right. I'll go right in."

Judson hurried past him along the long narrow corridor, opened the door and announced. "Mr. Emmanuel Gollantz," in a tone which would have done credit to a sergeant-major. Emmanuel entered and stood just inside the door surprised and dismayed. The room was full of people—Bill

77

was evidently giving a party. He felt horribly self-conscious as he stood there in his tweed suit, and heard Bill Masters' voice: "I say, this is nice! How splendid!"

Bill drew him into the room, and his heartiness struck Emmanuel as just a little overdone. Stupid of him not to have telephoned first. Equally stupid of Judson not to have said that there were people there. Still more stupid of Bill to be so damned hearty, because Bill had a perfect right to give parties and not ask all the Gollantz family if he wanted to.

He said: "I'm frightfully sorry, Bill. I didn't know you were having a party. I thought I'd just slip round for a talk. You must let me go away again at once. I feel like the chap who hadn't got a wedding garment."

Bill said: "What nonsense! Come along. Delightful to see you. I've been spending the evening with your wife, did she tell you?"

"She did. Said she had enjoyed it tremendously. I've been down in the country all day. You see, with my father away—"

He stopped, and said in a new and rather tight voice: "I think I'll get along, Bill. It's unpardonable to butt in like this."

It was little Gilbert who had come forward and stood in front of him; little Gilbert with his fair hair and nervous manner, smiling and holding out his hand, saying as he did so, "My dear young man, how very pleasant!"

78

Juliet did not move. She stood leaning against the piano, her face expressionless, her eyes never ceasing to watch the tall, good-looking young man who looked down at Gilbert and murmured some polite commonplace. He had not changed. Perhaps he looked a little older, his face had lost its almost boyish curves, and his eyes were graver. His mouth did not seem to smile so easily, and his whole bearing recalled old Emmanuel very plainly. There had been a second's dismay when Gillie spoke, then he had mastered himself, and was talking to Gillie as if it was the most ordinary meeting in the world. She caught her breath. In a moment Gillie would bring Emmanuel to her, he would take her hand, she would hear his voice again, listen to his queer little unEnglish trick of rolling his "r's", and be forced to remember that everything was changed. He was married, settled down, a partner in a great business—happy, successful, established.

Then a little spurt of anger flared against him. She had written to Angela, had tried to tell her that she didn't want to meet him, she had even hinted as much to Bill when he broached the idea of a supper party after the concert. Was Emmanuel so dense, so insensitive, so cruel that he actually wanted to make difficulties for her? Angela had written that he would be in Paris during her visit, that he was taking his wife there for a holiday. She had felt secure, safe and almost content. Now he appeared, obviously uninvited,

79

to disturb her peace and force her to remember those things which she had tried so hard for the past two years to forget.

He stood, his head held very high, and across the room his eyes met hers. Very calmly, unhurried and apparently very much master of himself, he came towards her and stood before her.

"How are you, Emmanuel?"

"Ver-ry well, and you?"

"A little tired, but very well, and delighted that London hasn't forgotten me."

"There are some things which even London cannot accomplish."

Bill limped up to them. "Lucky his turning up like this," he said. "He wants to go, but I tell him that's out of the question. You'll agree with me, I know, Juliet."

"Of course. How is Angela? And Max? I was so sorry to miss them."

"Angela is very well, and I heard this morning that my father is better. I r-really came round to find your address, because my wife, who was at the Queen's Hall tonight with Bill, wondered if you'd dine with us one evening."

His voice, his very attitude, were formal; only his little nervous trick of doubling his "r's" showed her that he was not quite so detached as he seemed. His wife—surely, though, that was a little unnecessary. He might have found some other excuse.

"How kind, but I'm afraid it won't be possible.

It's terribly difficult to keep any time free, and I'm singing again the day after tomorrow and again on the fifteenth. On the sixteenth I go back to Paris. I'm dreadfully disappointed. I'm sure she's charming."

"Then we are all three disappointed, myself, my wife and you. I mustn't keep you, other people will be hating me. Good night."

He moved away, his heart beating very heavily. She hadn't changed. She was as lovely as ever, her voice was still the most perfect music in the world, but it had been like talking to her through a thick curtain—heartbreaking. They had stood saying nothing, nothing, nothing, only uttering commonplaces. She had not given the smallest sign that she remembered anything; she seemed to wish to assure him that she had forgotten, that she was glad to have forgotten.

Gilbert was at his side again, asking if he wasn't going to have a drink. Babbling on, as he used to do two years and more ago. Kindly, silly Gilbert, who was the finest accompanist in the world, Juliet said. "A clever man wouldn't be nearly so good," she had said once when Emmanuel had declared that Gilbert was almost a half-wit. "He has no definite personality, and so mine never suffers as it might if he were clever at anything except his own job."

Once when Emmanuel took out his cigarette-case, Gilbert laid a hand on his arm and said in what Emmanuel remembered Juliet called his rather "churchy voice":

"Do you mind, not yet? I believe that she's going to sing. Old Lord Rendal is here. He's very old, and he's a great friend. She likes to please him."

Emmanuel thought, "I can't bear it—I can't bear it. I must get away. If she sings I'm done. If I can get away, almost hating her, I might be safe. O God, don't let her sing."

But a moment later she made a sign to Gilbert, who walked over to her and sat down at the piano. Emmanuel never forgot the scene. Juliet, tall and slim, her face rather white, her eyes never meeting his; Bill Masters leaning on his stick, frowning a little as if something puzzled or worried him; and old Rendal seated in a gilt armchair, his hands, with their knotted veins showing plainly, grasping the arms, his thin neck stretched forward towards the piano as if he could not bear to miss a single note. Round the walls, people—to Emmanuel they seemed to be only ghosts—clustered to listen. They had no real individuality. No one in the room was real except Juliet, and because of her—Gillie, Masters, and old Rendal, who belonged to a past age anyhow, and who was almost a ghost already.

She bent down, as he had seen her do a hundred times, and said something to Gillie, who nodded and whispered something back. Then, as she stood upright, she looked across at Emmanuel and for one brief fraction of a second smiled. In that flash it seemed to Emmanuel that she had explained everything. He felt that the curtain which had hung between them had been rent in two, and that the whole world was flooded with sunshine.

She sang a song which old Emmanuel had loved, "Das Lied im Grünen", and it seemed to his grandson that old Rendal's figure changed as he listened in to the magnificent body of the first English-speaking Gollantz. To his excited imagination, he seemed to be back at Ordingly with his mother and father, with Leon Hast, Bill Masters, and old Emmanuel—listening. The song ended, and he almost heard his grandfather's voice saying, "Dear Schubert—and dear Juliet. Thank you both."

Then the dream ended and once again he found her watching him, though she spoke to Rendal, smiled and laughed at what he said. She was leaving. He saw her move towards the door, with people crowding round, almost like a royal progress. He turned and followed her and Bill Masters into the hall.

Bill said, "Going, Emmanuel?"

"I must, I have to work early. Good night, Bill, and thank you for letting me stay for your lovely party."

"Thank Juliet, my boy."

"I do," he said gravely; "she knows that I do. May I take you down?"

They passed to the lift in silence, in silence they descended, and only when they reached the car which was waiting, Emmanuel spoke.

"Juliet, may I see you again? I won't worry you, my dear. Only there are things which I want terr-ribly to say to you."

"Must you say them?"

"I think so—I can't help myself."

"Then tomorrow at four. I am staying at Lauderdale House."

"Good night, Juliet."

"Good night, Emmanuel."

6

EMMANUEL woke the next morning, having only fallen asleep when dawn was breaking, with his mind swinging between content at the prospect of seeing Juliet and a sense of disloyalty to Viva. He knew that it was sufficiently easy to justify his visit. She was an old friend, he had known her for years—Viva knew that, and would certainly raise no objection. But there were the other facts which Viva did not know, and which he could not—after two years' silence—bring himself to tell her. Two years ago it might have been relatively easy, now it was almost impossible. On the other hand, he felt that he might with some justice consider his own mental attitude. For nearly three years he had tried, both consciously and by filling his life with other interests, to forget Juliet. He had failed, and even before he heard that she was coming to London his desperate need of her, his longing to see her again, had grown unbearable.

He was twenty-nine. He had made—apart from his father's position—a place for himself in the world of connoisseurs. He was married, and it might be that a meeting with Juliet would prove to him that, when faced with reality, he had outgrown his love for her. With a kind of cold brutality, which had something of the strength of despair in it, he told himself that Juliet was ten years older than he was. Three years ago she had been thirty-five, now she was nearly forty. A meeting with her might show him that age did make a difference, a difference which nothing could render insignificant.

Scarcely knowing which section of his thoughts had been honest and which sophistry, Emmanuel dressed slowly, and knew that he was taking additional trouble over his appearance. Always carefully, even rather eccentrically, dressed, he discarded first one thing and then another until he found the exact clothes which pleased him. All the time the less devious side of his nature pleaded with him to be wise, to be honest; while the other side—the side in which imagination played so large a part—applauded his care and attention concerning his appearance.

In the hall, Viva's maid Caroline told him that her mistress had not yet rung for her orange juice, and he heard it with a queer sense of relief in which shame played a not too small part. Leaving a message that he would telephone during the morning, he left the house and walked to the office in Bond Street.

The day dragged out its unending length. Nothing seemed to hold any particular interest. The prints which he had bought the day previously proved to be less good than he had believed, and Reuben Davis threw cold water on the idea that the so-called Morland might be genuine.

During luncheon people came and talked to him. He was irritable and bored, only longing for the time when he might get away and see Juliet again. Arbuthnot, with his out-of-date high collar and his enormous buttonhole, came and tried to sound him about the Reynolds.

"Dear old boy, is it true that you and Max are after the Sir Joshua on the fourteenth? Times are bad, 'nobody knows the troubles I've seen', and can't we get together over it? Y'know, united we stand, divided we fall, and if—as they tell me— Peters is coming over, it's going to break the Bank at Monte Carlo! Now, let's get together. Put your cards on the table and mine shall go down beside them."

Emmanuel wondered how much he cared about the Reynolds, and if it would make the slightest difference in his life if it went to America. What a bore Arbuthnot was! The only one of the big Jewish dealers who had bothered to change his name—he'd been born Abrahams, Emmanuel remembered.

"I have no cards, sir," he said, "to lay on the table. My father has left me certain orders, and I am going to carry them out to the best of my ability. One of them was that we're going to act alone. I'm sorry, but you'll understand."

Arbuthnot sniffed, turned rather huffy, and left him to finish his luncheon. Then Charles

Wilmot wandered up and began to talk about some case in which Gollantz' were involved. Emmanuel knew very little about it. Reuben Davis managed these things, with Woolfe. Charles seemed to think that he ought to know, and became a little supercilious about leaving a huge firm in the hands of people too young fully to appreciate the ins and outs of a big business.

Emmanuel returned to the office worried and more than a little annoyed, and asked Davis why he didn't tell him more of these affairs. Reuben spread his hands wide, palm upwards, and protested that Emmanuel had enough to do without being bothered about something which was all cut and dried before Max went off to Aix.

"Very well," Emmanuel said a little stiffly, "I'm glad that you can manage without me. Very good for me to be put in my place." Reuben cocked his rather large head on one side, blinked his bright brown eyes and said: "My dear fellow, that's unjust. We can't get on without you, and you know it. We only wanted to save you trouble, that's all."

"Sorry, Reuben. I was rattled. Forgive me."

"My dear Emmanuel! Forgive! Nothing to forgive."

For the rest of the afternoon he only marked time, and knew it. He listened to Mason's reports concerning the new furniture they were making, he gave his verdict concerning some offer to supply a special horsehair stuffing, he signed letters and dictated replies to others, while all the time he felt that he was acting a part, pretending to be Emmanuel Gollantz, the junior partner of the firm of Gollantz and Son. In reality he was only waiting for the curtain to ring down so that he might assume his real character again, might become Emmanuel Gollantz who had only one real concern, and that to see again the woman he loved.

He pushed the last letter over to Hannah Rosenfelt and said, "I'm leaving early today. I have an appointment at four. There's nothing else, is there?"

"Nothing, Mr. Emmanuel, everything finished." Then the telephone rang, and someone from the outer office spoke to her. She carefully laid her hand over the mouthpiece and said, "Mr. Julian to see you."

"Very well." After all, he had five minutes to spare, and Julian might have news from Aix. He knew that Angela wrote to him almost every day.

Julian entered, beautifully groomed, looking as usual remarkably handsome, and at peace with the world in general.

"Hello, Emmanuel. How are you, Miss Rosenfelt?" The last question in a voice which was cordial but impersonal. Julian never treated his father's staff without civility, but never with any show of real interest. Hannah gathered up her letters and went out. Julian sat down opposite to his brother, and smiled.

89

Emmanuel said, "Want anything, Julian?"

"To see you," he replied, still smiling.

"Well, you've done that. Pleased with the look of me?"

"Not particularly. Horrible business those socks that you wear. Pseudo artistic, smacking of the lower purlieus of Chelsea. No, seriously, I wanted to talk to you. I met a fellow who is very keen to get this picture that Howark's selling on the fourteenth. He swears that it's going up to a huge figure, that—well, that somebody is determined that it's going to leave England, and that bidding against this chap will only send the price soaring, and quite uselessly."

Emmanuel sat stiffly upright in his chair, his fingers closing rather tightly on his ebony ruler.

"Go on, please," he said, "this is interesting."

Julian shrugged his shoulders. "Nothing much more to tell you. Only this chap told me that at forty-two—thousand, of course—Howark will get all he wants. Naturally his American friend will go higher, in fact he is prepared to outbid everyone. I thought I'd give you a hint, that's all."

Emmanuel nodded. He looked very much like old Emmanuel at that moment; even his voice seemed to have taken on the same inflections.

"That is more than kind of you, Julian. Why didn't you telephone this to Max, telegraph it— give the information to him? I have his orders, and I must stick to them."

"I didn't see the use of bothering the Guv'nor—"

"And what time"—Emmanuel's voice was very smooth—"did you meet Arbuthnot today?"

"I didn't say that I had met him."

"No, I did," his brother said. "It's no use asking what he offered you in the event of the Reynolds going to America at forty-two or under, is it? Keep out of it, Julian. It takes people like old Emmanuel and Max to come into this business and keep their hands clean."

Julian was not in the least disturbed. His smile widened, and he flicked open the big cigarette-box which always stood on the table. "Admirable," he said, "a very neat little homily. There's something of the lamented Sherlock Holmes about you, isn't there? Don't you include yourself among the clean-handed members of the furniture and picture trade?"

Emmanuel lifted down the telephone without replying. He hated to lose his temper with Julian, and nearly always came perilously near doing so.

"Get me a taxi, please. Ring through when it's there."

Julian said pleasantly, "Leaving the shop early?"

"I have an appointment."

"Which way are you going?"

"Park Lane."

"Splendid. Give me a lift, will you? I have to go to Gloucester House to pick up Amanda."

For the least fraction of a second Emmanuel hesitated, and knew that Julian's smiling eyes noticed the pause. Then he remembered that Lauderdale House was nearer Oxford Street than Gloucester House, and said that he'd be very pleased.

They drove in silence, but more than once Emmanuel felt that his brother was watching him with an expression that was half curious, half amused.

The car stopped. Julian said: "Here we are. Thanks for the lift. Give my love to Viva. Will she be at the Claytons'?"

Emmanuel got out. "I'll walk, it's only half a dozen yards. I don't know, we might be there. Depends. Good-bye, Julian."

He watched his brother turn away and enter the huge modern building, then walked quickly on towards Oxford Street. He did not turn, and therefore did not see that Julian emerged a moment later and also walked briskly in the same direction that Emmanuel had taken. Emmanuel's heart was beating very heavily as he entered the hall and walked into the lift. A few moments later Julian entered the hall.

Julian walked over to the porter, magnificent in uniform, and stood for a moment hesitating. The porter came forward and asked if he required anything.

"Well," Julian said, "I do, and you might be

able to help me. Are any of these flats ever let furnished?"

"Certainly, sir. Frequently. Messrs. Huntly and Rideway in Hanover Square are the agents."

Julian nodded. "I see—I can't possibly get round there. Haven't time. I shouldn't want to be fobbed off with something stuck away in the roof. Could you give me an idea which flats are to let furnished?"

The porter considered a moment. "Number sixty-five, that's a bit high up, sir. Number twelve is a nice flat. That's let at the moment. Only on a very short let, about a week, I believe."

"Ah! Is that the one let to Mr. Peters, the American?"

"No, sir, that's not the name. Not Peters, sir."

"But an American has it?"

"No, sir. A lady singer—a Miss Forbes, sir."

"Oh." Had the porter been a person of any great mental activity he might have noticed the change which came over the face of the good-looking young gentleman with the pleasant manner. He was not a person of mental activity, and he noticed nothing.

Julian said: "For about a week, you said? That's worth knowing. It might suit me very well indeed. I'm very much obliged to you."

He walked out of the building whistling softly, and the porter, placing a substantial tip in his pocket, decided that it would be a very agreeable thing to have the gentleman as a tenant in number twelve.

Julian returned to Gloucester House, found his wife surrounded by a number of very smart American women, stayed long enough to make a very good impression on them all, and then carried off his wife to their own house for tea.

"Have you had a hard day, Julian?" she asked as she poured out tea for him, while he moved about the room with his usual restlessness.

"Hard, my sweet? No, a little disappointing perhaps, but that can't be helped. I thought that I was on to something rather good, only wanted a little information from my brother to clinch things, and he refused to give it to me. Annoying, eh?"

"Now that's too bad! I call that mean. Why wouldn't he give it you?"

Julian shrugged his shoulders. "God only knows. Just cussedness, I expect. You see, my brother doesn't really like me much—again God only knows why, I've always liked him enormously. Don't mention it to him, will you? I suppose it was nothing to him, only a matter of three hundred quid! He's a partner in the firm, and as such thinks in thousands. My wretched three-hundred flutters seem very small beer to Emmanuel, you see."

"What was it—stocks? I don't know anything about these things, but if it's a real good investment I could always let you have three hundred, Julian. I'd love it!"

He came over and kissed the top of her very smooth head. "I wouldn't have it if you offered it," he said. "I owe you too much as it is. Only" —he laughed, and the laugh was a little wistful "—only it's not much fun being so damned poor. Never mind, sweetest, we shan't always be poor. I'll make money for us both."

"Oh, Julian, we're not poor! Surely I've got enough for us both! No one could call Papa a tight-wad, now could they?"

Laughingly he laid his fingers on her lips. "S-sh," he said. "I hate to hear you even mention money. Only you must learn to remember that while I have to, I accept your help and your father's with very sincere gratitude; but I want the day to come when your money will be just for you to play with, and no concern of mine at all."

"Poor Julian," Amanda said. "But your father was pretty good, wasn't he? I mean he did act very well by you."

Julian looked at her with a half-humorous expression of doubt, then said: "Did he? Yes, I expect so! Oh, don't think that I'm trying to belittle all he did, but what my father can't realize is this. If I am to make a success of my job—and being a Member of Parliament is an expensive job, I can tell you—I must make something of a splash. Well, you can't make splashes if you've only got little pebbles to throw into a biggish pond, can you? My grandfather left everything to Max and to my mother. My father allows me—as you know—a couple of thousand, and reminds me that I get free railway fares to my constituency, and four hundred a year. It's laughable! That's what really gets me on the raw. When I do try to make a little, Emmanuel promptly puts a spoke in my wheel. Oh, don't let's talk about it. It only makes me miserable. Smile, darling, we'll roll in money before we've finished."

He was in debt, and knew that, living as they did, even with the very generous support which Amanda gave him, it would be impossible ever to get out of it. He liked to live well, he liked to know that people praised the dinners which they gave, liked to entertain at smart restaurants, and liked best of all to be pointed out as one of the coming young men.

He knew that he had something more than ability, that facts, figures, statistics all came easily to him, might be stored in his active and essentially well-trained brain, and relied upon whenever he needed them. His manner in the House was admirable. He knew how to treat his superiors with respect which never degenerated into servility. His opportunities had never been wasted, and already he had made a name for himself both on the floor of the House and in Committee. His constituents adored him, though, as Julian said, the huge and ungainly piece of plate which they had presented to him on his wedding was from an artistic point of view poor evidence of their devotion.

He had no scruples, and yet had sufficient imagination and balance never to take any grave risks. There had been more than one occasion when Julian Gollantz might have made money, but his common sense had warned him that the result might be a series of difficult questions, judicious inquiries, and the possession of certain facts by people who envied him which might be disastrous. Now, today, when old Arbuthnot had whispered that it would be worth three hundred pounds to him if he could persuade his brother to let the Reynolds go to America, Emmanuel had turned pi, preached a little sermon, and generally adopted an attitude which ended the matter.

But, as he dressed that evening, Julian smiled at his reflection in the glass. He wondered if Emmanuel had returned home, and, if so, if he had included his visit to Lauderdale House in his account of the day's doings. Julian felt pretty certain that Emmanuel over dinner embarked on a long and exceedingly dull account of how he had spent his day. Emmanuel was so damned serious, lacked the light touch, treated everything as if it were a matter of enormous weight. He wondered if he and Viva got on well in the privacy of their own home. Difficult to say. Viva never gave anything away, they were always apparently excellent friends, and yet—and here Julian's smile widened—there had been moments when he felt they were just a little on each other's nerves.

Three years before, Emmanuel had taken the burden of a particularly unpleasant scandal on to his own shoulders. He had saved Julian from a cataclysm which would have ended his political career for good and all; and Julian—brilliant, intellectual, super-intelligent—lacked that touch of greatness which could be grateful to the person who had sacrificed everything on his behalf. He had never cared a great deal for either of his brothers. Emmanuel was too serious, and Bill was too heavy. They bored him equally, but into the scale which was weighted against Emmanuel was the fact that he had placed Julian under a very great obligation to him. Julian was never likely either to forget that fact or to cease to resent it.

His character was in almost direct contrast to that of his family. Max was incapable of the smallest dishonesty, not only from a moral point of view, but because his innate pride in his house, his business and his father's memory would have rendered any conduct which deviated from the strictly honourable utterly impossible to him. His mother, although she had told old Emmanuel years ago that she was a definitely unscrupulous young woman, had a rigid creed as to what was permissible and what—though it might be poss-ible for other people—could never enter into the calculations of the Drews, the Wilmots and the Heriots.

But there was a weak place in the family heritage of pride, and that weak place had evinced itself twice in the past eighty years. Old Emmanuel had married Juliana Lara; she had been charming, beautiful, and he had loved her with all the passion of which he was capable. But there had come a time when Emmanuel—old Emmanuel, who had been "young Emmanuel" in those days—set out on one of his journeys round Europe. Juliana had begged to go with him, but he, knowing the dangers and the discomforts, had refused to take her.

She had been very angry, and had told him frankly that if she became bored in his absence she would not answer for the consequences. Months later, she admitted that she had been unfaithful to him, that she had been desperately bored in London, and that she had gone to Brussels with her first cousin Jules Alessandri, while her husband toured Europe for furniture, antiques and pictures.

Emmanuel had forgiven her, had put the whole dreadful episode behind him because he adored her, and had never mentioned it to a soul.

Their eldest son, Algernon—if indeed he was Emmanuel's son, which later events certainly seemed to point to, because Algernon's own son, Frank, was exactly like an old photograph taken of Emmanuel when he was six—had possessed that queer streak which made him so different from Max, which sent him away from his father's house, and finally caused him to find his death in Switzerland during the War, an international— and not too trusted—spy.

There was no definite weakness about Julian; rather the weakness of Algernon, the inhumanity of Juliana, had turned in him to a queer un- scrupulous strength, a kind of horrible Puckish trait, which made him actually enjoy waiting and working in order to pay off some real or imagined slight or wrong. At the same time, he never failed to turn such an action to his own advantage. He had believed that Emmanuel had left him to go and see Peters, the American dealer, a thing which Julian would have done himself, had he believed it to be to his advantage. Instead, he had stumbled on a piece of information which appeared to him to be not only valuable but very amusing. That Emmanuel, the Industrious Apprentice of the House of Gollantz, should be sneaking off to visit Juliet Forbes seemed to Julian to contain the elements of farce, a farce which at the right moment might be turned into tragedy for Emmanuel, and used as a very useful weapon by his younger brother.

Julian tied his tie with precision and descended the stairs, a smile still touching his well-cut lips.

7

THE room into which Emmanuel Gollantz was shown was typical of the expensive and totally unimaginative style of furnishing. It was luxurious, ordinary and utterly undistinguished. He looked round, and for the first time it occurred to him that Juliet must hate travelling all over the world, living in such rooms, while her own villa waited—empty and untenanted—on the shore of Lake Como.

His nervousness had left him and he stood there feeling strangely cool and controlled. His doubts had vanished, and he knew that, suffering from that state of mind which had possessed him for the past weeks, this was the only possible solution of his problems. To see her, talk to her, listen to her, might force him to some definite conclusion which, however disastrous it might be, would be eminently more satisfactory than that state of hungry longing to which he had become almost accustomed. Last night at Bill Masters'—that meeting had been nothing. It had been too brief, too public, and he had returned home only hearing her voice more clearly than ever.

He walked to the window and stood looking out over the trees of the park. Autumn had laid her fingers on them and they were already begin-

101

ning to look naked and stark. The whole outlook was cold, grey and a little depressing. His mind turned like a flash to the sunny days which he had known in Italy. He remembered how blue Lake Como had looked one Christmas Day, how the snow-topped mountains in the distance had assumed a new and almost impossible whiteness against the clear turquoise of the sky.

A sound made him turn, and he stood facing Juliet Forbes. For a moment neither of them spoke; Emmanuel because his heart seemed to leap in his breast, Juliet because the sudden sight of him brought back the past so vividly to her.

"It's very good of you to let me see you," he said. "I am more than gr-grateful."

She came nearer and stood directly before him, watching his white face intently as if she tried to see what troubled him most.

"Emmanuel," she said at last, "I don't want to let you say anything which you might regret. If I can help you—let me, but if you only want to go over old things, go away and try to forget it all."

With a touch of his old impetuosity he said: "Forget! My dear, that is what I have tr-ried to do. I have only come to you as a last resource. You are the only hope I have left. I have tried everything else in the world, I think."

"Very well. Only, remember that it is not very easy for me either. You will try to remember that, won't you?"

He took her hand and, with that dignity which reminded her of old Emmanuel, led her to the big, ugly, comfortable sofa which stood along one side of the room. He waited until she sat down, then took a chair facing her and began to speak very rapidly.

"It is nearly thr-ree years since I saw you. At first it was not too difficult. No, I am wrong, at first it was agony even to be alive. Then"—he shrugged his shoulders—"I think I became too numb to feel very much at all. I was tired of pain. I love Viva very much, but I love her very sensibly." He broke off and made a little gesture of impatience. "Oh, it is so difficult to explain and still be decent. Whatever I say will sound wrong, not only to you, but to me as well! I knew how good Viva was for me. She is so clear-cut, so definite, she knows exactly what she wants—always. I know her very well. I could answer questions about her and never make a mistake. You—I never knew what you were. I never knew or cared if you were clever or intellectual. I never cared. I only knew that I loved you. Juliet, when you can be sane and sensible about love—it ceases to be love at all. It may be friendliness, affection, companionship, but it's not love."

"But," Juliet said gently, "you married Viva."

"I know, I know"—eagerly. "I have tried to tell you why. I was lonely, numb with pain—the result of pain. I think that half of me was dead. So long as I remained half dead, ever-rything was

103

all right. Now things have changed. I am alive again; I can see, I know—and, what am I going to do? Oh, Juliet, why did you send me away?"

The room was growing dark, the light had left the sky outside, and he saw her as through a thin haze; not through darkness, but through what was merely a consciousness of lack of light. Her face, always pale, with that lack of colour which has nothing in common with ill-health, seemed to him to shine out like a magnolia blossom. She had always been a beautiful woman, and now, nearing forty, there was an additional fineness about her, a wonderful line from ear to chin, a lack of flesh in her face which made her look almost ethereal.

There was about her the almost unbearable loveliness of an autumn day, which has its own flowers, its own especial beauty, but which is rendered additionally wonderful by the knowledge that it has passed the zenith of the year and must inevitably begin to decline. To Emmanuel, watching her, came the knowledge—and with it a rush of tenderness that was almost painful—that the years of her obvious beauty were over. In their place was a loveliness which carried with it a faint sense of wistfulness, of half-regret.

Bill Masters had said that she was lovely when he and Hast and Seyre first met her in Verona. That must, Emmanuel felt, have been the beauty of youth which believes that youth will last for ever. A beauty which is unquestioning, which rouses no particular speculations, which is accepted and rejoiced in. It seemed to him that even three years ago she had lacked something which she possessed now; nothing tangible, nothing which could be named, but something which was a definite quality.

In the dusk he could see the faint outline of her figure, tall and slim, her hands, clasped tightly, lying on her knees. He could see the whole beauty of her, realize that all she had suffered, all the toll which the years had taken of her, had gone to make her what she was now.

"Juliet," he said, "tell me, why did you send me away?"

Her lips did not move, her eyes still regarded him steadily.

"Because you did not love me?"

"No," she said, very softly, but very clearly, "I always loved you. That was why I sent you away—that and my own fears."

"Fears—for what?"

"You and myself. Listen, Emmanuel." She closed her eyes for a moment, and it seemed that the whiteness of her face, with the light of her eyes shut out, shone like a flame in the half-light.

"I am listening."

"I know Max, I know Angela, and I know what you mean to both of them. They—and you—love Ordingly. You have that wonderful pride which has made you what you are in England today. I shouldn't have—fitted in to Ordingly.

Remember, I was Vernon Seyre's wife, I was Leon Hast's mistress, and—everyone knows it. I have never tried to make anyone forget what Leon was to me. Angela loves me, Max respects me, but neither of them would have wanted to welcome me as a daughter. Then—you were twenty-five and I was ten years older. I couldn't face the day when you would look at me and remember that. Think—'My God, she's growing old.' I promised to marry you—you were practically exiled. I was lonely, so were you. We loved each other, and I was blind to everything else. Then Max sent for you to go home, he wanted to reinstate you, he found out the whole horrible muddle—and I sent you back. There is the story —I let you go because I was afraid, for you and for myself."

She paused, leant back, and pressed her hands over her eyes as if she wished to shut out the pictures which her words had called up. Emmanuel sat perfectly still; his face was white but composed. Only his eyes, those dark Jewish eyes which were part of his heritage, were alight, wide and full of life.

"Perhaps," Juliet said, "I ought to have lied to you now as I did then. It might have been wiser, kinder—I don't know. I never meant to tell you. But I'm tired, utterly tired of going on and on, alone, and—I gave way to an impulse. I don't ask you to forget it, but I do ask you to believe that it's all over, and we can't alter anything now."

"If I were free, would you marry me?"

She answered very calmly. Whatever storm she had been through during the past moments was over, and she was herself again.

"I do not think that I would marry you, Emmanuel."

"If I were free—if I obtained my freedom in a way which did not, could not, implicate you in any way—"

"By lies, by pretence, by all the dirty little underhand ways that people follow to get the better of the law? Never, never, never! It's impossible. I have too much pride, too much pride in you."

"Pride!" he repeated. "Pride! It's a poor thing. My grandfather used to say, 'That wild lie, which men call pride'."

"But we all believe in that wild lie," she said.

The light had died in his eyes, his whole figure seemed to have lost its youthful elasticity. His pale face was set and twisted into lines which she had never seen in it before. He looked older, tired, terribly unhappy.

When he spoke, his voice sounded like the voice of a man who is puzzled beyond all hope of understanding. It lacked colour, its whole tone was dead and heavy.

"Juliet, what am I going to do?"

"My dear, what we all do—go on."

"Alone?"

She shook her head. "Not alone, only—without me."

"That is—going on alone."

"You're twenty-nine, you have a career, a home, a wife—whom you tell me you love. That's a great deal, Emmanuel."

"Weighed in the balance against you—nothing!"

"Responsibilities to your father, to Angela, to the woman you married. Don't they count for anything?"

"God of my fathers!" Emmanuel burst out. "Have I no part in this? Am I nothing? Is my life to go on and on, one perpetual aching for you day and night, week after week, growing, growing, growing until I can scarcely bear the pain of it? I can't bear it, Juliet! If only it would kill me! Tell me, what can I do? Is there any way I can forget you! I've held you in my arms, I've felt your lips on mine, we loved each other, we were happy. I left home because I was supposed to have done what would have branded me as unfit for decent society. When I first went to Italy, I was wretched. After I met you, knew that I loved you—how much did I care? I had escaped, I had flung free of everything, everyone—I had found you. I scarcely disliked my brother Julian, because through shouldering his stupidities I had found a road which led to you. Now I loathe him, loathe him because through him I went away,

108

and indirectly, through him, I was brought home again. The first—what did it matter? The second —meant separation from you. Juliet, if you loved me, if you still love me a little—help me, for God's sake help me."

She rose and laid her hand on his shoulder. "Help you by allowing you to see me, talk to me, by never allowing you to forget that you love me? Emmanuel, I can't, my dear. It's not possible. To allow you to leave everything, end your career, your future, let you trail round Europe, America, Australia, with me. What a life for you! Or else to be your mistress, to meet you—whenever it is possible, until we both grow to hate each other, and the deceits we practise because of each other? My dear, let us both keep something, not run the risk of losing everything."

"Then you are sending me away?"

Very slowly she said, "I am sending you away."

"You won't let me see you again?"

"Not here. Only if we meet somewhere, perhaps at the Claytons', and must"—she smiled —"observe the decencies."

"We shan't meet there. I cannot bear to hear you sing again. It makes me remember too much. The villa and the windows open on to the garden and the darkness. Gillie playing, and your voice —no, I don't want to hear you." He caught the hand which lay on his shoulder and pressed it to his lips. Still holding it, he stood up and faced her. "Juliet, let me see you again. I promise you on my word of honour not to talk like this again. I will be ver-ry ordinary. I will say nothing to hurt or worr-ry you. Only, for the sake of everything—for perhaps nothing but charity, let me see you once again before you go away."

He saw that she hesitated, knew that she was fighting against herself, realized that they were necessary to each other, and that Juliet felt it as he did.

"Once, Juliet. I pr-romise not to speak of these things again. Only to say good-bye, only to give me something to help me—to go on. I love you so. . . ."

"It's not wise, Emmanuel."

The sight of his drawn face hurt her. She wanted to take it in her hands, to smooth away the lines of pain that seemed to scar it, she wanted to have done with fighting, to accept what happiness offered, and to think of nothing and no one except Emmanuel and herself.

"I'm being weak," she said at last; "it's so foolish. I ought to be able to refuse and go on refusing. I shall leave the Claytons' early. I have to leave for Paris the next day. I shall be back here by eleven o'clock. I will see you then for half an hour. Only, it mustn't be like this, Emmanuel. I can't bear this again."

"I pr-romise," he said. "I am very, very grateful. Dear Juliet."

"Go now," she said, "I can't bear any more."

He lifted her hand to his lips, then, with one long look at her, turned and walked out.

But in spite of his declaration that he did not want to hear her sing again, Emmanuel went to the Albert Hall, and in that most hideous of all buildings listened to her voice, feeling while she sang that he was back again in Italy, happy, content, and loved. It was terribly painful, but he believed the pain to be less than that which he would have felt had he stayed away.

On the morning of the fourteenth he remembered the sale of Lord Howark's pictures and suddenly was attacked by nerves. He usually enjoyed important sales, for though Max generally made the bidding for super-important lots, Emmanuel had frequently taken his father's place for acquiring less notable items.

He went down to the office feeling nervous and strung up. He knew that Peters, the American dealer, was in town, knew that old Arbuthnot would be against him, and felt generally young and lonely.

Viva had forgotten about the sale and Emmanuel had not reminded her. Only once had she come down to watch Max bid for a world-famous piece of china, and had declared that she found it insupportably dull. In the middle of the morning Bill Gollantz wandered in. His essentially English, still boyish face made Emmanuel feel happier. Bill perched himself on the edge of the big desk and said:

"Hello, old chap. I've come round to second you this afternoon. I felt somehow that it might be a bit of a gut-twister for you, and that my stolid presence, to say nothing of my stolid form, might help a bit."

"That's nice of you, Bill."

Bill went on, speaking rather fast, his tone almost expressionless and ordinary.

"I was at Ordingly last night," he said, "and it struck me that it might be rather amusing if you carried old Emmanuel's cane. I fancy that it knows its way to the salerooms on its own, don't you? Anyway, it's there with my hat and coat. Got a top coat with an astrakhan collar, by the way?"

Emmanuel's face lit up. His smile was sufficient reward for Bill, who grinned back contentedly.

"I have—at home. Bill, I believe it's an idea."

"There may not be anything in it," Bill said, as if half ashamed of his powers of imagination, "only it struck me that it might—what d'you call it?—create an atmosphere. Same name, same looks—only younger clothes at least reminiscent, and the old ivory-topped cane. Send home for the coat. Tell 'em to bring it round to the Savoy, and I'll blue my all in giving you a damned good lunch. Are you on?"

His brother nodded. "Like a shot. Good fellow you are, Bill. I was getting into a panic over this afternoon."

He reflected as they drove to the Savoy that there was no one he would have preferred to Bill on that particular occasion, in fact that there were very few occasions on which he did not prefer his younger brother to most people. There was a clean-cut quality about him, a directness, and a sense of good fellowship radiated from him. Charles Wilmot with whom he worked prophesied that Bill would do well, that his brain and intelligence were above the average. Bill shook his head, declared that he might manage to make a living, but that he would never be a "star performer at the Bar".

"I like the Savoy," Bill said, as they sat down at the table which he had reserved for them; "always full of nice cheery people, and pretty women. Hello, there's my revered chief, the Admirable Charles."

Charles stopped and spoke to them. "Thought you were hard at work, young William."

"I am. New job, sir. For one night only, stage-managing a show."

"What the deuce d'you mean?"

Bill winked at his brother. "Wait, my revered friend," he said, "and when you read the papers tomorrow remember what I said. I'm going to save the Reynolds for England!"

Charles said: "Good God, Emmanuel, you're not goin' to let this idiot bid for you! No? Oh, well, don't let him make a mess of it for you. Good luck, old fellow."

When he had gone, Bill said: "Funny relationship a first cousin is. Charles is a first cousin, isn't he? Sort of uncle without portfolio. By Jove, what did I tell you about pretty women! Women are so menacing when they begin to get a bit haggard, aren't they? No flappers for me. Give me the woman with a sunken eye and a jaw-line every time. Now—"

Emmanuel said: "I know her. So do you, only you've forgotten. It's Juliet Forbes."

"No! I remember her at grandfather's funeral —with Bill Masters. And once before at Ordingly. She's Mrs.—Mrs.—what the devil is the chap's name? Painter fellow—Sawyer?"

"Seyre," Emmanuel said. "She isn't Mrs. Seyre any longer."

"Dead? No, I saw some of his pictures the other day."

"Divorced," his brother said shortly.

"Him or her?"

"I believe that he divorced her."

Bill stared across the room, his face full of frank admiration.

"Pretty fool he must be," he said. "I'd have hung on like grim death to a woman like that. Shall we go and speak to her?"

Emmanuel suddenly felt weak, that he was incapable of putting up the slightest resistance. He felt that he could only acquiesce in whatever his brother suggested.

"If you like."

"When we're through our food, then. They'll be there for ages, they came in long after we did. Very dangerous for me, I'm so susceptible. Ten to one I might ask her to marry me on the spot. I'm a sentimentalist, Emmanuel, y'know—arrant, rank, confessed and utterly unashamed. Dare me to!"

"We all are—except Julian," Emmanuel said. "Viva always says we're romantics."

They finished their coffee and walked over to where Juliet sat with two people.

"The Claytons," Emmanuel said. "She's singing there tomorrow night."

Juliet looked up as Bill came nearer. Her face was blank until she saw Emmanuel's taller figure, and to Bill it seemed that a light radiated from her eyes.

He bowed over Mrs. Clayton's plump hand, held Juliet's for a second and then presented Bill.

Bill, talking very fast as usual, said: "I insisted on being brought over because I do really know you, you see. That was the first reason. The second was that I want to collect good wishes for this fellow. It's his field day today."

Clayton said: "By Jove, Howark's sale! You're after the picture?"

"He's practically caught it, too," Bill said. "You ought to come down and watch him. It's going to be great fun."

Clayton turned to his wife. "Like to go? We

115

can easily get in, I know them pretty well there. Great show! What about it?"

Juliet spoke for the first time. "Won't it make you nervous?"

The youth in Emmanuel asserted itself. Juliet had never seen him work except in that little shop in Milan; she had never seen how he could pit himself against older men, retain his heart and his courage, and play for high stakes. She should see him now; he would show her what he could do. He looked at her and smiled, a smile which seemed to her so young, so pathetically boyish, that it was almost painful.

"I'm nervous already," he said. "I shall have London and New York against me." He laughed. "If there is any betting, sir," he said to Joseph Clayton, "you can take it from me that Gollantz and Son are the people to back."

Clayton nodded. "Interesting," he said; "we'll come along. Join us in something first, to drink to your success."

8

MORRESBY'S celebrated salerooms were crowded. For two days a certain portion of the public had surged in and out, looking at the treasures which the Earl of Howark was selling, he stated, because of the increased cost of living and the burden of taxation.

On the fourteenth of November, at three o'clock, the Reynolds was to be offered for sale. Speculation was rife as to the figure it would reach, and dealers had gathered together to watch a fight in which very few of them could possibly participate.

Marcus Arbuthnot, in his tightly waisted overcoat, tall white collar and black satin tie with the diamond pin, was there early, whispering behind his hand to a little man with a yellowish skin, horn-rimmed glasses and padded shoulders. The three Morrises—old Sir Augustus leaning on the arm of his elder son Joseph, with his other son. Samson—entered and nodded right and left. The old man walked up the room, puffing his lips and growing more and more congested with the effort he was making. Jacob Lane followed, his face slightly blue round the nostrils and lips. His secretary, whom people said would be his heir because he had never married and had quarrelled with all his relations, followed him, his small, dark eyes darting everywhere, missing nothing.

At ten minutes to three there was a little stir near the door and Joseph Clayton entered with his excessively smart, excessively stout little wife. Clayton was something of a collector, and Arbuthnot, only too willing to demonstrate his knowledge to the American, whispered: "Hello! He-ah's a surprise. Joe Clayton. Money to burn. Clayton's Custard Powders. Shouldn't be a bit surprised if he's he-ah to spoke all our wheels!"

Juliet Forbes followed with Bill, unrecognized by the dealers, for he had none of the Gollantz features, and looked—what indeed he was—a typical young Englishman. And lastly, a figure which made Jacob Lane go still more blue about the lips, and caused Sir Augustus to puff and blow like a grampus—a tall, erect figure in a tight coat with an astrakhan collar, carrying in his hand a broad-brimmed hat and an ebony cane with a huge ivory knob. Even the familiar eyeglass swung from a wide ribbon.

"'Tisn't pothible!" Morris whispered to his elder son. "It's Gollantz ath I knew him thixty yearth ago!"

Jacob Lane dug his secretary in the ribs when his fit of wheezing was over and muttered: "Der picture stays vhere it iss—in Englant. Der portents is too strong! Vell, vell! Dot's a cleffer poy!"

"That's young Gollantz," Arbuthnot said

behind his large white hand. "Play-acting fell-ah! Coming here dressed for the part."

"I only had the pleasure of meeting the late Gollantz on one occasion," Peters whispered back, "and I must say that the likeness is most marked. The effect on nerves less strong than my own might be overwhelming."

Emmanuel did not sit down, he was too nervous; also he wanted to stand so that he might look towards where Juliet sat with his brother. Bill was talking hard, and once or twice Emmanuel saw that Juliet smiled and afterwards looked over to where he stood. He wondered what Bill was saying.

The auctioneer had stepped into the rostrum. He began with a short account of the sale and the lots which were to be offered. He dealt very briefly with the silver, the china and the pictures, merely giving some small piece of information here and there. Finally he dwelt for a moment on the Reynolds, gave a short history of its career, and announced that he was going to begin with Lot 105, the previous lots having been disposed of before the interval for luncheon.

Emmanuel bit his lip and glanced at his catalogue. Not that he didn't know it, he could have recited the dozen lots which came before the Reynolds by heart. God, how quickly they were bidding! Twice the hammer had come down with its metallic little click while he looked at numbers which he knew already. Only three lots to go! Two—one!

"And now, gentlemen. we come to the great feature of the sale. Here is—" But Emmanuel did not hear. His eyes were fixed on the beautiful painting which two men had placed with reverence due to its value, if not its artistic merit, on an easel. The auctioneer had finished his little lecture, the bidding had started. Emmanuel stood perfectly still, his face very grave, almost impersonal, as he listened. Five, six, seven, eight thousand. This was playing at bidding. No one really expected such bids to be taken seriously. He would save himself until later. Once Jacob Lane got a laugh from the dealers by announcing in his thick, husky voice, "T'irteen t'ousand—Lane." That was old Jacob's idea of fun.

"Twenty," Emmanuel stiffened slightly; the voice was American. A second later: "Twenty-fo-ah." That was Arbuthnot.

"Twenty-eight." It came with a wheeze. Morris.

Emmanuel spoke for the first time, "Thirty thousand."

The bids were coming more slowly now. No more jokes came from old Lane, and Morris offered no further bids at all. Once an unknown voice from the back of the room said, "Thu'ty-fower."

That was Bradly, the cotton magnate, who had recently given a Gainsborough to the nation.

"Thirty-five," said Emmanuel Gollantz, and turned and met Juliet's eyes watching him. His father had told him to go to fifty. He had that in writing in Max's last letter. "Don't go further than fifty; I estimate that figure should be sufficient to keep her in England." Max had caught the habit of calling pictures "her" and "him" from his father, Emmanuel remembered.

Slowly the figure crept upwards. It reached thirty-six thousand, and then it seemed that everyone except Emmanuel and the American had lost heart. At intervals Bradly would throw in an advance, and more than once Emmanuel felt that the whole thing had resolved itself into a fight between the three of them. Arbuthnot was scowling and biting his nails, the American looked pale but inscrutable. Emmanuel remained leaning against the wall, apparently nonchalant, but in reality almost stifled by the beating of his heart.

"Thirty-seven," Emmanuel said, and this time there was no hesitation.

"Thirty-eight," came like a pistol-shot.

"Thirty-nine"—with the last word drawn out very long.

Two voices rang out together, the one young and clear, the other dry and nasal: "Forty thousand," said one. "Forty," said the other.

"Forty thousand in two places—"

Old Lane lisped, "Vath it guineath or poundth?"

121

There was a titter; the listeners' nerves were on edge, and they were glad of a second's relaxation. The auctioneer replied suavely, "Guineas —as usual, Mr. Lane."

Another titter, and again the auctioneer said, "Forty thousand guineas in two places."

Emmanuel, watching the American, saw him slip the gold pencil with which he had been making notes into his waistcoat pocket. The movement was so small that had his eyes, and in fact his whole body, not been keyed up to snapping-point, he might never have seen it. The American had retired from the contest.

"In two places," the auctioneer said again. "Mr. Peters and Mr. Emmanuel Gollantz."

Lane said: "They musth thtoss for it!" and got another titter.

Very coolly, only his fingers on the ivory knob of his stick betraying him, Emmanuel said, "Forty, and one hundred."

He met Peters' eyes, made a very small, beautiful, courteous little bow, heard the auctioneer say: "Mr. Emmanuel Gollantz—forty thousand and one hundred guineas," then turned and, greeted by a splutter of applause, walked from the salerooms. Gollantz' had come to buy the Reynolds, they had achieved their objective, and they left the rest of the admirable collection of the Earl of Howark to other dealers to whom such things were of interest.

For a moment Emmanuel stood at the door,

uncertain and hesitating. Should he wait for a little to see if Juliet would leave the salerooms, and try to snatch a word with her, or should he walk back to the office immediately? His sense of what was due to Max and his firm won. He turned and walked quickly back to Bond Street, rang for Hannah and dictated a telegram to Max.

Bought it at forty thousand and one hundred guineas.

He made no further attempt to see Juliet again. His business occupied him, and he regarded the sudden rush of work as something of a boon sent by Fate. His time was literally not his own, and he was forced to spend long hours at home working out various estimates which Mason had submitted from the works on Camden Hill. Once when he sat at his desk, while Mason's stubby forefinger pointed out first one item and then another, the clock on the mantelpiece struck the half-hour after eight. For a moment, Mason and his modern designs, his prices for time and overhead expenses, faded into the distance. In spirit, Emmanuel had entered the Albert Hall and stood waiting for the appearance of Juliet Forbes. Then, with an almost superhuman effort, he dragged himself back and listened to Mason once more.

"By usin' the second quality—and that's a sight better than what most firms uses for first quality

—we might save a bit on the frames of the big couches, but the point is, Mr. Emmanuel, that once you start mixin' wood, it's like mixin' drinks —you're never goin' to know where you get to, nor what you land yourself in for."

Emmanuel did not answer immediately. He sat with his head resting on his hand, apparently giving the matter his consideration. In reality he was fighting one of those battles which were growing more and more difficult as time went on.

"My dearest, I mustn't think of you. I daren't think of you. Half London may be listening to you now, and I'm the one man in London who mustn't even think of you!" Then, pushing the thought of her from him with what seemed to him almost physical force, he nodded and managed to say convincingly to Mason:

"I believe you're right. Stick to the first quality, it will pay in the end. More reliable. The difference in cost isn't sufficient to warrant taking risks."

On the morning of the day of the Claytons' party, Viva asked him what time he would be back in the evening.

"We might dine somewhere first," she said; "make a night of it. I've seen nothing of you for months!"

Emmanuel smiled. "I have only the usual excuse to offer and you must be tired of that by this time. I'm getting just a little tired of it myself.

I was hard at it until after eleven last night. Where were you, by the way?"

"Went to see Hammond's new play at the Queen's. Had supper afterwards at the Hungarian. Bill was there. We shall have to watch William, he wasn't alone. Guess who was with him."

"Couldn't—I never even knew that Bill went in for escorting young women to theatres."

Viva grinned. "Not so young, very attractive though. Your terribly menacing Juliet Forbes! I talked to them during the intervals, and wasn't terribly impressed. She's lovely, just a little haggard, but dull, y'know. Nothing much to say for herself. You didn't tell me that she and Bill were at the sale the other day."

Emmanuel, feeling like a schoolboy discovered in some crime, knew that his explanation sounded horribly weak. It was really so simple and his story seemed so elaborate. Bill and luncheon at the Savoy, catching sight of the Claytons, going over, what Clayton said, and how, after the sale of the Reynolds, he had left and returned to the office.

Viva still smiled. "Leaving Bill a fair field? Kind, but possibly not very wise. We can't have William losing his heart to a woman old enough to be his mother. You're coming tonight, aren't you?"

"Yes, I can manage it. I'll get home early and

take you wherever you like first. It doesn't begin until ten, does it?"

He came over to the bed and kissed her, telling himself that his sense of irritation was ridiculous. What did it matter if Bill had taken her to a first night? What did it matter that Viva said she was dull, or old enough to be Bill's mother? Nothing —not a damn, and yet it was difficult not to show that he was almost angry.

He was going to see her that evening, speak to her, touch her hands, and hear her voice again. He had said that it would be the last time, and now he knew that there could never be a last time. He could never put her out of his life, never allow her to put him out of hers. It was impossible; they belonged to each other. Everything else faded into insignificance. He could never go on alone; could never face with equanimity the life which he had lived for nearly three years. He doubted if he could even face it with sanity.

The day passed. It seemed to Emmanuel that the hours alternated between racing and dragging. Seemed too that his own state of mind swung between excited expectancy and dreadful misgivings. Hannah Rosenfelt, watching him, decided that it was time that Sir Max came home and allowed Emmanuel to take a holiday. He was losing weight, there were shadows under his eyes, and she noticed at his temples that the grey hairs, which a few months ago had only been a few in number, had increased, so that when the light caught his hair it shone silver.

"My father writes that he will be back in a week or ten days," Emmanuel said. "He's very much pleased about the Reynolds."

"I'm glad that he's coming back," Hannah said. "A thing like buying a picture—even a picture as famous as that one—isn't really much. Oh, I don't mean that it wasn't courageous, or splendid! But it's the small everyday things that tell. That's what's wearing. The going on day after day, having to attend to everything, to give opinions on this, that and the next things. You're tired out."

Emmanuel looked at her intently, and something which she saw in his dark, rather melancholy eyes startled her.

"Mr. Emmanuel—"

He smiled. "What's the matter, Hannah? Don't worry about me. I'm all right. It's only—as you say—the going on, day after day, that gets a little wearing." Then with sudden intensity: "But it's going to be all right! It must be!"

She went away to work at the letters which he had dictated, to attend to the memoranda which he had made, her mind disturbed and perplexed. She had loved Emmanuel Gollantz ever since she had first seen him, a tall, good-looking boy calling to drive his father home, long before he had any part in the business. She had known him when he used to sit, silent, attentive, watching, and

127

listening to old Emmanuel, his grandfather, transacting business. Her love had been, then, the romantic love of a girl for a young man. Now it had changed and become merely protective, fiercely resenting anything that could hurt him. Once she had allowed herself to dream, to weave stories round him, romances in which he suddenly realized her devotion to him and admitted that he had always loved her. That had been many years ago. Now, when she looked at her heavy, intelligent face in the glass, noted her features so marked by race, she realized that her dreams had been only the sentimental yearnings of a young girl. She had grown wiser, and had transmuted her affection for Emmanuel Gollantz into something which might be less colourful, but which in its selflessness and intensity was very beautiful.

At five o'clock he came into her office, asked if there were any other letters to sign, and sat down at her desk to put his name to the letters which she passed over to him. As she watched him, she longed to ask him what was wrong, to beg to be allowed to help. Once before when he had been in trouble when he had left England so suddenly she had been able to offer him sympathy and comfort which he had valued. Now her love for him made her senses so alert that she knew instinctively he needed help, and that he had no one in whom he could confide.

He finished the letters, pushed them away, and

128

said: "There, that's done! No tea going today, Hannah?"

"I had it at four," she said, "and you were busy with Mr. Lane. I didn't like to disturb you. I can send for some in a minute."

Emmanuel shook his head. "No, I don't really want any. I think I'll get along home. You could telephone to me if anything cropped up suddenly." He laughed. "I get nervous when I'm on my own like this. Always afraid that someone may come in and offer us the Portland Vase or the Elgin Marbles and I may miss them!" Then, suddenly: "Hannah, do you ever feel that you've been wandering about in the dark, that you're more than a little frightened, and yet you don't quite know how or where to find daylight?"

"I used to—I don't think that I do now."

"How did you get out of the wood?"

She looked at him very steadily. "The same way as everyone else gets out, Mr. Emmanuel. I walked out."

He nodded. "Yes—but what about the other people, the people who don't find that particular wood dark and frightening?"

Her eyes wavered, she nervously set some papers straight on her desk.

"I don't know," she said. "It's difficult to know how far other people matter. I don't know, Mr. Emmanuel; if there's anything I can do, I'll do it, but don't ask me riddles when you don't even know the answers yourself. Oh"—with almost violent intensity—"I wish Emmanuel Gollantz was alive still! . . ." Then more gently, as if she had regained her control: "You might apply his methods and rules to most things and not go very far wrong, Mr. Emmanuel."

Emmanuel rose and laid his hand on her arm. "Sorry, Hannah. I ought not to bother you, but it's a bad habit you've allowed me to get into. Don't worry. I was talking a lot of nonsense. Good night."

"Good night," she said abruptly; then added, "May the God of your fathers bless and keep you."

He went home, dressed and took Viva out to the latest and smartest restaurant to dine. Viva was in her most flippant mood. She was amusing, daring, and looking her best. Emmanuel, watching her, thought how much he liked her, what good friends they were, and how utterly lacking in any passion his feeling for her was.

As they left she said: "You'll stay and dance after your brother's young woman has sung, won't you?"

He wanted to tell her everything, wanted to say that he was going to see Juliet, and that he loved her and couldn't face life without her any longer; instead he said that he didn't know, that if Viva didn't mind awfully he wanted to go along and see old Lane. And in a flash he was telling a long idiotic story of how Lane had been in that afternoon, and what Lane had said, and how this ought to be settled and that ought to be clinched.

"I don't mind," she said. "I think you're a fool to work so hard. I think you're losing a devil of a lot. Once before, Emmanuel, you almost lost a great deal by this mania for carrying everything on your own shoulders. That was when Max was away, and when out of sheer annoyance I almost married Julian, d'you remember? But you must do as you wish. I've no doubt that Julian will be there for me to dance with tonight."

Emmanuel, leaning back in the car, feeling rather dreadfully detached, said easily: "Trying to make me jealous of Julian, Viva?"

"Not particularly. Oh, go and talk to old Lane. It's all right, Emmanuel, I don't really mind."

The next half-hour was a confused series of impressions to him. Red carpet and an awning, lights, the Claytons, kindly, smiling and stout. A huge room, gilt chairs, three great cut-glass chandeliers, people saying, "Hello, Emmanuel," or "How are you, Gollantz?" Julian, without Amanda. Amanda had a cold and couldn't leave her room. Bill asking if Julian was never at the House in these days, and Julian replying that Bill knew less about the House than he believed. "It's Friday, my poor child." Julian asking Viva about dances later, and Viva promising a great many, or so it seemed. Viva asking Bill questions about what he had been doing, Bill saying stolidly that

131

he had lunched with Miss Forbes, and Viva asking if he wasn't making the running there very well. Julian suddenly interested in Bill, and asking questions about Juliet.

"Nice woman, Bill?"

"Charming."

"But dull, eh?" Viva said.

"Most really good women are," Julian added quickly.

Viva said, "Is she really good?"

"Ask Bill"—Julian smiled.

Bill, suddenly sulky and on the defensive, said, "Oh, shut up!"

Julian began: "There is a refreshingly youthful quality in the conversation of brother William which no doubt makes an immense appeal to any woman who is past her first youth. His whole outlook is one which lacks—"

Bill, his face scarlet, said: "Your whole outlook will be upset if you don't shut up! You are a damned cad."

Emmanuel stood and listened, and felt that he didn't belong to any of them, he scarcely knew them. Nothing mattered. He was only there to see Juliet, to hear her and to meet her again when it was over. These people couldn't affect him. They might talk, say what they liked, he had no part in them or their affairs.

Bill touched his arm. "Come and sit down. Bolitha is going to play, and then Miss Forbes is

going to sing. Only four quite short songs, because she's leaving tomorrow early for Paris."
He followed Bill, sat down, and waited.

9

IT was over. Bill gave a deep sigh and said:
"Lord, that was good!" People were moving,
and surging towards the supper-room.
Emmanuel wondered how much he had heard.
Nothing very consciously. He had only known
that Juliet had stood there, and that waves of
sound had swept over him and transported him
from London to the villa in Italy. He followed
Bill, and saw Viva ahead of them with Bill
Masters. He wondered how soon he could go,
and then the thought struck him that he might
borrow Bill's car. He didn't want to take his own,
Viva would want that, and he felt that to sit
cooped up in a taxi would drive him crazy.

"Got your car here, Bill?"

"Yes, why? Want it?"

"I do rather. I want to slip round to see old
Lane"—he was lying even to Bill, and lying quite
easily! "Viva will want ours. She'll give you a lift
back. I'll send yours round in the morning early."

"Right—do me splendidly."

"Thanks awfully."

Then quite suddenly they were close to Juliet.
She stood talking to old Carrington, who
quavered out: "Oh, my dear young lady, why
didn't you sing that French translation of 'My

134

love is like a red, red rose'? I heard you sing that one—now, where was it?"

For a moment Emmanuel caught the expression on her face that he had seen there the night he held her in his arms and whispered, "Lovely Juliet." She answered quickly giving the name of some hall which Emmanuel felt convinced was not correct. Carrington had heard her sing the song when she was with Leon Hast, and she could never bear to be reminded of that time. The knowledge that he alone had seen her expression change, and had known the reason for it, gave him a strange sense of closeness to her. It was as if they shared a secret.

Bill said: "How are you, Miss Forbes?" and she turned, smiling, herself again.

"Your much too elaborate luncheon almost killed my voice," she said, and Emmanuel knew that she had seen him, standing behind Bill's broad shoulders. "I am going home in half an hour. I have to start horribly early. Oh, how I hate the Channel!"

"Then stay this side," Bill said. "We should all be thankful."

Emmanuel moved forward, bowed, and tried to say something ordinary and conventional about her singing. He knew that his words came automatically, but her eyes smiled and were very kind.

Bill said: "Will you give me one dance?"

135

"If you will promise when it's over to take me to my car. Is that a bargain?"

"I feel as if I might be selling my birthright," Bill said; "there is a dreadful sort of finality about it, but—I promise."

He turned to his brother. "Why don't you ask for one too?"

"Because, having heard what Miss Forbes said, I obviously shouldn't get one."

Bill grinned. "Oh—faint heart never won—you know."

For one moment Emmanuel hesitated, then remembered that if he danced with Juliet, he must automatically dance with Viva, and so the moment passed. He felt a sense of unreality sweep over him, and wondered how much any of these people—except Juliet—mattered to him, or how much he cared if he never saw any of them again. The band was playing and Bill moved a little nearer to Juliet.

"This one—it's a topping good tune."

Emmanuel heard her say, "What is it called? —I've heard it somewhere."

"Auf Wiederseh'n, leb wohl," Bill said, and gave a little boyish laugh that held something of selfconsciousness in its tone.

They moved away and Emmanuel, still detached, watched Viva dancing with Julian. A man behind him said: "How like the Claytons! Juliet Forbes and her Lieder, and then Jimmy

136

Hartopp's band! The fair-haired poof will sing in a minute!"

The sound of a thin, sexless tenor floated across the room.

"Here in your arms . . . remain,
So let me kiss you . . .
Before we say 'Auf Wiederseh'n,
Auf Wiederseh'n', my dear,"

He shivered. It wasn't going to be "Auf Wiederseh'n" for him, it was going to be "good-bye". As Bill had said—"Dreadfully final." The dance was over. He went across to Viva and said that he was going, and would she give Bill a lift home. Viva, still laughing at some remark of Julian's, said:

"Going? Oh, I remember. Give old Lane my love and don't let him keep you up until all hours. Good night, my sweet."

Bill and Juliet were moving towards the door. She was stopping every few seconds to speak to someone, or to allow someone to speak to her; Bill followed, his face beaming. Julian walked slowly along at Emmanuel's side.

"So you got the picture," Julian said.

"Yes—we got it."

"The regal 'we' meaning the House of Gollantz?"

"Obviously."

"Peters told someone that you had paid through the nose for it."

"A hundred guineas more than Peters was prepared to pay, that's all."

"Going on to old Lane's to talk business?"

"Yes." His eyes were following Juliet; he answered automatically.

"The Industrious Apprentice, eh?"

Emmanuel did not reply. Juliet and Bill had vanished. He turned to get his hat and coat. Julian followed. At the door, Emmanuel asked if his brother was leaving. Julian laughed.

"No—one member of the family must stay and do their duty by Viva, mustn't they? I'll see her home: I didn't come in the car."

Bill, turning from a car the door of which he had just shut, stood watching it move slowly away, then faced them.

"Want my car, Emmanuel? It's over there on the parking place. Nice bright car to pick out, mine. Nothing like scarlet and white! Vulgar but visible. Good night. Send her back in the morning."

The two brothers stood watching Emmanuel cross the road, swing his legs into Bill's low and ultra-sporting model, then drive it out of the square, going northwards.

Julian chuckled. "Queer way to get to Lane's place. He lives in Prince's Gate!"

Bill, absorbed, answered mechanically: "P'raps the road's up."

Again Julian laughed. "Perhaps he isn't going to Lane's at all!"

Bill came out of his dreams and said sharply: "What the devil do you mean?"

"Just what I say. Oh, well, it's none of my business. Good luck to him."

With a pleasantness which was dangerous, Bill said: "You enjoy trying to queer things for Emmanuel, don't you? Pity it never comes off, isn't it?"

Julian turned away, and as he went looked over his shoulder, smiling and saying: "One never knows. It might—one day."

The low scarlet-and-white car swung out of the square and into Park Lane. Emmanuel's hands were steady, but he felt dazed and terribly tired. Almost unconsciously he turned into the Park and drove round the circle, hoping that the cool air might soothe him a little. The wretched tune was running in his head. He could still hear the thin, effective tenor voice singing:

"Then let me kiss you once again
Before we say . . ."

He turned out of the Park by Marble Arch, back down Park Lane, and brought the car to a standstill outside Lauderdale House. Juliet's car had gone. Emmanuel climbed out, and on his way through the hall asked the porter if he could leave his car at the door. The porter peered out, then said that, as he hadn't left it "direckerly in front of the door", he thought it would be all right.

Juliet was standing by the fireplace when he entered. She turned and held out her hands. He said, in a tone which sounded in his ears ridiculously conventional: "It's very kind of you to see me."

He heard the door close, and stood holding her hand in his.

"Juliet," he said, stumbling a little over the words, "I promised that I wouldn't distr-ress you. I don't mean to. Only—oh, my dear, it's terrible, I think this is killing me. Can't you help me?"

"How can I help you, except by going away and never coming to London again?"

"The world is too small. We're bound to meet each other."

She smiled. "Lovers used to say that the world was so large."

He let her hand fall, walked to the fireplace, and stood resting his arm along the edge, watching her. She thought that she had never seen such pain in anyone's eyes as that which was reflected in Emmanuel's at that moment. She had loved him three years ago, she still loved him, and almost frantically she sought for something which might comfort him, stabilize him, and help him to forget.

"Emmanuel—you ought never to have come. I was weak—"

140

"Why did you let me come? Only because I asked? Juliet, for God's sake tell me the truth. It's too late for us to lie to each other. I've lied to everyone tonight, and it didn't matter. But you mustn't lie to me. Tell me that you wanted to see me again."

"I did—I did want to see you."

"Only to tell me to go away?"

"I don't know—"

"If I was free, would you marry me?"

For the first time she spoke with determination. "Emmanuel, we talked this over before. The same reasons which prevented it before prevent it now."

"If you loved me sufficiently you wouldn't care!"

She shook her head. "I can say equally truthfully that because I do love you, I do care!"

He came to her, took her hand, and very gently forced her to sit down on the big sofa. Then, sitting down at her side, he took her hand in both his, and began to speak in that soft, almost lisping voice, with the rolling "r's" which she remembered so well.

"Juliet," he said, "It's no use, we can't either of us risk everything for a scruple. I've starved for you. I've starved so long that I'm weak. I think I'd almost commit murder in order to see you again. I've lost all values concerning everything and everyone except you. You are the world, my world—no other world matters.

141

You're fr-ree. I can get my freedom. Life is in front of us, not left behind. I shan't starve, I can find work somewhere. I don't mind if it's away from you so long as I know that you will come back—and come back to me. Places don't matter to me—work doesn't matter. I'll do what I did before, keep a shop—anything, so long as I can see you, tell you that I love you, and know that you love me. Juliet, listen to me."

"I am listening, Emmanuel."

"I could face separation, if I could see meetings at the end of it—if it didn't stretch into infinity. It's the blankness, the endlessness that frightens me. Oh, Juliet, Juliet, don't condemn me to years of blank, aching nothingness!" His voice rose a little and, as she heard the sudden sharpness of his tone, she realized how near to breaking-point he had come, "I can't bear it—I can't face it!"

"Emmanuel—don't! Don't make me entirely responsible."

"You are responsible!" he flung at her. "Who else can be?"

"Oh, don't! It's cruel!" She moved so that she faced him, her hands pressed on the sofa on either side of her. "It's no use—can't you see that? You're the eldest son of Max Gollantz. You'll be the head of the house you're all so proud of. How can I let you leave everything—risk losing everything? I can't do it, it's not possible."

"Losing?" he cried. "Gaining everything! Not possible! I tell you that if you love me it is possible—it can be possible. Make what conditions you wish, only keep me in your life, and—oh, God, Juliet, if you love me, and you say that you do, be merciful!" His eyes narrowed suddenly, his face seemed to grow older, pinched and grey in the light of the shaded lamps. "Or is it that you loved me once, and that it's over and done with? Tell me. It won't make me love you less, nothing can do that. Only, I'd try to make it easier for you if you said that—r-really—it was past and done with."

She spoke so softly that he had to lean forward to catch her words.

"How can I say that?" The passion in her almost whispered words reached him. "How can I say that? It's not true! You know that it's not true!"

Without warning he put up his hands, drew her to him, and held her fast. She felt his kisses on her lips, her eyes, her forehead, heard the wild, half-delirious phrases which he whispered, and knew that her strength and determination were leaving her. It was as if every ounce of conviction, of resolution, were being drawn from her as she lay in his arms. She knew that she too had starved, had known what it was to be chilled, lonely, and wretched. For three years she had lived her life without love. She had worked, attained a greater measure of success than ever before, and had continued to drive herself to fresh efforts so that she might push away the thought, the image, of Emmanuel Gollantz.

Panic-stricken, she tried to put up her hands and push him away from her. Vainly she whispered: "Emmanuel, my dear, don't—don't!" His arms only held her more closely, and once his laugh, very soft and tender, reached her. When at last he let her go, only holding her very gently in the circle of his arm, she opened her eyes and found his watching her.

"Juliet," he said, "oh, my beloved, it's too late to be wise any longer. You know and I know, and we're done with pretence and talk of what is wise and possible. Everything is possible! We belong to each other. Tell me that you are happy, tell me that you've done with struggling and fighting against what is inevitable—"

She pressed her finger-tips against her eyes, sat very still and silent for a moment, then turned and laid her hands on his shoulders.

"Emmanuel," she said, "it's dreadful. I won't pretend, I can't pretend any more. I love you. Nothing really matters to me except that I should be with you. But there isn't anything new, things are as they were three years ago. You can't marry me. I'm not the sort of woman who makes a good mistress—I know, because I remember what I suffered when I lived with"—there was a second's pause before she went on—"Leon Hast. We've got to go on—as we are."

Emmanuel shook his head. "We can't," he

said, "because a moment ago I held you in my arms and knew what it meant to me, and what it meant to you. From now—it is different, and you know it."

"I shall leave England tomorrow."

He nodded. "I know, but I shall find you again. We shall find each other again." He smiled suddenly. "The world, my beloved, is such a small place. There, you shan't be wor-ried any more. You're tired. Lean back, there!" He pulled cushions towards her and arranged them so that she could rest against them. "Sit still and let me look at you. I've made so many mental pictures of you and I want to correct them all. How bad some of them were, too! None of them nearly beautiful enough. Like all the mental gramo-phone records I made of your voice—not one single one was r-right. All dreadful! Was there ever another voice like yours in the world? Tonight I never heard a word, I only knew that lovely waves of sound wrapped me r-round and r-round. It's such—such an effortless voice, Juliet. Why?"

For the first time she smiled back at him. She felt that she had been drained of all her strength, that she was powerless to do anything but lean back and listen to his voice. The very tones were healing. His little foreign accent, his lack of self-consciousness, were recalling so many nights when they had sat together under the stars in the garden with the high thick hedges, where the moon sought and found the little white marble faun and made it shine like silver.

"Effortless?" she repeated. "Only because I happen to know how to sing, nothing more."

He laughed, that soft, almost silky laugh which she remembered.

"How I adore you when you are conceited about your voice! It's your only conceit, and such a charming one. Is there another voice as good as yours in the world?"

Very gravely, for Juliet never contrived to think or speak lightly of her voice, she answered. To her, her talent was an almost impersonal thing. It was something with which you were born, and which you must, in duty bound, cultivate and use well.

"At this present moment," she said seriously, "I don't think there is—for my special type of work, of course."

Emmanuel threw back his head, and this time his laugh held a sound of youth which she had not heard before.

"Adorable person! Juliet, have you any sense of humour at all?"

"I don't think," she admitted, "that I ever had very much."

He caught her hand, raised it to his lips and kissed it.

"Wait," he said, "wait, and we'll laugh at everything! Not in this country, because the sky is too low and that makes laughing difficult.

Somewhere where the sky is like a great arc, a great blue arc; somewhere where there are masses and masses of flowers, people who have very white, strong teeth, and dark hair that is very strong too. People who walk easily, laugh easily, who love their food, and drink because they are thirsty with the heat of the sun."

In the distance a bell rang, and Juliet, lifting her head, listened and said: "Who can that be?" She rose and walked to the door, opened it and looked out. Emmanuel did not move. He was too content, too far removed from everything and everyone to realize what the ringing of a doorbell meant. He sat, his hands clasped loosely, his eyes watching Juliet.

Then her voice cut through his dreams. "Bill," she said, "what is it?"

Emmanuel started to his feet and walked to the door. Bill was standing in the hall, his round, pleasant face disturbed and worried. Then Juliet spoke again: "Come in, this is nice! Emmanuel is here."

She moved aside and Bill entered, and stood for a moment uncertain how to begin.

"Well," Emmanuel said sharply, "what is it?"

"Look here," Bill said, "Julian knows where you are. Oh, I don't mean to be beastly, Miss Forbes, but you don't know Julian. He's talking to Viva now, and God only knows what sort of a complexion he can put on things! He's a devil, and a clever devil, and he loathes Emmanuel.

147

Viva gave us both a lift home, and Julian told your man to turn down here because the road by Marble Arch was up. He told him at the last possible minute, so that we turned round here fairly slowly. He looked out of the window and said: 'By Jove, Bill, there's your car outside Lauderdale House!' Then added very quickly: 'No, of course it's not, what a fool I am!' Viva craned her neck and said of course it was my car, and hadn't I better do something about it. That gave Julian his cue and he started off with a long palaver about it couldn't be, and Viva mustn't think another thing about it, and rattled on at sixty miles an hour about all sorts of things. He made it so damned obvious that he knew it was my car, and Viva isn't a fool by a very long chalk. I—I hope you don't think me all kinds of an idiot, Miss Forbes, but—just because I do know my precious brother—I think—well, I think that Emmanuel ought to get along home, if you don't mind my saying so."

Juliet did not move. She stood looking at Emmanuel, thinking that she had never seen him look so utterly tired. All his youth, his gaiety, seemed to have left him. His face was white, and new lines showed round his mouth.

At last he said: "Very well, Bill, I'll come."

Bill said: "Then, if Miss Forbes will excuse me, I'll nip down and start her up. She's rather a brute when she's cold."

Mechanically Juliet said, "Good night, Bill."

She heard the door close and turned again to Emmanuel. "Well?"

He nodded. "It's all right, my dear. I'll go and see what Julian has managed to do. After all, there isn't anything very incriminating in my visiting you. It's only a quarter past one." Then he squared his shoulders and said more firmly: "Don't worry, promise that you won't worry. I can see this thr-rough. This isn't the end, it can't be, it mustn't be. Juliet, you're mine and I'm yours—nothing can alter that. We belonged to each other years ago. I loved you—do you remember?—when I came down with Angela to stay with you somewhere near Reading. I was eighteen—less. Ten years ago. Ten years is a long time, my sweet."

"Ten years," she said, "is just the difference between your age and mine, Emmanuel."

"I have been separated fr-rom you for three years," Emmanuel said. "Each year has seemed like ten. So, my dearest, I am r-really twenty years older than you are. I must go. Good night, my so-much-loved Juliet."

He caught her in his arms, held her to him, and when he tried to go Juliet knew that she was possessed by a sudden and overwhelming sense of fear. She clung to him, crying: "Don't go— Emmanuel, don't go!"

Very gently he moved her hands from his shoulders, kissed her very tenderly and whispered: "For the first and last time," he said, "I leave you when you ask me to stay. Auf Wiederseh'n, my dear."

10

THEY drove in silence until the car turned into Gloucester Place, when Bill said: "Can't think how you came to have Julian for a brother! Nasty bit of work."

Emmanuel, feeling terribly tired and utterly lacking in ability to care what happened, replied: "Oh, I don't know. Sorry to have dragged you into this, Bill." Then quickly and with more animation: "You mustn't think badly of Juliet, she only let me see her—because she's going away tomorrow."

Bill grunted something unintelligible and drew up at the kerb.

"There you are," he said. "No, I won't come in. I've had my bellyful of Julian this evening. Don't get rattled, Emmanuel. Good night."

Emmanuel climbed out, let himself into the house, and walked into the drawing-room. Julian was standing by the fire, smoking. He stood with one elbow on the mantelpiece, graceful, nonchalant and undisturbed. Viva sat on a low chair and watched him. Emmanuel stood for a moment in the doorway watching them both, wondering what he was going to say, and what the result would be. On one thing he was deter-

151

mined: he was not going to talk to Viva with his brother in the room.

Viva turned and said in her crisp voice: "Hello, Emmanuel."

"Hello, Viva." He waited for some word from Julian. Julian said nothing, only a smile touched his lips as he looked at his brother. Emmanuel faced him.

"Good night, Julian," he said; "I want to talk to Viva."

Julian's smile widened. "Belated but acceptable," he said. "Shall I wait until I hear that Viva wants me to go?"

Viva said: "Yes, I think you'd better go, Julian. Three-cornered conversations are difficult. Good night."

He bowed as if in assent to a command. "Good night. Just one word. Whatever I did or said, believe me, was not from any wish to—"

Emmanuel cut him short. "That's all right, no one is misjudging you."

As the door closed behind him, Viva laughed, There was no trace of annoyance or bitterness in the sound; it was, so far as Emmanuel could judge, a sound of sheer amusement.

"Exit the wicked fairy," she said. "Well, Emmanuel, you made a mess of it, didn't you? Why the devil couldn't you have said where you were going, instead of that tale about Lane?"

"I don't know," he said. "Honestly, I don't know. I beg your pardon. It was stupid of me."

"I agree," very quickly. "It's given Julian an opportunity to condone with me, to suggest that you're keeping two homes—not that anyone could call a flat in Lauderdale House a home!—and a dozen other things. He painted such a picture of a deserted young wife—me—deserted by an unworthy husband—you—that I almost burst into tears." Her tone changed. The lightness and the banter left it, and she asked crisply: "How much is there to it, Emmanuel?"

"In the sense that Julian would like to imply—nothing."

"She's not your mistress?"

"No."

"Was she—when you were in Italy?"

"Never."

There was a pause. Viva lit another cigarette and Emmanuel walked over to the little table and poured himself out a drink. He carried it back with him and stood as Julian had done, watching his wife. After what seemed an eternity, she looked up and smiled.

"Why didn't you tell me about Italy?" she said. "You knew her there. And loved her? Wanted to marry her?"

"Yes—all those things," he said. "I didn't tell you, Viva, because it was all over. She refused to mar-ry me, and at first I couldn't bear to talk of it. Then—it didn't seem necessary."

"And now you've seen her again?"

It seemed that their old friendship, comradeship, was re-established; that he was standing in this quiet room with his best friend, with the woman he liked best in the whole world, and that everything had miraculously become easy and beautifully simple. All fear had gone, he only felt a contempt for himself that he had understood Viva so little.

"Now I've seen her again," he said, "I know that nothing has changed. It's all as it once was. I can't help myself. It's too str-rong for me. It's something far bigger than I am. I ought to have told you. I met her at Bill Masters'. She let me call and see her the next day. I saw her at luncheon with Bill at the Savoy, and now again tonight. Perhaps a couple of hours in all. She leaves London tomorrow morning."

"Where for?"

"I don't know."

"You mean that?"

"On my word I do."

"Then she won't live with you?"

Emmanuel shook his head. "No—even if I were free she wouldn't marry me."

He saw Viva's lips smile again, this time with less mirth; they were twisted a little.

"Oh, you got as far as that, eh?"

He made a little appealing movement with his hands. "My dear," he said, "I didn't mean to hurt you. I'm trying so desperately hard to be honest with you."

"I'm sure you are. Poor Emmanuel. It's a

rotten business for you. I think it's permissible to ask if you ever loved me?"

"I don't know, Viva. I thought that I did. I think that I did love you, that I still love you—only—well, you're my best friend. I like you so tremendously. It's been such fun—"

She nodded. "Great fun. Y'know, I believe that I was in love with you once. I remember when you were away—when you played the fool and let Max think those letters were yours, not Julian's—I worked like a black to prove that you were innocent. Y'know, you really had me to thank for bringing you home. Good Lord, if I'd known, I should have been doing you a better turn to leave you there, shouldn't I? I still love you. I honestly believe, Emmanuel, that we have something between us that will last as long as we shall. I tried to say this the other night, do you remember? Only I had an idea that I should—want to break loose first. I might have done if Juliet Forbes hadn't come to London! Shall I go on and be quite frank, rather brutal?"

"Yes," he said, "say anything—anything."

"Give me a drink—make it fairly strong. Thanks. Sit down. You look so impermanent standing there, as if you might go off with your young woman at any moment. That's better. The first year was grand. You're good-looking, you dance divinely, and you're very nice to have about a house. Now, don't think this is sour grapes, because it's not. Honestly, for the last year I've been just a little bored, and for the last six months —in patches—unspeakably so. I know that you hate Julian. I do in spasms; in spasms I adore him. Oh, it's all right, I've not fallen in love with your brother. I use the word in its—modern sense, meaning like enormously. Given another six months, if your young woman hadn't precipitated things a bit, we should have had a bust! Only I should have been the person to do the busting, not you. You see, you're a Gollantz— I'm a Heriot. My father is a drunken English baronet, and my mother is an ex-chorus girl. I want a heap more fun out of life than you ever will. I'm restless, I'm always looking for something, and it's always just evading me. I thought that I had found it in you: decency, stability, all the sterling qualities—because you have them, you know. D'you know, Emmanuel, I don't really want those things at all?

"I don't want Walter's nasty little decadents, I don't want father's jaded aristocrats, I don't want the unwashed section of Chelsea with their elaborate disregard of convention. I want—something, and I'm damned if I quite know what." She laughed, "You know, I believe—in the end —I shall want you or someone like you; but not now, not yet. You're not fluid enough, you're too businesslike to be romantic, and too romantic to be businesslike. You're too intrinsically decent to be really amusing. Oh, damn, if only I wasn't

156

your wife, I'd ask you to call and see me every other afternoon from four till six!"

Emmanuel sat and stared at her, his dark eyes melancholy and puzzled. As he listened he remembered how often Viva had puzzled him. how so many of the statements she made seemed inexplicable to him. He had disliked many of her friends, while she had pronounced many of his crashing bores. Not that it had mattered, because she was right when she said that there was a bond between them, something which went deeper than common friendships and ordinary tastes.

"Fundamentally," she said suddenly, "I love you; extraneously—that's a good effort, Emmanuel—you irritate me. It's funny how this is working out. I ought to be playing the outraged wife and asking you a long list of most awkward questions. Here I am, putting myself in the wrong and saying, 'Oh, well, if it hadn't been you, it would certainly have been me.' It's all wrong somewhere." Then abruptly: "What are you going to do about it—about you and Miss Forbes?"

"I don't know, Viva. I should like to get away."

"Alone? Oh, I don't mean that you should take me with you. I mean do you want to get away to Juliet Forbes? I'll divorce you if you like—we could always get married again when we've settled down. It's rather a smart thing to do. In ten years, twenty years, we may both of us have 'found

157

ourselves', and the fundamental liking we have now for each other may be enough. I'm desperately sorry. I'm sorry because I hate to know that you're unhappy, I hate to see you with a dead-white face and looking wretched. I wouldn't go on living with you, even if you wanted it, knowing that you loved someone else. I mean none of this 'hoping that with care and love it may come right again'. That's a degrading sort of business. If you want to go, then go. If ever you want to come back, tell me and I'll answer honestly—that either we'll give it another chance, or that I've found someone else and don't want you. There'll be a hell of a row with the family. I should work the nervous breakdown if I were you. Say that you want a holiday and take one. Whew! I wouldn't be in your shoes for something! Max will be outraged, Angela will wonder what has been lacking in her that her eldest son wants to go off with someone other than his wife, Bill will wrinkle his snub nose and reiterate that you are the decentest chap he knows, and Julian—what a chance for Julian! For months he'll be so publicly attentive to Amanda that he'll be nauseating. Oh, well—let's get down to brass tacks. What are you really going to do? I've reached that question before and still you haven't answered except that you want to go away."

Emmanuel stood silent, his eyes clouded, his face very pale, looking, Viva thought, terribly pathetic. With all his business acumen, with all his apparent poise and his modernity, he was utterly incapable of applying any of these things to his present position. He looked what he was —a very handsome, slightly romantic-looking young man, utterly wretched, entirely without plans, ready to launch out on an unknown sea without chart or compass.

"I don't know," he said, "I only wish that I did."

"You'd like to get away? Have you any idea where you want to go?"

He shook his head. "Not r-really."

"Can't you go to her—to Juliet Forbes?"

"Not as her lover—she—oh, it's impossible! It's no use, Viva, I don't know. Write me down as a fool, an incapable fool. It's all been so dreadful, it's so difficult to speak of. I—I don't know where I am. I only know that I can't go on any longer buying and selling furniture and pictures. I feel half dead, and, my God, I want life! I want colour and sunshine and I can't find it here—"

"With me," she added. "That's what you mean. Why haven't you the courage to say it? I can only say that if you want to go—go you must, I shan't try to stop you. If you want this woman, then—find her, make her live with you, take what will give you sunshine and colour. If you can't, then you don't either love her or want her enough. You've got too many visions and not enough vision, Emmanuel. It's not a hanging

159

matter. The day's past when men and women had to stay tied together when one or both of them wanted freedom. Learn to be hard like Julian, learn to be practical like Bill, and learn to take everything lightly as I do." She rose and came over to where he stood and laid her hand on his arm. "Listen," she said more softly. "What have we got left, you and I? I'll tell you. We've got friendship and a certain trust in each other. You believe that?"

"Yes," Emmanuel said with sudden energy. "Yes, I do believe that."

"Then go—go where you like, do what you like, and know that I shall do the same. Only if one day either of us wants the other, really and truly, let's trust that friendship and say so. If I write and tell you that I've met the one man in the world I think I can be happy with, either give me my freedom or write and tell me that the idea gives you a horrible tug at your heart and ask if we can't give it all another chance. Will you do that?"

"Yes, yes, I will"—eagerly. "But that's only one side, Viva. What about me? If I go now, if I meet Juliet and she—does love me enough—what then?"

Viva's hand slipped from his arm, and she moved an almost imperceptible distance away from him. "Oh, I'm facing that from the word go," she said. "I'm accepting that already. You may not know it, you may be able to deceive yourself, but that's why you're going away. To find her."

"Is that why I want to go away?" Emmanuel said. "I wonder. Honestly I don't know. I don't even know where to find her."

She moved again, this time with a certain half-tolerant impatience.

"You may not know," she said, "but I do! Take my advice, get away quickly. If you want romance go and find it, don't stay here haggling and arguing with the family—yours or mine. There's sufficient money. I have some of my own, Max will go on making us an allowance. That can all be settled when you've gone. What you'll have I don't quite know, but after all, in the role of troubadour you ought to be able to travel pretty cheaply. For heaven's sake, Emmanuel, brace up. Go and find her, catch her by the hair and live with her, and either get over it quickly and start again, or live happily with her ever after, only—don't moon." She yawned, walked back to her chair, finished her whisky-and-soda and said abruptly: "I'm going to bed. It's all right, but this modernity is a strain. The Edwardian rages and Victorian hysterics must have been much easier. Good night, Emmanuel. I should advise a couple of medinals or you'll never sleep."

He followed her to the door and opened it.

"Good night, Viva," he said. "I thank you so very sincerely. I do think you're the best friend anyone ever had. You're quite, quite wonderful. I'm terr-ribly grateful."

Once again she yawned, frankly and without concealment.

"That's something anyway," she said. "Good night. Make a bolt for it, my dear, that's my advice."

She walked upstairs and entered her bedroom. Her maid was waiting for her and, rising, came forward to take her cloak.

"I can manage." Viva said. "Get along to bed. It's late."

"I'll just take your things, madam."

"No, get along. You can put them away in the morning. Good night."

"Good night, madam, thank you."

She began to undress slowly, lighting a cigarette and dawdling about the room. She was tired. The whole business had been horribly tedious, except the part when Julian had been tactfully sympathetic. Julian, assuming that she was the heartbroken wife, betrayed and deceived, had amused her enormously. She reflected that after all the whole Gollantz family lacked imagination. They could usually be counted on to act conventionally. Bill, silent, outraged, and stolidly believing that, whatever happened, his hero, Emmanuel, was not to blame. Julian, immediately convinced that Emmanuel's defection had wounded her terribly, offering carefully worded sympathy—sympathy which carried with it the unspoken assurance that he was always ready to serve her.

"He's getting just a little tired of Amanda already," Viva thought. Then Emmanuel, constrained, puzzled and miserable, yet never able for one moment to speak what was in his mind, or to state exactly and clearly what was the position between himself and Juliet.

"Can't bring himself to speak of her—intimately—even to me whom he calls his best friend! Poor Emmanuel, he's so damnably nice and so terribly conventional about women."

She sat down and began to pull off her stockings, very slowly and reflectively.

"And me?" she thought. "What am I feeling in all this? Julian amuses me, Bill makes me laugh, and Emmanuel—having bored me for weeks—suddenly becomes interesting. Damn, that's laddered! They're too thin, these stockings. I ought to be suffering tortures, but I'm not. It can't be that a latent nobility is evincing itself in my character and that I want his happiness first. That's not a bit like me! It must be that I really don't care a great deal. He says that he wants life and love and all the rest of it. Possibly that's just what I want too, and it's just what's been lacking in this ménage for the last year. Let him go and look for it and I'll look for it too, and when we've got through this stage—who knows? I can't see life with Juliet Forbes being one long round of gaiety and fun, but then he has never really cared for gaiety and fun. He likes glasses of wine under boughs and dishes of herbs and a Mozart concerto by way of comic relief. Poor old Emmanuel, he's so eternally old and so perpetually young. Really the only time I have ever felt romantic about him was when he was away, banished for Julian's sins! Then I saw him as a sort of super-handsome Napoleon on Saint Helena, and wondered who darned his socks."

She ran her hand down the leg of the stocking, estimated the extent of the damage done by the ladder, then threw it aside and, slipping her feet into slippers, walked over to the dressing-table where Emmanuel's photograph stood in a leather frame. She picked it up and looked at it intently under the light.

"Nice feller you are!" she said softly. "Far too nice for me. She's a fool if she doesn't take you. I might even send her a note and tell her so. 'I am sending my husband to you—placing his happiness first,' and so on. If only we could have steered clear of this last year's bad patch, we might have been in smooth water. Oh, damn, I don't want smooth water, do I?" She grimaced at Emmanuel's picture, and went on, "Silly old stick! I'm going to miss you horribly sometimes and going to be so genuinely relieved not to have you at others. Two years, ten years—things may have settled themselves, or we may have settled ourselves. Anyway—off you go!" She laid down the picture and laughed. "And if I feel like it—off I go too."

The telephone by the side of her bed rang sharply and she wandered over to it without hurry, saying as she did so:

"Oh, shut up! Horrible noise! Damn the thing! Yes! who is it? Mrs. Gollantz speaking. Yes speaking!"

Julian's voice answered and Viva grinned, her vivid face animated and full of amusement. For a moment she wished that Emmanuel could have been there to listen with her and laugh at her asides.

"I couldn't sleep until I knew that you were all right."

"Nice of you, Julian. Yes, I'm all right."

"And Emmanuel—"

"I left him drinking a last whisky-and-soda."

Julian's voice, suddenly much softer, said: "My dear, you're making my poor little attempt to help terribly difficult, aren't you?"

She answered very lightly, allowing a laugh to interrupt her words. "Do I want help? Emmanuel hasn't beaten me, and I'm not weeping in the solitude of my room."

"By God, you've got pluck!" The sincerity was just a little overdone.

"Thank you, Julian. Always generous, aren't you?"

"Why are you so consistently unkind to me?"

165

"Because everyone else is so consistently kind to you."

"And if I told you that—everyone else didn't matter to me?"

"I should say—Ugh!—sorry, that's a yawn, Julian—that you're a remarkable fool. Good night, sleep well."

"Viva—just one minute—"

"Sorry, I honestly am asleep. Goo'night."

She hung up the receiver, stood looking at the telephone for a moment, then pursed her lips and emitted a low whistle.

"Whew-w-w! I'd hate to be Amanda Gollantz!"

Then, turning, she got into bed, let her head sink into the soft smoothness of the pillows and slept immediately and peacefully.

Book Two

Book Two

1

HE had sat up all night going through his papers, arranging odds and ends of work which were part of his own particular job. Once or twice he paused, stared at the sheets before him and wondered why he, Emmanuel Gollantz, should be spending the small hours of the morning arranging costs, instructions, passing designs and adding various small memoranda to estimates and cost sheets which he would never see brought to fruition. Then, pushing away his vague wonderings, he set himself again to his work with that thoroughness which was characteristic of him in his business dealings with his father's workmen and customers.

It was nearly five when he finished, pushed back his chair, and reached for the big tortoise-shell box in which he kept his cigarettes. Leaning back in his chair, smoking, he tried to order his thoughts and formulate some plans. Viva had advised his going away, seeing no one, but his mind rejected the idea. It looked too much like running away. He must see Max and his mother however painful the interview might be. They were still at Aix, and if he left at once he might catch them there. To have his interview in an hotel sitting-room would be less painful than at

Ordingly. Ordingly held so much. It had been the house which his grandfather chose, the house in which they had all three of them grown up. It had been the scene of his grandfather's death, his mother's illness, of the first days when he met and loved Viva.

Leaning back with his eyes closed, a little giddy for want of sleep, he saw so many scenes reacted for him. The lawns, with Angela seated under the big cedar tree waiting to pour out tea. His grandfather walking out very slowly, leaning on his ebony stick. Himself and Viva in the kitchen garden gathering strawberries. His father, white-faced and worried, walking restlessly up and down waiting for Meyer Bernstein's report when Angela lay fighting death in the big bedroom with the open windows which looked over the lawn. The day of old Emmanuel's funeral when all the Foreign Contingent had gathered together, when the crowd of dark-faced men had entered the big drawing-room, and he had seen Juliet Forbes standing beside Bill Masters' chair.

No, he couldn't face Ordingly—Ordingly belonged to the past. He was concerned only with the future.

He opened his eyes and stared round the room. It seemed that he had never seen it consciously before; as if now, for the first time, he looked and realized that this room in his house was his, and had been for over two years. Two years spent with Viva—years which had begun so delightfully. That was the right word—delightfully. His wounds had ceased to smart and ache quite so badly, and Viva had laughed and been amusing, and it had all been great fun. The house, the furniture, their plans for everything. And over all and through all Viva's definite personality which had seemed to draw a heavy curtain between himself and his memories of Juliet. He had returned from Italy three years ago, stunned. Looking back, he felt that he must have been only partially alive. Juliet had sent him away and he had returned to England and Ordingly, hurt, angry and utterly wretched.

That first winter at Ordingly had seemed to him to be months of perpetual rain, mist and wind, but it had healed him—or so it had appeared at the time. With Juliet away on a tour to Australia and later to America, replying to none of his letters, he had allowed Ordingly to wrap him round in its comfortable blanket of warmth and kindliness, and for months he had drifted. Viva had come and gone, had driven with him, ridden with him, and gradually her companionship had begun to take a definite shape in his mind. She had come to stand for something valuable, warm and brilliant. His mother had been glad to see her, had encouraged her to come and stay, had encouraged Emmanuel to go with the Heriots to Cannes for a month, and when he told her that he was going to ask Viva to marry

171

him, she had smiled, and held his hands and assured him that he had made her very happy.

He remembered his wedding day, standing with Bill at the altar steps waiting. Somewhere near him among the masses of white flowers he had smelt the scent of magnolia, and had felt suddenly shaken and uncertain, had known that his heart moved within him and that the old aching for Juliet had asserted itself. Then Bill's voice, rather thick with nerves, had brought him back to the present.

"She's here—they're coming! Now then, Emmanuel!"

Later, the people, the congratulations, the crowds had driven away the pain. He had looked at Viva and smiled, and she had laughed back and said: "Let's make a really star exit when we leave, shall we?" They had driven away, and Victoria had seemed thronged with more people than ever. Even on the train a man came to them, a man with heavily marked features and a lisping voice, and asked in French if he was "Maxth Gollanth's son" and offered his good wishes.

He didn't like Paris—he shared his grand-father's dislike of that city—but Viva said they must break the journey there. The hotel had been terribly over-decorated. Men had bowed them to their rooms, had been over-attentive, and their eyes had been curious and a little disconcerting. Later they dined and went to a show—was it a revue or a rather improper comedy?—and Viva

172

had got bored and said that she wanted to go and dance somewhere. They had danced until four, because Louis Lara had found them and danced with Viva alternately with Emmanuel.

He had driven back to the hotel with them, had bowed over Viva's hand and held Emmanuel's a second longer than necessary and had said that he wished for their happiness. Viva had whistled as she undressed, and he had wondered when was the right moment to enter her room. When he did go in she was in bed and reading a book in a paper cover.

She looked up and said: "Hello, old thing. Tired? So'm I. Hope the bed's comfy in your room." Then after a second's pause: "We needn't be conventional tonight, need we? Good night, sleep well."

He had kissed her and gone back to his own room, feeling at once chilled and relieved. It was cold, but he had opened the window and stood looking out on the Champs Elyseés for a long time before he got into bed. The next day they had left for the South.

They had liked the sunshine and Viva had wanted to rush here, there and everywhere. She had been excited and happy, had spent a great deal of money, and once or twice had almost frightened him because she had declared: "The South is no place for married people. Let's pretend that we're just nice, pleasant sinners, shall we?"

The first year had been, as she said, great fun. He had worked hard, but from the moment he entered the house he had been caught in a whirl of excitement. Sometimes he had felt that it was rather artificial excitement, manufactured because there was a demand for it, but it had served to make him live in the present.

Viva said: "Fill the something or other minute with sixty seconds' worth of duty done, and when it's over thank Heaven there's always another minute waiting to pop into its place."

Only after twelve months had he shown that he was flagging. He couldn't work all day and dance all night. Viva laughed at him and said: "Good old Industrious Apprentice! Did you never learn to burn a candle at both ends? It's most amusing once you get the knack of it."

He didn't like her less, in fact when he wasn't too tired, he loved her laughter and her keen-edged remarks, only sometimes he did wish that Colonel Saxe might have died before he ever invented an instrument which was rapidly becoming, to Emmanuel Gollantz, an instrument of torture. He knew that he was growing dull, that Viva noticed it and resented it, and he flogged himself to fresh efforts and knew that he failed. It seemed that his life was filled with noise, with people, with the perpetual sound of feet moving on parquet floors, of the chatter round a dinner-table and of syncopated music.

It was then that the memory of Juliet had

begun to reassert itself, and gradually he had realized that he was always looking back, and, later, that he looked back with regret and definite pain. He had fought, and fought hard; he had forced himself never to think of Viva for a moment without adding some mental eulogy—how clever she is, how amusing she is, how attractive she is! More than once he had even whipped himself into a sort of passionate desire for her, and he had found a certain relief from the drug. Then he had caught Viva's eyes, watching him, half amused, half mocking.

"If I didn't know my Emmanuel," she said, "I should believe that you were repenting some minor infidelity. You're not, by any weird chance, are you?"

He had answered: "Me? No, what makes you think that?" And once again his mind had swung violently back to Juliet. He had heard her voice, seen her moving slowly in her garden, and the pain for her had become an aching, desperate thing once more.

Now he was going away. He didn't know where; his ideas were vague, uncertain, nebulous. He scarcely knew whether he should try to find Juliet or not. All he did know, all he could see with perfect clarity, was that he must get away, leave everything and try to regain some measure of stability, even sanity.

Once again he glanced through his papers, slipped them all into one of the firm's big envelopes, addressed it, and walked upstairs to his own bedroom. He got out his suitcases and methodically began to pack, while always the sense of unreality persisted. Once, he stood staring down at the pile of dress shirts in his bag and wondered why on earth he had packed them. He didn't know where he was going, what he was going to do—but still automatically he packed suits, shirts and dress-ties.

It was finished, and very slowly he undressed and bathed. As he re-entered the room he saw the heap of clothes lying where he had thrown them on the chair, and felt that he was escaping. He was throwing off a disguise, he was going to be himself again.

At nine Viva's maid knocked on the door and said that "Madam would like to speak to him before he left for the office".

She was lying, as he had seen her so often, on a pile of pillows, sipping orange juice, with opened letters, scattered over the counterpane. She looked up as he entered and said, "Hello, Emmanuel," just as she had said it every morning for two years.

He said mechanically: "Hello, Viva, sleep well?"

"Like a top. Sit down—you can spare ten minutes?"

"As many as you wish."

"What are you going to do? After a night's sleep things sometimes look differently. P'raps

176

you didn't sleep? Poor old thing. You mustn't take things to heart so, Emmanuel. I never thought that you'd sit up worrying. I'd have stayed with you."

"I was working," he said. "Putting things straight."

Viva laughed suddenly, throwing back her head and giving vent to a shout of laughter.

"The ruling passion! Eighteen Hepplewhite chairs at three pounds ten apiece! You are funny! Darling, I'm not being unkind, only you are so astonishing, you Gollantzes. Are you taking my advice and getting away from it all for a time at all events? That's the only thing—get away from London, me, dances, nigger bands: for the rest —let it take its chance."

He stood, his hands on the decorated end of the bed. He felt more secure with the smooth wood under his fingers. That was something he understood, and loved—beautiful, sound wood. He said, speaking very slowly: "Yes, I'm going away. I've packed everything—"

Viva interrupted. "My dear, why didn't you ring for Benson?"

"I wanted to do it. I'm going, I don't know where, except that I must see Max and Angela —I can catch them at Aix. After that—I don't know."

Viva stretched out her hand, flicked open the lid of a big cigarette box and took one of the cigarettes which she averred were the only decent ones in London. Emmanuel moved forward, offered her a light, and pushed the little enamel ashtray nearer to her. She drew hard on the cigarette, inspected the lighted end, then said: "Thanks, angel. Good manners you have! Take my advice, find your Miss Forbes and be happy. Be nice to her, Emmanuel. If she loves you she must have had a devil of a time these last years."

Again he said, "I don't know—"

Viva glanced at him, half tolerant, half amused.

"I know," she said, "You're not very sure of anything just now, are you? Don't be frightened, it will clear. You'll get used to it. Don't let Max high-hat you, and don't let Angela get all self-condemnatory. Make life—or the world or fate or whatever you like to call it—give you a decent show." Her voice softened a little. "You've not had much of one up to now. I began all right, in fact I was something of a little Goddess in the Car, but I've not been frightfully considerate lately. I do like you frightfully, and this morning—when you're rather white and heavy about the eyes, I feel slightly maternal about you."

He stared at her, his eyes heavy and sombre. "You're awfully good to me, Viva. Again, I do hate myself for having lied to you. I ought to have known that it wasn't necessary."

She made a little gesture of sweeping the fault away.

"Poof, all men tell lies to their wives!" Then, with that grin which was almost boyish, she added: "Except the Gollantz men." They remained silent for a moment, Emmanuel trying to believe that it was true, that he really was leaving what had been his home and the woman who was his wife; Viva smoking contentedly, and wishing vaguely that Emmanuel would go and get it over. She was conscious that she was just a little tired of this interview. She wanted to telephone to half a dozen places before she had her bath. She had an appointment with her dressmaker at half past ten, and another with her dentist— Emmanuel was a dear, but why couldn't he pluck up sufficient courage to say good-bye and go?

She dabbed out the end of her cigarette, then held out her hand.

"Good-bye, Emmanuel," she said, "there isn't anything to go on talking about. Remember there isn't anything to be ashamed of—these things happen. If it hadn't happened to you, it would have done to me. We're both free, and I'll divorce you whenever you wish, and I expect you to let me divorce you if I want to marry someone else. I'm still conventional enough not to say that you can divorce me! If I want you to come back, if you want to come back, then we'll be frank and decent and say just how we feel, won't we? Good luck, old thing; you've been frightfully nice, and I shall always like you terribly."

He took her hand and held it in his, and stood looking down at her. How pretty she was, how charming, and how little she mattered to him!

179

"Good-bye," he said, "and thank you for everything, Viva. I'll remember all you've said. Goodbye, my dear."

Without waiting for her to speak again he turned and walked out, closing the door behind him. He stood for a moment leaning against the closed door. It was over, he was going away, he might never see Viva again, might never enter that room again, might never—Viva's voice reached him, clear and vital.

"Sloane seven six four two—yes—four two." And a few seconds later: "Is that you, Mary! I'll lunch at one instead of a quarter to, if you can make it. I've got a busy morning. I have—"

He turned and walked away, and a few moments later drove away from the house which had been his and Viva's.

The journey passed like a dream. On the steamer he looked back, saw the coastline disappear, and sighed—not certain if with relief or regret. Paris was crowded, and he scarcely left his hotel. He wanted to see no one, not even Louis Lara. He wanted to think, to try to find out what he really wanted to do, and how he was going to accomplish whatever he decided upon. The following morning he walked into the huge hotel at Aix and asked for Max.

He was told that Max was taking the waters, but that he was expected back immediately. Lady Gollantz was with him. Emmanuel went up to

180

their suite and paced restlessly about, until he heard his mother's voice in the corridor calling: "Emmanuel, Emmanuel—where are you?"

The door was flung open and she stood there, holding out her arms. For the first time, Emmanuel felt a sense of security and reality sweep over him. Here was the one person who had always understood, who had always believed the best of him no matter how black things looked against him. At that moment he wondered if the love of any woman—even Juliet—counted with him as much as the love of his mother; he wondered if any other woman possessed the same wide tolerance, the same wisdom, the same limitless affection.

His arms were round her and he felt her lips on his cheek. "My darling, what a lovely surprise! No one's ill, nothing happened? Everyone well?" Then, holding him at arm's length: "But you're fagged out. Let's have coffee and talk for hours."

His father said: "Very nice to see you, Emmanuel. I can congratulate you personally. Letters have been a poor substitute. I'm very proud of you, you've handled everything splendidly."

Angela was issuing orders, arranging flowers, throwing open windows and talking all the time. Emmanuel wondered if she sensed that something had happened and wanted to put off the moment when he must speak.

"Lovely to have you, even though it's only for

181

three days. Yes, we're staying until Monday. Max is better, aren't you, Max? Did you ever see anyone look so brown and disgustingly young? He looks younger than you do! How's Viva, and Bill and Julian? None of them ever write letters telling one a thing that matters. Ah, the coffee! Max, coffee—oh yes, it won't hurt you, just for once. Now, darling, sit down and be comfy and forget all the worries at Gollantz and Son for three days. We'll have a gorgeous time, won't we?''

Emmanuel looked from her to his father. Max sat near the window. The light fell on his grey hair and showed up his handsome, kindly features. To his son he looked the embodiment of uprightness and integrity, the soul of kindliness and the essence of what was honourable. He looked again at his mother, her eyes shining with excitement and pleasure, her fair skin looking beautifully smooth and cool, her every movement quick and certain, the light catching the stones in her rings as she moved. Once she looked up, met his eyes and smiled at him. A smile which seemed to offer him encouragement, to give him courage and steadfastness.

"They're all very well," he said. "I haven't come for a holiday. I've come because I wanted to tell you something. Viva and I have agreed to separate."

Max turned his head quickly. "What?" he said. "You have agreed to do what?"

Angela said, very evenly and without a trace of

182

surprise: "Why have you agreed to separate? Don't you love each other, don't you get on happily? What is it, Emmanuel?"

Emmanuel put down his coffee-cup and walked over to the window. He wanted to put what distance he could between himself and his parents. He stood at one end of the long balcony window facing his father, a good six feet separating them, and felt that it was easier to speak if he stood alone.

"It's not very easy to say," he said, speaking slowly and without passion. "We don't quarrel, we're very good friends. Whatever is wrong is my fault. I am going away. Viva will stay in London."

"You haven't done anything"—Max paused as if the very word was difficult to speak when applied to his own son—"disgraceful?"

"I've done nothing for which Viva could divorce me."

Once again Max seemed to nerve himself to speak.

"Is that a quibble, Emmanuel? Don't try to be clever with us. I want facts, not evasions. People don't leave each other for nothing."

"Don't you love each other?" his mother asked gently.

Speaking now very quickly, Emmanuel said: "We talked this over the last night. I don't love Viva any more. She doesn't love me. It's only friendship, and that's not enough—for me. I

183

haven't done anything wr-rong. Nothing which even you could find r-really disgraceful. It was inevitable. I r-realized that I love someone else and I told Viva. She understands. In many ways I think she's a little r-relieved. I've been terr-ribly dull lately. Viva hates dull people. So I'm going away."

Max rose and stood facing his son. Angela, watching them, thought how handsome they both were and how dearly she loved them. She thought, too, how hard Max would find it to understand his son, and how impossible it would be for Emmanuel not to feel that his father's attitude was both harsh and unjust.

"You don't leave your wife because you find that you love someone else," Max said, his voice hard and intolerant. "Neither do wives allow their husbands to leave them because they find them —dull."

"Max darling, that's the one reason you do leave your wife," Angela said, "because you find that you love someone else. What other reason, except that she loved someone else, could there be?"

He turned on her sharply. "Angela, don't adopt that tone. I'm old-fashioned. I hate this changing wives, this running away from responsibilities, making promises and breaking them. Emmanuel, I want a plain, unvarnished statement of facts. Let me have it at once, if you please. I'm waiting."

184

2

HE seemed to have been speaking for hours, telling a story about someone else, not Emmanuel Gollantz at all. It had been difficult to remember never to use Juliet's name, to refer to her always as "this woman" or "the person who really meant everything to me". He had tried to remember all that Viva had said, suppressing her remarks about herself and the possibility of her wanting to marry again, or the probability that "if it hadn't been you, it would have been me". He neglected to mention the facts concerning Julian, and told the story confining it to main issues alone.

As he finished he realized that his father's face was very stern, his eyes very cold. He had made no comment, he had not interrupted, only sat very upright, very still, terribly aloof.

". . . And I left yesterday morning," Emmanuel concluded.

"And the sooner you make up your mind to return," Max said, "the better for everyone concerned. I have rarely listened to a more fantastic story. Your attitude is astounding. Viva's is impossible. Your behaviour—well, I never believed that you could be so foolish. The lady—whoever she is—is fortunate. I advise her to discontinue this habit of allowing married men to visit her in the early hours of the morning."

Angela said, "Max dearest, that's unnecessary, I think."

"I beg your pardon, Emmanuel."

He turned back to his wife, making that little Hebraic gesture with his hands which was one of old Emmanuel's legacies to his son.

"It's unthinkable," he said, suddenly stumbling a little over his words and losing something of his coldness. "Unthinkable! Make him understand that he can't do these things. It's not possible. Why, the woman herself refuses to marry him. She isn't even his—I mean, he isn't even her lover in the accepted sense of the word!" He turned back to Emmanuel. "Listen, my boy, you can't break ties so easily. It isn't right that you should be able to do so. Go back, give things a chance to come right, make allowances for each other, you've everything to make you happy—"

Emmanuel, young, very tall, his face sombre, replied: "Only one thing can make me happy. I couldn't go back. Viva doesn't want me to. She sees the impossibility of it all."

His father stared at him intently, his brows drawn into a frown, his face puzzled and uncertain. Angela's hands clenched suddenly. She sat a little rigid, as if she waited for a blow to fall.

"This—lady," Max said. "Do we know her?"

"Max, must you ask that? Is it quite fair?"

"I think so. Do we know her, Emmanuel?"

186

"My mother is right. I don't think it's a fair question."

Max moved abruptly from his place near Angela and walked to the window. For some time he stood looking out, silent, motionless. When he turned, his face was composed and cold.

"You've answered me," he said. "Whatever you had replied you would have answered me. There is no more to be said. Do you remember when I visited you at a villa near Como? You do? You denied then that there was anything between yourself and this lady. I believe you now when you say that she won't marry you. She didn't find her métier lay in marriage, I remember."

"Oh!" The exclamation came from Angela. "You don't blame her for that, Max? Seyre was impossible, you always loathed him!"

She wanted to make Max sit down and listen to her, she wanted to take away the look of wretched uncertainty on Emmanuel's face, she wanted them all to contrive and plan what would be best for this son of hers. She loved all her three children dearly. Once she used to admit that Julian was nearest to her heart, but that was over. Now, Emmanuel, who had suffered for Julian, who had suffered through his love for Juliet, and who now had torn adrift from all that had seemed permanent and lasting, occupied a place in her life which neither Julian nor Bill could ever hold. Her love for him lacked the joyous pride that she had felt for Julian, it was without that safe solidity of her affection for Bill; it held a queer protective element which determined that he should not be hurt again if she could prevent it.

Max had always held those rigid ideas of honour, of right and wrong, from which old Emmanuel never deviated. To him divorce under any circumstances was regrettable, but that two people should amicably agree to part when no legal guilt existed on either side seemed to him unthinkable. A man whose whole life had been stainless, filled with kindliness, whose utter devotion to his wife had never changed during thirty years of marriage, found it difficult to view with any toleration such an attitude as Emmanuel stated existed between himself and Viva. To Max it argued a laxity, an unstable moral code, and an evading of responsibilities.

She looked at Emmanuel standing by the window and noted the lines on his young face; and remembered that he was not yet thirty. The remembrance filled her with a passionate determination that he should not suffer, should not be hurt again if she could prevent it.

Angela Gollantz counted herself a happy woman. There had been moments of horrible pain in her life, and at the worst of those it had been old Emmanuel who had eased her pain, soothed her fears and solved her problems. She had married Max and—except for short periods of anxiety when he was fighting in France, later when he was employed in the Secret Service, and afterwards when everything seemed to go wrong, and she and Max wandered in a dark forest filled with terrible thoughts, dreadful doubts and uncertainties from which old Emmanuel had delivered them—they had been ideally happy.

Four years ago tragedy had almost touched them. Four years ago young Emmanuel had left England under a cloud which it had taken her months to dispel. He had allowed himself to be accused of a social crime in order to protect his brother Julian. It had ended, and Emmanuel had returned to England and Ordingly to pick up the threads of his life again. He had wanted to bring Juliet Forbes back with him as his wife, and even Angela had felt a certain relief when Juliet refused to marry him.

She had known and loved Juliet Forbes for years. She had known her as the wife of Seyre, the painter, and as the mistress of Leon Hast, the millionaire collector. She had sympathized with her when Seyre proved so insensible, so utterly insensitive, that he had killed any love which Juliet had for him. She had loved her, helped her, been her friend when she went back to Leon Hast, and after Hast's death, had been, perhaps, the only woman who knew fully what Juliet suffered.

Both she and Max had helped her to gather together the threads of her life again. They had offered her every possible kindness, and they had seen her from time to time when her engagements made it possible. They had admired her as an artist and liked her as a woman. They had never allowed what they knew of her history to influence them in the least—until the question arose that their son wished to marry her.

Then for the first time that strange conventional strain which ran through all the Gollantz cosmopolitanism asserted itself; and Max was horrified at the thought that his eldest son might marry a woman whom all Europe knew to have been Leon Hast's mistress. To Angela it came as something of a surprise that her own family conventions asserted themselves. She loved Juliet Forbes, she knew her to be beautiful, brilliantly artistic, successful—but she knew too that she shrank from the thought that she might marry Emmanuel.

Now, in the slightly stereotyped room of a de luxe hotel, she watched Max's white face and knew that he was suffering, knew that he was hating the thought that Juliet Forbes, ten years older than the son who loved her, might one day reign at Ordingly as that son's wife. She looked back to Emmanuel, and his youth touched her, touched her so deeply that she turned away her eyes to ease the pain. He was twenty-nine, and for nearly five years had known only such happiness as had come to him for the few months when he had worked in Milan, and spent his brief periods of rest at Juliet's villa on Lake Como.

Something of dead-and-gone Walter Heriot,

who had made a friend of an unknown young Austrian Jew, Emmanuel Gollantz, solely on the strength of a chance meeting in a saleroom, asserted itself. Ordingly with its lawns, its great old trees, its treasures and its dignity—what did it matter? Max's great position, his title, his wealth, his high standing in the world of art—what did it matter? Nothing mattered if they could wipe away that look of misery from Emmanuel's face; nothing mattered if they could find some way by which he might attain happiness.

"Emmanuel," she said gently, "come here. I want to speak to you."

Very slowly he walked over to where she sat, and stood looking down at her.

"Yes," he said, "what is it?"

"Can you, will you give me your word—your word of honour—that Viva is not breaking her heart for you? Will you assure me that you parted without bitterness, without recrimination, and that you have done nothing which broke promises you made to Viva when you married her?"

He answered, speaking very slowly, gravely but without emphasis.

"I give you my word, darling," he said, "that Viva and I talked this thing over two days ago. I told her everything and she was very frank with me. Viva is the best friend in the world. She likes me enormously and I like and admire her. But we don't love each other—not as men and women

191

need to love each other to make marriage poss- ible. There was no bitterness, no recrimination, and I have done nothing disgraceful, nothing . . ." He paused, then said with an obvious effort, "Nothing except that once—I couldn't help it—I took Juliet in my arms and kissed her, and knew finally that I should never be happy again without her. It wasn't Juliet's fault. It was mine. I was lonely, I hadn't seen her for three years—three years is such a long time, darling."

"You are quite certain that you love her?"

For the first time his lips curved into a smile. "Entirely."

"She loves you?"

This time he did not speak, only bowed his head in silence.

"You say that she won't marry you—wouldn't marry you if you were free—why not?"

He answered with a sudden burst of passion that almost frightened her:

"Because she is afraid for me. Because she knows that I am the eldest son of my father, because she knows that Gollantz and Son are the gr-reatest art dealers in the world, because she was divorced by Seyre, when it was too late for her to marr-ry Leon Hast, because everyone knew that she was Hast's mistress, and because she is ten years older than I am. Those are her r-reasons! And," he dropped his voice so that it

192

came as a whisper, "to me they matter nothing, nothing, nothing."

Angela took his hand and laid it for a moment against her cheek. She had made up her mind that she was going to fight for this son of hers. She would throw convention to the winds and make Max join her in doing so. Max, who stood with his back turned to them, his whole attitude indicating disapproval and intense dislike of the scene, should be made to understand. He might never approve, but at least he should be persuaded to do nothing to prevent Emmanuel finding happiness if he could.

"Go and rest," she said, "I'll send for you later. Now rest, my dear, promise me."

Again he smiled at her. "At least I'll promise you that I'll try."

"Very well."

As the door closed behind him she rose and walked over to Max, laid her hand on his shoulder and said, "Are you very angry, Max?"

He swung round and met her eyes, frowning and angry.

"Angry?" he said. "Rather—disgusted, amazed and quite determined that this folly must be ended."

She fell back a little and regarded him coolly.

"Disgusted! By what right? Amazed? Because you don't realize that young people refuse to make pretence of things which matter vitally to them? Determined? How can you determine matters for Emmanuel? He is of age, he is old enough and wise enough to run your business successfully, to buy and sell in the markets with men who are years his senior. You can't treat him as a man in business and as a child with regard to his own affairs. Be reasonable, Max."

Again, almost astonished at her intensity, Max made his little Jewish gesture with his hands. "My dear, it's all so—so undignified."

"Undignified!" she flung at him. "On the contrary, it seems to me that Emmanuel and Viva have both displayed a considerable amount of dignity. Viva might have stormed and railed, might have insisted upon immediate evidence for a divorce. Emmanuel might have—at least—persuaded Juliet to live with him as his mistress. They've done none of these things. I admire them —yes, all three of them."

"Three? Oh, you include Juliet!" Then with another little flare of anger, "You'd welcome Juliet Forbes as your daughter to Ordingly?"

This time Angela laughed frankly and openly.

"Darling Max, you are amusing! One's sons don't marry women because their parents will or won't welcome their wives to the family roof. I don't welcome Amanda van der Hoyt, I probably shan't welcome some pleasant solid young woman whom Bill will discover in the near future. It's not our concern. The only question is—can she, will she, make Emmanuel happy?"

"You really mean that? You really mean that

194

it wouldn't affect you for him to marry a woman ten years his senior, a woman whose past is, to say the least of it, unconventional?"

"My angel, don't be so horribly Victorian. In these days no one has any past, we've only got futures and presents."

He shrugged his shoulders. "I don't understand you when you talk in this way."

"That's because I am naturally much quicker, more adaptable, really cleverer than you, Max. I may not be so sound, but I don't carry the weight of so many conventions on my shoulders. Four years ago—oh, I'm not ashamed to admit it—I didn't welcome the idea very wholeheartedly. But four years have taught me a great deal. Or made me forget a great deal, I don't quite know which. At twenty, I quite definitely knew everything—that was why I made you so miserable, my sweet. At thirty, I knew a little less, and by the time I'm seventy—if I live so long—I shall probably be a very delightful, sensible person and admit that I know precisely nothing!"

"You'd agree to allow Emmanuel to wander about Europe, following in Juliet's train, deserting his wife, his home and his work? My God, Angela, you can't mean it!"

Angela lifted her hands, laid them on his shoulders and shook him gently. "Max, Max!" she cried in amused horror, "where do you find these dreadful archaic words—agree, allow, deserting home, wife and work? You're talking like Mr. Dombey of pious memory. His work—his work isn't the primary matter. His happiness is the first thing and the last. How old are you? How old am I?"

"You know how old I am—fifty-eight, and you're fifty and manage to look like thirty!"

His control was returning, his anger was slowly leaving him. He was still puzzled and a little disturbed, but Angela knew that the worst of the storm was past, and smiled.

"Thank you, O pleasant but untruthful one. I've been happy—terribly happy—for thirty years, Max. You've been happy too. We've both had perfectly lovely lives. Oh, the bad patches only helped to accentuate the good ones. Are we going to be so mean, so ungrateful to whoever it is who has given us these good lives, that we're going to deny Emmanuel his chance? Max, we can't, we daren't, we mustn't! Let him work out his own salvation in his own way. He may not find this content, this love he's craving for. Then he can come back to us. We'll be waiting to 'make him better' as we used to when he fell and cut his knees as a little boy. That's our job, Max darling. To be ready either to kill fatted calves if everything goes right, or to be waiting with basins and lint and nice cool salve if everything goes wrong."

He moved away and began to pace slowly up and down the room. His hands were clasped behind him, his head was bent. Angela watched him a little anxiously, but with no evident signs of impatience.

Max began to speak as he paced the room; he spoke slowly, dispassionately and without heat.

"You see, Angela, you can't run a world on these lines. Young men can't run away from responsibilities whenever they get a little tired of them. My dear, we should all be at sixes and sevens."

"I should have thought that we were already at sixes and sevens under the old order. And how well was the world run under the old régime? Was it such a howling success? My dear! You wouldn't condemn Viva and Emmanuel to live together without love, with Emmanuel eating his heart out for another woman? They're both decent young people—decent healthy young people. You're going to condemn them both, because of that decency and frankness, to lives of celibacy, unless they both take lovers for—well, for necessity's sake."

"Then what," he demanded, "do you propose that I should do?"

"Do? Do nothing. Emmanuel has a little money from his grandfather. I'll allow him a little more. You can make his allowance over to Viva; she can keep up Gloucester Place if she wants to. Let him have enough to live on—not exist, mind! We can't live at Ordingly in comfort, keep Viva in comfort, while Emmanuel wanders about looking at both sides of a penny before he spends

197

it. The rest—well, that's his affair. And if he suddenly arrives home with a wife (for eventually Viva will divorce him, I fancy; I know my family —after all, she is my cousin), then we'll be the same nicely mannered people we've always been, thank heaven, and make her very welcome."

"Seems to me that everything is going to be made remarkably easy for him!" Max grumbled.

"And why not? What the devil are we here for but to make things easy for our sons? What particular merit is there in making things difficult?" Then, more gravely, she added: "Emmanuel once made things quite remarkably easy for other people, ourselves included. We might do well to remember that, don't you think?"

For a moment they stood looking into each other's eyes, remembering that but for Emmanuel their lives might have been touched by a scandal so dreadful that it might have broken them both. And with that remembrance came the assertion of the love which they had for each other. Max saw her as the woman he had always loved, and she saw him as the husband who had been her devout lover for thirty years. She stretched out her hands and he took them in his.

"We almost quarrelled, Max," she said.

"You tried to force a quarrel," he answered and smiled.

"I'm a very clever woman."

"A very unscrupulous one, at least," Max admitted.

"But—you'll try to be kind to Emmanuel?"

"I don't think that it will be very difficult. I'm old-fashioned, I distrust this easy breaking of ties, these separate lives—"

"So do I! But I hate unhappiness still more. If I believed that Viva was unhappy, I'd resent it keenly. She isn't. Emmanuel is. I won't allow my son to be unhappy any longer. If he loves Juliet and she loves him—then let them find happiness. We've had ours, we still have it. We mustn't be dogs in mangers, Max."

He drew her to him and kissed her. Still holding her closely, he said:

"I distrust your theories. I could smash your arguments to pieces. You're cunning and have a sort of low cleverness. You bully and bluster—but you win every time through a queer forceful humanity. Incidentally, I love you very much. Let's go and find the boy and talk to him. And help me to talk wisely and sanely, won't you?"

Together they walked to the room which had been given to Emmanuel. With her finger on her lip, Angela opened the door and looked in. She turned and beckoned to Max to come nearer, whispering: "He's asleep. We won't wake him."

Standing at the door, Max watched her enter and very carefully draw the curtains so that the light was shaded from Emmanuel's tired face. She bent down and drew the coverlet higher round his shoulders, then kissed him softly and came back to Max, smiling.

"Let's go and work out how much we ought to allow him," she whispered. Then, catching his hand and holding it tightly, she added, "Dear Max, you are the nicest man in the world."

3

AS the long train drew into Como station, Emmanuel looked up from his papers and smiled. Until now he had felt that he would never reach Italy, that the whole journey was something imaginary, a foolish dream from which he must inevitably wake. Now, as he sat staring at the big scarlet letters which spelt Como, he smiled because he had been wrong. This was no dream, this was reality, and soon he would be in Milan station, soon he would feel Guido's over-soft hand shaking his, perhaps hear Louis Lara's voice bidding him welcome.

The past ten days had been difficult. The interview with his father and mother had shaken him, and later his father's sudden gentleness and essential kindness had touched him deeply. Max had explained that not even Angela's arguments could move him in "those opinions which I have held, rightly or wrongly, for fifty years", but he had added that the fact that he was unable to move with the times did not prevent "the times moving, and moving very quickly, without me".

"I should prefer," he said slowly, "that you went back to your home, to your wife, and tried to rearrange your life. In pursuing this present course—a course which seems to me to lie in an uncharted sea—you believe that you can find happiness. I hope, and hope very sincerely, that you may. Your mother believes that happiness is the main object of everyone's life if it can be achieved without pain to other people. She may be right. I think perhaps that she is. So you must go your own way, and believe, Emmanuel"—and Emmanuel remembered how very kind his voice had been as he spoke—"that whatever you do, whatever venture you may embark on, I am always there, and always ready to help to the best of my ability. Once—years ago—I acted impulsively; I shall always be in your debt, and you can always count on me to try and pay that debt. Don't keep us in the dark, your mother and me; and if I don't understand your motives, or don't think them very wise"—he smiled—"there is always your mother at hand to bully me until at least I pretend that I understand."

Emmanuel had written to Louis asking if there could be room for him in the little antique-shop in Milan. Max had offered to finance the business, to make it a foreign branch of Gollantz and Son, but Emmanuel had refused. He had a little capital, and he wanted to go back to work at a business which was unhampered, unassisted, which was in fact practically as he had left it four years ago.

Louis had replied ecstatically.

"It would appear", he wrote, "that fortune

favours me always, with a regularity which possibly ought to engender fear in my heart. Olympia loves me, you wish to come back to work with me and for me in Milano, and last week one of my horses won a magnificent victory. Come back and know that two hearts—mine and that of Guido—will beat faster for your coming. Olympia is at Cannes, and she will spare me to you in order that we talk the business for three days—a longer absence she assures me would break her heart, and certainly be the death of your loving Louis".

Max read the letter, shrugged his shoulders, sniffed the sheet and said: "Poof! The fellow uses scented note-paper! It's incredible that he should be a very astute business man, and yet he is, you know. Do you know this lady with the fantastic name?"

Emmanuel shook his head. "I've never seen her. I only know that Louis adores her. She's a dancer, quite famous, I believe. Then that's settled! I go back to Milano."

His mother had come to his room at night and sat on the edge of his bed talking for hours. He had never known her so understanding, so tender. Again and again she reiterated: "Oh, Emmanuel, be happy." Now, watching the word Como slip away as his train moved out, he wondered if he would ever find the happiness he sought. He had no plans, he had not even written to Juliet to tell her of his return to Italy. His only plan, and that was sufficiently nebulous and unformed, was to go back so far as was possible to the conditions which had existed when he first met Juliet in Italy.

The little shop was waiting, he would work there, travel round the country in the car picking up bits of furniture, lengths of old brocade, china and glass. He would spend his Sundays in the country in the sunshine, living very simply, and —wait. Perhaps Fate might send Juliet to the little shop again, perhaps she might hear from Angela what had happened and write to him, perhaps—later—when he had regained some of his peace, when his flayed nerves were soothed, he might find sufficient courage to write to her and tell her everything. He didn't know, and at the moment it was sufficient to him that he had returned to a country where he had known the only real personal happiness that his life had held.

His childhood had been delightfully carefree; he had been surrounded with love, care and luxury. Looking back, Emmanuel felt that even then there had been moments of pain which had tinged the beauty of his days. His mother's over-whelming love for Julian, her pride in Julian's achievements, his good looks and his success, had all contributed to create in Emmanuel a queer self-effacement, a strange belief in his own unimportance. Then his absorbing love for his mother had brought pain with it. He could remember as a little boy that any slight delay in her return home, any minor illness, any evidence of worry, even a headache which concerned Angela, had made him feel utterly wretched. As he grew older he had learnt to control his fears a little, he had learnt to accept the fact that Julian was the best loved of his mother's sons; but his love for her had never changed fundamentally and to him she remained, apart from Juliet, the only great love in his life.

Not that he had ever demonstrated his love in any obvious fashion. He made fewer charming speeches than Julian, he used fewer terms of endearment than Bill, but his love burnt with a clear, steady flame, and with the years it had grown and strengthened. Bill treated her as any young man might treat the mother he loved very dearly. Julian talked to her—now as ever—as some young lover might have spoken. He offered her a thousand little attentions, he praised her clothes, her hair and her eyes, he sent flowers every few days and never forgot affectionate tele-grams on her birthday and on other anniversaries. But between Emmanuel and his mother there had grown during the last few years a new relation-ship, one of devoted comradeship. She had told him more than once that he was satisfactory because he was her friend, her brother and her son, "and so very satisfactory in all your roles".

He leant back in his corner, his eyes on the passing country, and recalled their last conversation on the evening before she left Paris to return to Ordingly with Max.

Max had gone to dine with old Henri Cremieux, who had discovered a Van Eyck in a back attic in Montmartre and wanted Max's opinion on it. Emmanuel and Angela had dined alone, and had sat very long over their coffee, talking of the past and the future. Neither of them spoke much of Juliet. Emmanuel said only that he loved her, and that he could only hope to find happiness with her. Angela had accepted his statement and made no attempt either to challenge it or enlarge upon it.

"I wish that you weren't going away," she said. "I shall miss you."

"We haven't seen very much of each other like this, talking alone, quietly, for the last two years," he said.

"No"—reflectively—"perhaps not. But you were always there. Now you won't be there, you'll be somewhere else. Oh, my dear, don't think that I'm grumbling, I'm not. I only want you to be happy. I hate unhappiness for anyone, most of all for young people. It's horrible. The world just now isn't fit for young people. We old ones let it get into such a mess—we allowed wars and horrors to stalk about unchecked. They say—the old ones who are still believing that they're alive, when really they're dead, and ought to be buried —that you young people have no values, no standards! What values, what standards did we leave

206

intact for you? Scarcely one. Christianity—oh, I don't mean the Church kind, I mean the ethical kind, the kind that you believe in as you believe in good manners and cleanliness—kindness, loving your neighbour as yourself—we taught you that we could fling all that overboard if we wanted to snatch something from someone else. We taught you that might is right—by implication at least —that cruelty to children is all part of the great machine of war! Oh yes, we did. In England we didn't cut off their hands or their heads, but we didn't mind starving them because it was part of the great game called the Blockade, which was very, very clever! We taught you how to lie, how to break promises to people who were weak, and poor and hopeless, we even taught you to talk about a Dole paid to the poor. Why, the attitude of mind which permits anyone to use that word is poisonous! We taught you to be suspicious and mean and petty. We taught you to be inefficient and often lazy. Then we attack you because you have no standards!

"We brought you all up to open your eyes and see that nothing was of any real value except money. That whatever happened money must be protected and safeguarded. Not lives or happiness or health, but money! When men had sufficient courage to talk about protecting intangible things, we taught you to laugh and call them sentimentalists, or else to throw up your baby hands and

207

scream that they were driving the country to ruin, and wasting money!"

She paused, looked at him and laughed. "Lor'! How I am talking! Poor Emmanuel, your last night with me, and I'm boring you." She took another cigarette from the case which lay open before her and let him give her a light for it, then went on more gently, but with very real regret: "You see, I don't talk in this way to Max because he and I are two of the old ones, and Max could never bear to remember that we old ones made you young ones in the mess you are today. It comforts him to see too many cocktails, night clubs, nigger dances, dope, divorces and murders as causes; I see them as results. Do you know one of the things which hurts Max most? The younger generation of rich Jews and their attitude to life in general. I never realized how proud Max was of his race until I saw how it pained him to see the post-war Jews.

"You see, they always do everything a little more than anyone else. Have you noticed that? They're gayer or sadder, they're finer or far more base, they're generous or unbelievably mean. And this new world—you don't remember how we were told that after the war to end wars there was to be a new world, do you?—has affected them terribly. They'll emerge, you'll all emerge, bless you, but I do wish you could emerge a little less painfully—less painfully both for yourselves and other people."

Emmanuel said tentatively: "Oh, we don't all need to emerge. Look at Bill, look at Julian—"

"Bill," she returned quickly, "is one of those almost uncomfortably normal people that not even the end of the world will shake. Julian is as hard as nails, my dear. Julian has no standards, that's why he's able to make such a success of his life. If he found a standard tomorrow morning on the breakfast table, he'd throw it over the Embankment as he walked down to the House. But he's not happy! You—you're not able to find any standards that satisfy you, and God knows you're unhappy enough, my sweet. You have them in yourself, and you can't understand the lack of them in other people."

"Don't worry about me," he said, "I'm going to be all right."

"I know, I know"—eagerly; "and don't be too hard on us old ones. We weren't really intentionally wicked, only frightfully and crassly stupid." She lifted the liqueur glass and smiled at him. "Here's to a brave new world for you all, my blessing!"

Closing his eyes for a second, Emmanuel could see her again, could see the soft light from the little table-lamp shining on her hair, see the laughter in her eyes which was encouraged to keep back tears, see her mouth curving softly in a smile that was so completely tender that it seemed to reach his heart.

They had sat in silence after her toast, very

much in tune, very much in sympathy with each other; then Angela had begun to talk again of other things, of her plans for the winter, of how she might come out and see him next year, of a hundred things which made no call on their emotions. Only as they drove back to their hotel had she talked once more of personal matters.

"Don't worry about Viva," she said almost abruptly, "she'll be quite all right. I like Viva very much. She'll be a fine woman one day. Perhaps a little hard, but very fine stuff. And, Emmanuel—no, don't speak, don't look at me, I'm trying to be terribly matter-of-fact, and it's difficult. I don't want to get emotional—if Juliet will marry you—if you are in a position to ask her to marry you, don't be afraid. Age won't matter, nothing will matter if you love each other really and truly and decently. Tell her, when you ask her to be your wife, that your mother will be very happy if she'll say yes. That's all!" Then, speaking very fast, in the way which made old Emmanuel once call her "a most agreeable rattle": "Shall we go and call for Max? Old Henri is great fun when he hasn't gout. Besides, he has some Waterloo brandy which you ought to taste, it's part of your education. If his taste in pictures was half as good as his taste in wines and spirits, he'd have beaten Max from the field years ago and we should all be begging for bread. Tell him to drive to Henri's, and you and I will enter like whoever it was like wolves on the fold. 'Their

210

cohorts were gleaming with purpose and gold', or was it scarlet and gold? No, that's one of Cicely Courtneidge's songs about the King's Horses, the other is Lord Byron. Nasty uncomfortable person he was! But so was she! Ever read a life of Lady Byron, Emmanuel? The sort of woman, I always felt, who wore flannel petticoats and liked them."

The train was running into Milano. He rose and looked out and saw the great signal cabins, the wide stretches of rails, and in the distance the great stone arches of the station itself.

He caught his breath with a little sob as he looked.

"It must all happen again," he said softly, "it must—it will." The blue-bloused facchini, the railway officials with their red velvet-banded caps, the little representative of the American Express very busy as usual, Cook's man—a new one that Emmanuel didn't remember having seen three years ago—and two figures looking like birds of Paradise among the soberly clad waiting crowd—Louis and Guido.

Louis, in the lightest of light overcoats, with a hat so pale and delicate that Emmanuel felt it could never survive three days' wear in Milano, his shoes shining like polished ebony, two splashes of brilliant colour which were his tie and handkerchief. Guido, wearing checked suiting so loud, so truculent, and so obtrusively what any foreigner believes to be typically English that Emmanuel could have laughed with delight. His

211

shoes were so thick, so heavy and so completely brogued, his tie and handkerchief were so very restrained and yet noticeable, and his gloves made of such thick hogskin that Emmanuel wondered how he ever got them on his hands.

They were waving. Louis shouted some greeting, obviously of an impassioned character, which Emmanuel could not catch, and Guido produced his huge silk handkerchief and waved it wildly. Emmanuel knew that his eyes smarted suddenly. They were just the same. It was a good omen; nothing was really altered.

"My dearest cousin, welcome!" Louis seized his hands and kissed him affectionately on both cheeks. Emmanuel, suddenly shy and uncomfortable, hoped that no one noticed, then remembered that it mattered very little if they did—he was in Italy. Guido grasped the hand which Louis dropped, held it in both his own and said in English, his voice broken with emotion:

"Cheerio! This, old top, is a first-rate occasion. Let us all binge together quickly. I feel that it is what you call in England a Bankers' Holiday!"

Emmanuel said: "Hello, Louis, nice to see you! Guido, how splendidly you speak English and how marvellous you both look!"

Louis became the complete Frenchman, Guido the complete Italian. They took entire charge of Emmanuel's luggage, they shouted good-temperedly at porters, they both lost their platform tickets and yelled with laughter when

Emmanuel had to pass the barrier, get two new ones from the automatic machine, and pass them over the head of the ticket-collector to them. Emmanuel walked down the wide flight of steps between them and felt that he had never been away, or at least only away long enough for them both to have bought new clothes.

"You look superb," Louis said, "untired by the journey."

"He looks as he always looked," Guido said, "the magnificent Englishman. Have I not made myself one successfully, Emmanuel?"

Emmanuel glanced at the suit he wore and replied that it was not a suit of clothes, but a miracle.

"I'd no idea you were so big," he said. "By Jove, you've got a wonderful pair of shoulders, Guido!"

Guido smiled, showing his beautiful teeth. "These are a 'regalo' from my tailor. It is in the coat, not in the skin of Guido. But you are pleased, my first master in how to dress correctly, and I am satisfied."

In the taxi they talked without ceasing. They told him of Olympia and her success in Milano three months ago, they told him of the beautiful ladies who, since Guido wore English clothes, came regularly to the shop every week. "They come only to see me," Guido said modestly, "and they have the faces of sheep. They spend very little but they have no taste and buy whatever is cheap. All what you used to call Yonk."

"Junk," Emmanuel said, "not Yonk."

"Yes, junk, is sold, cleared away. It reposes in the apartments of these very, very old tr-rrouts." He paused for a moment, then said: "Did you notice the expression—very, very old tr-rrouts? That is exclusively English."

Miraculously they were at the shop. The window had been enlarged and there was more stock. Emmanuel looked round and found it less dark and more orderly than it had been formerly. But it smelt the same, it felt the same, and for the first time he lost a little of his control. He stood turning to look this way and that, waves of remembrance breaking over him; regret, memories, pictures all crowded in on his mind.

Guido and Louis watched him, sympathetic and comprehending. They knew something of Emmanuel's tragedy, and, being the one a Frenchman and the other an Italian, tragedies which were caused by love, the lack or loss of it, were the greatest tragedies in the world. They did not turn away and pretend not to notice his emotion, they watched, and in their minds applauded him for his sensibility, for his feeling and his unhappiness. There was nothing to be ashamed of in emotion, it was one of the natural and right things of the world. To realize that an Englishman could feel as either of them would have felt under similar circumstances forged an additional link in the chain of their affection for Emmanuel Gollantz.

But being what and who they were, they felt that it was incumbent on them to identify themselves with his emotion; and with a gesture which was unstudied and very beautiful Louis moved towards him and took his hand.

"Emmanuel," he said, "do not hide what you feel, do not be ashamed. What you feel, we feel too. Perhaps we do not know everything, and there is no need—now or at any time—to confide in us unless you wish. But what we do know is that at this moment you are unhappy, and for that reason we suffer with you because we love you. Now it is night for you, but your star will rise and after that your sun. Then your world will be flooded with the light and the warmth that once were yours. Meanwhile, there is work for you, for work is the best drug in the world, and it will never harm you. Drug yourself, my very dear cousin."

Emmanuel looked at the over-exquisite figure and met those dark eyes, realizing fully for the first time the depth of kindness which lay in them. The words might make him feel slightly self-conscious by their wealth of colour and sentimentalism, but the kindness which prompted them was real enough.

"Thanks, Louis," he said. "It's good to be back."

Guido moved nearer and smiled with the tears

215

still hanging on his long, dark lashes. His large dark eyes were liquid with tenderness.

> "Nessun maggior dolore
> Che recordarsi del tempo felice
> Nella miseria,"

he chanted in his beautiful voice, which to Emmanuel always contained an almost fluid quality.

"My Italian's not quite good enough for that, Guido," he said, "but I'm sure that it's very beautiful and very apt."

Guido lifted his hand, commanding silence and attention.

"It is Dante," he said. "He says—never is there greater pain than in hours of misery to recall hours of happiness. We understand."

But Emmanuel's training and upbringing asserted itself. His weakness was past, and he felt suddenly hot and uncomfortable to be standing here talking of miseries and joyless hours with Louis and Guido.

"You must teach me sufficient Italian to read Dante," he said. "You're both awfully decent to me. I appreciate it very much."

4

IT astonished Emmanuel to find how quickly he fell back into the old life. For a few days he found the shop terribly small and cramped, and, after the type of antiques which filled his father's showrooms, the stock seemed ridiculously poor and worthless. But after forty-eight hours his sense of values became adjusted and he looked on the things which composed Louis's stock-in-trade with a more tolerant eye. At the end of a week he found it as simple to enthuse over a Capo del Monte cup and saucer as he had done over the masterpieces which passed through the huge galleries of Gollantz and Son.

Louis, after spending an hour in concentrated business conversation during which Emmanuel grew to wonder at his grasp of facts and his knowledge of figures, departed for Cannes and the arms of Olympia. Louis, Emmanuel reflected, was one of those happy people who can do as much work in one hour as most people do in four. While he worked, he worked with an intensity, a grasp and an essential clarity of mind which made it possible for him to cover a tremendous amount of ground. Once the necessary work was ended, Louis dismissed it from his mind and set out resolutely to enjoy himself.

217

For an hour he sat at the table with Emmanuel and Guido making notes for Emmanuel's guidance, asking short, clear questions of Guido and refusing to accept any answer which did not supply him with exactly the information he required.

"Here then," he said, "is the amount of the stock. These are for our own information alone. To you, my dear cousin, they must seem foolish and poor, but this is the day of small things, and this little venture of ours is in no way to be compared with the House of Gollantz. Your expenses—here is the total. Rent, taxes, light. You must live and so must Guido. You will take what is agreed upon. For the rest buy and buy and buy. China and glass and materials are all good. Furniture—not so good, because we have very little room for storage. Pictures—be very careful of pictures. Arms, armour, pikes, swords and so on—never, never, never. There, I have done." He laid down his pencil and with it his business manner. Once more he was Louis Lara, who cared for nothing but enjoying himself and making money to spend on a very beautiful if slightly overblown cosmopolitan dancer who awaited him at Cannes.

Now, left alone with Guido, Emmanuel set to work to make himself conversant with the stock in hand. Some of it was amusing, a little of it was good, and most of it was nothing more than attractive rubbish. Guido, Emmanuel remembered, had a weakness for buying what appealed to him, and Guido's taste was not always very good. It was not very well kept, some of it was distinctly dirty, and only Guido's dog-like devotion made it possible for Emmanuel to insist upon a thorough cleaning of everything. In a fortnight the meticulous neatness, order and cleanliness of the Gollantz galleries was reproduced in the little antique-shop in the Via San Francesco in Milan.

As he worked Emmanuel thought continually, "I am doing this to make it possible for Juliet to come here again to buy materials. One day she will come into the shop, and find it just as it was before. I'm getting it ready for her."

Every day when the door opened he felt a little spasm of expectancy which was half fear, and he held his breath for a second because Juliet might enter. But she did not come, and usually he realized that the client was only one of Guido's "very very old trouts" who spent half an hour poring over a trayful of junk and listening to Guido's panegyrics on some bit of twisted and discoloured metal.

"Things are horribly quiet," he grumbled to Guido.

"What would you?" Guido replied. "No one has money to spend on antiques. I sold only ten lires' worth of rubbish this morning after being charming to an old sheep for half an hour."

"Ten lire a day won't pay for light!"

"No, indeed"—very cheerfully—"it will scarcely pay for salt."

"Then we've got to find something that will pay, and for a good deal more than salt. What's happened to the decorating side?"

Guido sat down on a table and polished the nails of one hand reflectively on the palm of the other.

"That was a personal matter. You understood it, you created it, and when you left, it died. I know nothing of decorating, except of a type which you dislike. I decorate for my friends. I have just decorated an apartment at the back side of the Scala."

"Back—not back side," Emmanuel said.

"Why, when you say right side and left side, why not back side?"

"Because you don't say it, it means something else—"

"I shall remember. I take it that its meaning is rude, eh?"

"Childishly so, perhaps. Let's get on with this business."

For the next month Emmanuel Gollantz turned himself into a canvasser, he literally touted from house to house. He visited everyone of importance in Milan. He was employed by Guido, officially, and thus became the representative of an Italian firm. He thought gratefully of Louis's foresight in arranging these things before he came and so freeing him from the small tedious questions which might have been put to him by the authorities.

He never told anyone how much he hated calling upon people, how often their charm and kindness hurt him more than their abrupt refusals. He had made sketches, had worked out schemes of decoration, which he felt suitable for Italian houses, and gradually he came to know that he was making an impression. Orders were small, but there were promises and inquiries which would certainly bear fruit sooner or later.

There was the redecoration of a lounge here, a small boudoir to be furnished with painted furniture there, and a reception-room for a well-known specialist somewhere else. Small things, but Louis expected small things at first. Emmanuel forgot his hours of trudging from one great house to another, and felt that he was beginning to get his foot once more on the ladder in Milan.

He was horribly lonely, for he knew no one except Guido's friends, a group of pseudo-artistic young men, very elegant, mostly very poor, and all too remarkably beautiful. They were nice lads, simple and very ready to laugh, drink a little and admire every good-looking woman they saw; but Emmanuel felt out of tune with them. He was too old, too serious, too lonely for their rather simple gaiety to reach him.

Night after night, when the shop was closed and he had arranged his work and plans for the following day, Emmanuel would wander about Milan alone. He grew to know it intimately, to watch with quiet expectancy for this or that little bit of loveliness which he knew waited round the next corner of the street in which he walked. Glimpses of the Duomo, a fountain where Saint Francis—most lovable of saints—stood and preached to a group of pigeons, the castle of the Sforzas, grim and terrible, with their dreadful coat of arms cut into the everlasting stone, all these things and many others grew to be part of his daily life and in some queer way comforted him.

Sometimes he would wander through the Galleria and sit for a few moments at one of the cafés watching the crowd passing up and down. Once or twice men came and spoke to him, rather shabby-smart men with an overdone pleasantness of manner, speaking his own language, saying: "I say, forgive me, but you're English, aren't you?" In the beginning, his loneliness was such that he let them stay and talk, offered them drinks, and tried to like them. But they talked with such bombast of England and their position there, of public schools, race meetings, men of title, and lastly with ghastly intimacy of women they had known, that he left them and decided that he preferred to walk alone.

Once or twice women smiled at him, inviting him with their eyes to speak, hinting possibilities of favours to come. Sometimes he wished that he could have accepted the invitations, for it would have meant at least temporary warmth and cessation of loneliness.

There were days when he almost determined to find out where Juliet was, to write to her, to go and beg her to see him, but after a mental struggle he decided against it. He was possessed by a conviction that she would eventually come into his life again as she had done once before, unsought, and that until then he must wait and work.

Once he had become convinced that his love for her burnt as brightly and steadfastly as it had always done, his one wish had been to leave London, to put behind him a life which irked him, which seemed useless and utterly foolish. It would have been unbearable to continue to live with Viva, to exist in the same state of intimacy, once he acknowledged his love for Juliet. Freedom had been the primary necessity, and that had—though only in a limited sense—been granted to him.

His first impulse had been to seek out Juliet Forbes, to beg her again to share his life and as soon as possible to marry him. That impulse had died when he came back to Italy. He wanted to forget the intervening years, he wanted passionately to take up their life again where it had been cut short three years ago. It seemed to him that after so long a parting they must both have time to wipe out the memory of that separation and all that had followed it.

To have written to Juliet, to have followed her over Europe and have been importunate, seemed to Emmanuel to jeopardize all the happiness which lay in store for them both. He never doubted that she would come, never doubted that he would find her, and least of all doubted that one day they would take up the severed threads and live again a life which was simple, beautiful and utterly complete.

So the autumn slipped into winter, and the winter ended and the flower stalls began to be filled with spring flowers. Emmanuel worked harder than ever. The winter had tried him a little, for Milan is as cold, as wet, and almost as misty as London in winter. He was thinner and his face had grown a little haggard. People got to recognize his tall, thin figure walking quickly from one business house to another, his portfolio under his arm, his eyes intent and keen. Men pointed him out in the Galleria as a young Englishman, and speculated as to what had driven him from his own land. The women still smiled at him, but the invitation had faded from their smiles. They realized that he did not wish for their favours.

Max wrote kindly, even affectionately, and once or twice was able to put small orders in his way. He constantly offered financial help, and protested when Emmanuel replied that he could manage very well and did not need money. Angela sent him papers which he rarely read, and it was Guido who pointed out more than once photographs of Mrs. Emmanuel Gollantz, and remarked that she was very beautiful.

Emmanuel, tired to death after a long day, would glance at the pictures and feel that he was looking at the portrait of a stranger. An attractive stranger, but someone he had never met in his life.

"Queer," he said once to Guido, "to think that's my wife."

"Had she been mine," Guido replied, "I should never have left her for Milano! Tell me, Emmanuel, why did you leave—all this?" He drew an imaginary circle with his finger on the page, as if including all that was best and brightest in London society.

"I didn't belong," Emmanuel said, "I just didn't fit in."

Guido sighed gustily. "Ah, that is life."

Emmanuel sniffed. "I wish you'd eat less garlic, or get out of the habit of sighing," he said.

Guido laid his over-manicured hand over his beautiful mouth, "Peccato!" he exclaimed. "It was the salami. I love it and I fell! Mea culpa!"

Then, one morning in early February when Emmanuel sat entering new items of stocks in the books, the telephone rang.

"Mr. Emmanuel Gollantz?"

"Speaking."

"Oh, Emmanuel, it's me—Viva. Can you come round and see me here at the Continental, or I'll meet you somewhere? I only got here last night. Angela gave me the address. It's important."

"I'll come round at once. How are you, Viva?"

"Frightfully well—and you?"

"Very fit. I'll be with you in ten minutes."

As he walked through the Piazza della Scala and through the quiet side streets, he wondered why she had come. The question disturbed him a little. Possibly to ask him to go back, possibly to tell him that she had determined to marry again; in any case the interview would be difficult. She was certain to mention Juliet, and he shrank from the idea of even speaking her name. She had become something so infinitely precious to him that he hated the thought of the question which Viva would inevitably ask.

She was waiting for him in a sitting-room full of spring flowers. She looked exquisite, charming and just a little artificial. Her clothes were delightful, and she welcomed him with obvious pleasure which did not conceal a trace of nervousness.

"Hello, Emmanuel. Kind of you to come so quickly. I want to talk to you. Is it too early for a cocktail? No, it's never really too early, is it? Can they make a decent one here?"

"I don't know. I'm a working bloke, and things don't run to cocktails and the Continental."

226

She glanced at him sharply. "You don't mean that you're poor?"

"Oh, I have quite enough to eat and sufficient clothes to wear. Don't worry, Viva, I do very well."

"That suit's damned shabby." She eyed him critically.

"His suit was shabby," Emmanuel said, smiling, "but well brushed and still bearing the evidences of a Savile Row tailor, eh?"

She laughed. "Sit down and smoke an English cigarette. Never paid a penny duty. All done by smiles distributed impartially to customs officials. That's better. Now, Emmanuel, let's get down to things. I want—well, I want to divorce you. D'you mind?"

"I don't think so. Only tell me what to do, what evidence you want, letters and so on."

He had expected it, and yet when it came it disturbed him. Like Max, he hated publicity, and the thought of his name appearing in the lists of well-known divorces, even though there were nothing but the one line, "Gollantz v. Gollantz", gave him a quick sense of nausea. Then, lest she should have heard the faint note of dismay in his voice, noticed his instant's hesitation, he said again with additional firmness:

"No, of course I don't mind. We arranged this, didn't we, before I left?"

Viva nodded. "It won't be difficult. Miss Forbes' name needn't come into it."

Always pale, Viva thought that at that moment Emmanuel looked ghastly. Then, making a great effort, he said: "There is no reason why—her name should come into it."

"But you're living at her villa!"

"Who told you that?" His voice sounded like that of old Emmanuel.

"No one told me. It seemed pretty obvious when you dashed off to Milan. Julian said that she has a villa on Como."

"Julian is better informed than I am," Emmanuel said very coldly. "I have never even been to Como—to find out."

Viva sipped her cocktail reflectively, swinging one silk-clad leg backwards and forwards. How damned touchy he was! As if it mattered one way or the other. Quibbling! Typical of the whole family, this "never mention a woman's name" attitude. They were almost amusing, and yet she liked him better than any man she had ever known. Not loved him most, perhaps, but always liked him tremendously.

"Sorry," she said. "No offence meant, none taken I hope! Oh, for God's sake, Emmanuel, don't gloom and glower! I want to get married and I want to divorce you. It does seem a bit unfair to ask when apparently you're living a blameless life. At the moment so'm I, but heaven only knows how long it's going to last. You remember Toby Tatten? Oh yes, you do. His father's old George Tatten. Makes or lets other

228

people make brushes. I'll send you a new shaving-brush as a divorce present!"

He did remember Tatten; remembered too that he was a pleasant fellow with a toothbrush moustache. Viva swung herself off the table, walked over to the mantelpiece and came back with an enormous leather folding-frame which she offered to Emmanuel.

"That's the lad," she said. "Not good-looking but terribly nice."

Emmanuel took the frame and looked at the rather plain, well-groomed young man in the photograph. The sort of face you might remember but ten to one you'd forget.

"Are you very fond of him, Viva?"

She laughed, and this time the nervousness in her voice was apparent.

"I suppose I'm really rather desperately in love with him," she said. "It sounds damned silly, but there it is. There's nothing to him, he's just terribly sweet and frightfully nice. I don't want to go off the rails with Toby before we're married, he's too decent, but he's human and so'm I, and —oh, it's rather hell. Sure you don't feel badly about this divorce, Emmanuel?"

He rose and walked to the mantelpiece and put the photograph back in its place before he answered. Viva thought, "That's so like Emmanuel. Any other bloke would have just laid it down on the table rather superciliously."

"No," he said, "I don't mind. It's inevitable. We must get it put through as soon as possible."

"Soon!" she echoed. "A year's a deuced long time! I do think it's weak—don't you? This waiting and hanging about and giving perhaps four wretched people a devil of a time! I'm all for Divorce Reform, aren't you? Well, there it is. I'm leaving again tonight. Write and tell me that you won't come back to me and that you have lived with half the women in Milan, and then my lawyers will write back and tell you what a hound you are and ask a heap of impertinent questions, and we shall all be jolly boys together in no time! Oh, what a game! I do apologize, Emmanuel, it's not awfully fair, is it?"

"That's all right, Viva. I hope you'll be awfully happy. Tell Tatten that he has all my good wishes and that he's a very lucky fellow, will you?"

"Not likely!" she returned. "You don't know Toby. If they stuck him in a witness-box, or some lawyer talked to him, he'd be certain to say, 'Y'know, I like Gollantz awfully. Sent me all his good wishes and said I was a lucky feller,' then we should all be put in jail for collusion or whatever it is. He's an angel, but the biggest fool. Going?" —for Emmanuel had risen. "Won't you stay for luncheon? No? I've got some people coming to take me out. Friends of Toby's—very stiff and proud and English."

Emmanuel held out his hand. "I won't stop,"

he said. "As your ex-husband it would scarcely do, would it? Besides, I have work."

"I'd like to have seen your shop, and bought masses of things. Still—I expect you're wise. Good-bye, Emmanuel, and thanks awfully. You are a nice person, only too thin. Take care of yourself. I don't understand why you aren't with that attractive person, but I suppose you both know your own business best. Good luck."

"Good luck, Viva."

He walked back, feeling shaken in a foolish way. He had expected it, he had known that it must come sooner or later, but the fact that Viva had found a man she loved seemed to make his own position additionally lonely. It seemed to intensify the fact that he was terribly alone. He didn't like the idea of being divorced much, but he had given Viva his promise and he consoled himself with the thought that at least it would be permissible to tell Angela the truth.

He got back to find Guido talking very fast and very loudly to an elderly man who had come to sell something or other. As Emmanuel entered, Guido began to exercise his usual "carpet-selling" methods of decrying whatever clients offered for sale.

"The beads—there are millions such in Venice! The earrings are pretty but only pinchbeck! The fan—charming; but tell me, where will anyone buy a fan of chicken-skin in these days? No one, nowhere."

231

Somewhere the echo of Juliet's voice rang through Emmanuel's mind. "Fans—I have a sort of unholy passion for fans! Useless, out of date, but oh, so attractive!" He stepped forward to the table.

"Let me see," he said. "No, only the fan. I might find a buyer for it."

Guido added hurriedly: "If the price is right, of course."

Five minutes later he locked the fan away in his private drawer, and in some inexplicable way he felt that the end of his probation and of his loneliness was drawing near.

5

THE days passed. He heard from Viva, from her lawyers, and still there was no sign of Juliet. Emmanuel began to lose some of that self-control which had been tried to breaking-point so often. Time after time he would open the little drawer, take out the fan with its delicious little paintings of ladies and gallants, and, holding it in his hand, would try to exercise his will to make Juliet come to him. But nothing happened and the long days dragged on, filled with work, with business worries—for Italian workmen are very different from their English brothers—and weariness. His keenness had lost some of its edge, it had become blunted and dull, and though he worked harder than ever, he worked mechanically.

Guido watched him with grave attention, noting his little bursts of impatience, his sudden flares of anger, and making allowances for them all. Never during the whole of that time did Guido resent anything that Emmanuel said to him. He was gentle, kindly, even tender. When, after some show of temper on Emmanuel's part, he would come to Guido, penitent and ashamed, Guido met him more than half-way. In fact, it seemed sometimes that Guido apologized to him, not he to Guido.

He was sleeping badly. Hour after hour he tossed from side to side, waiting for the day when he might fly to his work as the only drug he knew or cared to use. It was the end of March before Guido spoke.

They were checking a mixed lot of goods which Emmanuel had bought at a sale, when some small item evaded Emmanuel, who looked for it with that passionate irritation which is the outcome of frayed nerves.

"Damn and blast it!" he burst out. "Where the hell has the thing got to? I'm sick to death of the rubbish. It's not worth a fiver anyway. Let's put it away, Guido. Leave it! I can't stick this any longer. My God, I think sometimes I shall go crazy."

Guido, usually so easily moved, answered very quietly.

"No," he said, "We shall not leave it. This is work and must be done, and you know it. Today it is a bore, tomorrow it would be a damned bore! The day after that—it will be pushed aside and never done at all. Courage, my friend. Another ten minutes and it will be over."

Emmanuel glowered at him for a moment, then said: "Come on, then, let's get it finished. Here you are—a silver snuff-box."

It was later in the evening when Guido, who now lived over the shop with Emmanuel, had donned a smoking-suit of purple velveteen and red leather slippers, that he talked frankly to Emmanuel. They sat by the grey china stove smoking in silence, Emmanuel's eyes sombre and wretched, staring at nothing, Guido watching him.

"Emmanuel," he said suddenly, "this cannot continue. You are making yourself a very sick man. Something must be done, and done quickly. You eat your heart away and live in horrible darkness. Perhaps I know why, perhaps I know nothing. I beg that you will take the car tomorrow and go to that lady's villa."

"Mind your own business, please, Guido."

As Guido met Emmanuel's cold eyes there was nothing in the world he wanted to do so much as to mind his own business. Coldness from the man who was his hero wounded him terribly.

"This is my business," he said. "You gave me the right to make it my business when you came here and I grew to admire you and love you. Oh, I know that Englishmen hate to hear men talk of love, especially love for other men. That is one of your little childishnesses. You think that men must always be full of heartiness, and spend their time smacking other men on the shoulders, and asking them to have drinks! There is nothing bad in my love for you, it is not like nasty little boys' love, it is just like bigger and littler brothers."

"All right, it's very decent of you. God knows

I've given you little enough cause even to like me lately."

"That is why I take my courage in two hands and speak. Go to the villa, even if you do no more than look at it, and return here. You are beginning to have doubtfulnesses, to believe that the time you were so happy is an over-long-ago dream." He rose and came to Emmanuel, laying his hand on his shoulder. "I beg this, with a hole in my heart—I mean a wholly heart."

Emmanuel lifted his white tired face, and Guido knew that his own eyes smarted at the sight of such misery. He had known this man when he was loving life, when they had laughed and joked. He remembered when Juliet Forbes used to call for Emmanuel when work was over, and how the sight of his hero and her beauty together had almost moved him to tears.

"I wonder if you're right?" Emmanuel said.

"I am betting you two to one that I am."

Emmanuel's lips curved. "Not very long odds! Very well, Guido, I'll go tomorrow. I'll call and see old Hugo in Como and drive back—the other way. You're a good fellow; I'm very fond of you."

"'God bless you, Mister Copperland'," Guido said, his smiles returning, as he explained: "You see I have studied the work of the undying Dickens—that is a quotation. Oh, Dio mio, it is a dull book! The loving is so bad! So stiff, so rigida."

The next morning he saw Emmanuel drive

away, and with a sudden burst of energy set to work to rearrange the little window and clean the shop. At twelve he was so tired with his exertions that he closed the shop for siesta with a sigh of relief. He washed and dressed to his own great satisfaction and, putting a little extra scent on his hair, adjusted his hat in what he believed to be an exact imitation of Emmanuel and sallied forth.

It was nearly five o'clock when he returned. He opened the shop and sat down at the desk smiling contentedly. What did he care if a hundred customers had come and gone away disappointed and angry! Not a rap! In a high, sweet tenor voice he began to sing "Santa Lucia" with tremendous expression, beating time with a carved ivory paper-knife.

It was half past five when Emmanuel entered. He came in and stood swaying a little like a man who is utterly exhausted. His face was white, his eyes heavy and bloodshot. Guido stifled a sudden longing to lead him to a chair and fold him in his arms. He wished at that moment that Emmanuel had been anything except an Englishman.

"Hello, Guido," he said, his voice colourless, "you were wrong. The villa is closed. The garden's like a wilderness. I asked the gardener next door. The villa was given up some time ago —nearly a year past." He sighed and sank on to a chest which stood near, covering his face with his hands. Guido had never seen him so listless, so broken as he was at that moment.

He went into the little kitchen, put the big coffee-pot on the little gas stove and presently carried back a cup of the strong, bitter liquid to Emmanuel.

"Drink this," he said. "I have a great deal to tell you and you must have a clear mind to listen."

"Thanks, that's good. But I don't want to hear about sales at the moment, Guido. Just let me alone, there's a good chap."

The little shop was almost dark. Emmanuel's pale face seemed to shine out of the gloom; to Guido it looked like some old cameo. The pieces of hanging brocade, old pieces of carved furniture, the wooden chests, all took on strange shapes in the half-light. Here and there a piece of china caught what light remained and shone clear in the dusk; here and there a bit of metal, polished silver, or a gilt frame glimmered as the last rays of the spring sun entered the shop only to leave it again very quickly. Over all was that strange smell of old things which is not dust or dirt or decay, but a queer regretful perfume which emanates from things which have been in the world too long, which have become friendless and unwanted. Guido, sentimental and sensitive, shivered suddenly. The spell of the shop caught him and held him. Emmanuel had no real place among these poor little pieces of flotsam and jetsam; he had nothing in common with old, worn-out things, with a little out-of-the-way antique—shop from which daylight was fading.

"Oh, Emmanuel," he cried with sudden passion, "if only you would study Italian so that I might speak easily with you!"

"I'll study it this next winter, Guido. You shall give me lessons." The tone was kind, even gentle, but its lifelessness hurt Guido.

"No, no, next winter you will be happy," he said. "Only I have a great deal to say, and shall speak it so badly. All you know is how to tell workmen to paint, curtain makers to hang, carpet men to lay—prices, totals, money. What I have to tell you has no price. Drink your coffee and listen. The villa is closed, but a very beautiful apartment is open in Milano! Listen to me. Today I have lost a great heap of old trouts' money, for the shop was closed from mezzo giorno until seventeen o'clock, and I care nothing. I walked this morning round the back side of the Galleria, and I saw before me a little man, a mosquito of a man, a nothing! With him—the goddess Juno walking the earth again! Yes, yes, per Bacco—do not interrupt me. Already the words tumble over my teeth and my tongue is too large—it is terrible. I hurried forward, like an Englishman I lifted my hat from my head and spoke. I said: 'Please to forgive me—I think that we have met before.' The little man—you remember a little rabbit of a man called Jilly—Billy—it does not matter—was angry. But she turned and stopped and said: 'It is Guido—oh, dear little Guido, how are you?'"

Emmanuel licked his dry lips. "You mean that it really was—"

"Miss Juliet Forbes, yes. She wore a very beautiful—"

"I don't give a damn what she wore," Emmanuel said roughly. "For God's sake tell me what she said—how she looked. . . ."

Guido smiled, took out his carefully folded silk handkerchief and frankly and unashamedly wiped his beautiful eyes. When he spoke his voice shook a little.

"She said was I still at the littler shop. I said that I was, but now, thanks be to all the Saints, not alone. I gathered my courage and said, 'Please do me that honour to drink coffee with me.' She did not speak for a moment, then said to the littler Rabbit, 'Do you mind? I shan't be very long, Jilly. It is important.' We went to Biffi's and sat down. I spoke a great deal. I said you— mio duca, maestro e signore—had returned, a long time went. No—past, not went. I said that my heart was broken for you. I told her that you were very littler fat, very pallido, very triste'. Her face was like a mourning woman in a picture by dei Libri. I spoke with great feeling, very beautiful words spoken from the heart. I wept, and she wept a little—less than I did, though!"

He paused to wipe his eyes again, and Emmanuel said thickly: "Kind little devil you are! Go on, old chap."

"I was exhausted by emotion," Guido went on,

240

"and while I drank a doppio cognac she told me that she had left the villa. Imagine my distress at that moment, knowing that you had gone there! My tears returned! The Galleria was dark as night for me. I reproached her. I said 'Tell me why you left there, when my friend, my brother, loved it dearly and has gone there to find you!' I said that it was unhuman."

"You did, eh? Reproached her! I've a good mind to wring your neck, Guido."

"But the best was to come. Her apartment is in Milano—I have the address. Here it is, and the number of the telephone. She said: 'If he'— never once did she say your name!—'wishes it, that is where I am.' Then, my dear, a thought came to me. I remembered the past time. It is very good to sometimes put clocks back again. I said: 'In the shop there is a fan of chicken-skin, painted with ladies and flowers and cavaliers. It is put away in a drawer and not offered for sale, though it was bought many weeks ago.' I laughed and said: 'Now, I am a shopkeeper again, mees, and perhaps it might be of interest to you. If this is the matter, my chief will be in the shop tomorrow, or better still, this evening. I regret that I shall not be there, but he will know which is the fan and will have pleasure in showing it to you.' I said: 'If you buy it, I do not doubt that I shall get a very large commission—the happiness of my dear chief.' She smiled, showed her beautiful strong English teeth, without any gold

241

in them, and said: 'Dear little Guido. I think that I must have that fan—though I shan't promise to pay for it.' Then I walked with her to her apartment, always on the outside of the pavement as you would do, and refused to go in because—I felt that it might displease you. I came back here and waited for you. Now tell me, was that not a beautiful regalo for you?"

"I hope it's going to be the only regalo in the world that I could ever want," Emmanuel said. "I don't talk much, Guido, but I know just how beastly I've been, what a rotten time I've given you, and now you make me a return like this—it's just a little too much. I can't talk about it. It's too big to talk about. I've nothing to say, except—thank you. If you'd been anything but the marvellous fellow you are, you might have bungled everything, and—oh, God only knows what might have happened. But that simplicity of yours, that lack of self-consciousness, saved everything. I do thank you—just open that drawer and give me the fan, will you?"

"And then," Guido said, as he passed over the delicate ivory and painted thing, "if you will excuse me I shall close the shop and go to a conversazione. I will wait only enough long time to allow you to go and wash, and—perhaps put on a smoking, yes?"

"A smoking—? Oh, a dinner jacket. I don't think so. It's not necessary, is it, d'you think?"

"It is necessary. There are only two places

you will dine. One is at the flat of Mees Forbes, the other is a restaurant. Both demand a smoking. Besides"—he paused—"your other suits are just a little shabby. I wish you to look your best."

When Emmanuel returned the shop was closed, and two tall yellow candles were burning on the table. They stood in high old gilt candlesticks, their soft beams touching everything with a light which was very tender.

Already some of his old doubt had seized Emmanuel. After all, Juliet had not promised to come; she had only hinted that she might. She might even have decided against it when she had time to think.

He said, with an impulsiveness which was new to him: "Guido, if she doesn't come, I shall die!"

"Have no fear of death," Guido replied; "she told me that she would come. Not in words, but with her eyes. Women in love speak very plainly with their eyes. You look very beautiful, very gentlemanly, like an English lord. I think that she will be tickled to death with you, your sveet'art. That is a beautiful word—sve-ee-et'arrt." He rolled it on his tongue as if it tasted good.

Alone, Emmanuel sat with his hands lying loosely on the table before him. He felt strangely light, as if he had been drained of all emotion. His fears had left him. He knew that she would come, and he waited with that strange, impassive patience of his Jewish ancestors. Somewhere a clock struck seven, then played a little tune of five notes only. A little childish tune with no particular charm, but it soothed Emmanuel Gollantz and he listened to it with a feeling of conscious happiness. As the last notes died away he heard a car drive up and stop at the door. Immediately afterwards it drove away, and he waited for the knock which he knew would come, his heart beating wildly. His time of probation was over.

As he heard the knock, his heart seemed to cease beating for a moment, and he knew that his knees were weak, that his whole body was cold. Only his mind seemed to remain alive and fully conscious. He walked to the door, moving very slowly, his hands hanging at his sides, then stood for a second immovable before he laid his hand on the old wrought-iron handle.

The door swung open slowly, and for the first time for nearly a year he saw Juliet again. She stood there, looking very tall and slim, despite her heavy furs. Her face gleamed white in the soft light which shone on it from the two tall candles. To Emmanuel it looked like a magnolia blossom seen in moonlight, strange, exotic, very beautiful.

He listened for the first sound of her voice, thinking almost wildly that it could never be as beautiful as he had imagined it. It came, very soft and clear. "I want you to show me a fan. Guido said you had one—"

Emmanuel said: "It has been waiting for you a long time. Please come in."

She entered and he closed the door behind her. They stood alone in the crowded little shop with friendly things about them. She looked round, smiling a little, and said: "It's larger, but really it's not changed, is it?"

"Nothing has changed," he said. "The clock has been put back four years, Juliet."

"May I sit down?"

He dragged forward the big chair with the high carved back. She looked at it, then back at Emmanuel's intent face.

"That was here before, wasn't it?"

"Yes, Guido bought it. He believed it to be fourteenth century. It's modern Milanese. We can't sell it."

"You can—I'll buy it."

Emmanuel came nearer. He took her furs and very gently slipped them from her shoulders, holding them to his face for a moment before he laid them down.

Then coming back to where she sat he stooped down and took her hands in his, and without speaking they remained so, in silence, while it seemed to Emmanuel that the past four years were wiped out, and they were as they had been before she sent him away.

"You've come back to me, Juliet," he said. "Really come back."

"I'm breaking all my resolutions," she said.

245

"I'm doing something which is weak and probably very foolish. I shall hurt you and you will hurt me. There will be all kinds of difficulties. People will blame me and pity you. I shall be spoiling your career, and one day you may regret it very deeply. Can you face all those things?"

"Anything—except losing you."

"Your—career?"

"I have none. You are my career!"

"The knowledge that I must go away very often?"

"If you will come back, and be glad to come back."

"I am nearly forty. I've worked very hard."

"To me you have no age—you are only Juliet."

"I shall grow old very soon."

He made a little movement as if he would take her in his arms. "Juliet, Juliet," he said impatiently, "You've come home, you've made it sunshine again, we're together and here we are talking of ages and years and growing old. How can either of us grow old in a brand-new world? Give me your hands; there—I know that you're real, not a dream. I've only lived in dreams since I left you that night in London."

He drew her to him and kissed her very tenderly and without passion. At that moment he was living on the mountain top, he was removed from all emotion except the joy that she was with him again. He had waited so long, had hoped and despaired, believed and doubted, and now his only feeling was one of immense peace and beautiful reality. He whispered her name, softly, as if to him it was the most beautiful music in the world.

"Juliet, Juliet, Juliet."

He felt her hand on his neck, knew that her fingers touched his hair as they used to do when they sat together in the garden of her villa.

"Your hair—just there, where it grows into a little peak—feels so young," she whispered.

He laughed. "Until an hour ago I felt so old."

"Guido told you? Dear little Guido, he was so delightfully miserable over you! And so discreet. He wouldn't come into my flat for fear it might seem too unconventional. You went to the villa? To find me?"

"To assure myself that it wasn't all a dream. To assure myself that you really had existed, that I had not only imagined you. I came back—oh, let me forget it all. You'll marry me, Juliet? As soon as it's possible. Viva is divorcing me, she wants to marry again. You will—say that you will."

"I don't know, my dear. I never want to make it irrevocable for you. I couldn't bear to hold you if you ever wanted to go. Can't we wait? There is so much to say now. I'm here, I've come back to you—and I love you."

With that lack of self-consciousness which was part of his nature, Emmanuel slipped to his knees, lifted her hands to his lips and kissed them. Then, still holding them, he laid his head on her lap and she felt his tears wet and hot on her fingers.

248

6

THE first days were ecstatic. Emmanuel was filled with tenderness and happiness which held a trace of recklessness in it. He lived at the shop, but spent every free moment with Juliet. To him she seemed to have grown more beautiful than she had ever been, and to be with her gave him a peace and content which he felt he had never known before.

"I feel that I've been travelling alone in some horrible desert," he said, "and now when I've reached the oasis I find it difficult to realize that it's not a mirage which may disappear at any moment. You won't disappear, Juliet, will you?"

His youth had reasserted itself, as youth will do when some heavy burden is removed from young shoulders. He lost his look of weariness, the little lines traced by worry vanished from between his eyebrows, and his mouth lost its downward curve. He smiled easily, and laughed as if he found life amusing, not "as if he mocked himself, that could be moved to smile at anything".

Juliet waited for him to tell her of his coming divorce. He alluded to it vaguely and without giving her much definite information. There was sufficient of both his grandfather and Max in his

249

mentality to make the whole subject distasteful to him; and to speak frankly to Juliet on the matter was positively repulsive.

He possessed that feeling, common among many Jews, that nothing unsavoury, nothing sordid, must be allowed to touch the woman they love. To Emmanuel, the bare statement, "Viva is going to divorce me. She's going to marry again," seemed not only sufficient, but almost too much to have confided to Juliet. Though he had done nothing actually to merit divorce in the eyes of the law, he felt in some queer way smirched by the coming proceedings. The fact that he would be called up to produce evidence of infidelity hurt his self-respect, and despite his intense love for Juliet, his ardent desire for her, and his youth, the thought of that evidence which must be given to Viva, of necessity, stood between them and in his mind made him unworthy to take all that Juliet would have given.

She was happy with him, she looked forward to his coming, she felt for him a passionate tenderness, and, having made up her mind as she had done when she talked with Guido, was ready to give him everything, to surrender herself completely to him.

Juliet had never been a very passionate woman, but she had always been a very affectionate one. Where she loved—and she had only loved one other man in her life—she had no reservations, no petty restraints. She was not, and never had been, what is called "clever" with men. She had allowed Leon Hast to wound her most delicate sensibilities, to break her self confidence, to bully her and treat her abominably. Those things had never affected her love for him. Even when she left him her love had never failed. She had gone because she felt that not only was he destroying her, but that she was actually destroying all that was best in him.

Three years before, when Emmanuel had been with her at the villa on Lake Como, she had hesitated to give freely and generously because she had feared the pain which might result when he was forced to return to England. She had realized his youth and her own rapidly approaching middle age, she had understood that rigidity in Max Gollantz' character which would make her unwelcome as the prospective mistress of Ordingly, and she had hesitated. She had suffered a great deal and had fought desperately to obtain peace and a measure of content; even her love for Emmanuel had not been sufficient to make her ready to risk those things at the outset. Only after she had seen him again in London, understood that age mattered nothing, position, social distinctions and approval or disapproval of other people were of no account, had she decided to go to him, if he still wished it.

For nearly a year she had made no attempt to write to him, to find him or get in touch with him in any way. She had worked, both on the continent and in America, and had deliberately waited, rather as Emmanuel had done himself. Guido had precipitated matters and she had flung pride, wisdom and convention to the winds and gone to him.

Now, after some days, his restraint puzzled her. In the midst of his most impassioned outbursts she noticed the sudden effort to become entirely master of himself again. There were times when he would push her from him with a roughness which, because of his innate gentleness, she knew was entirely foreign to him and which could only be the outcome of some mental struggle through which he was passing.

Juliet never doubted that he loved her, that he loved her absolutely and entirely; and, remembering his pleading and importunities of three years ago, his present rather violent efforts at complete control contained an element which was almost abnormal. He began to indulge in sudden outbursts of temper, short-lived but incredible to her. At first she was hurt and distressed by them, and only after hours of quiet thinking did she understand that they were the outcome of frayed nerves—nerves which were strained to breaking-point.

They had lunched together at a little restaurant near the shop, and as she was leaving him she suggested that they should dine quietly at her flat.

"No, let's go to Biffi's," Emmanuel said.

"I'm just a little tired of Biffi's," she said. "We

were there last night and the night before. The flat's much nicer, and—I pride myself on my cook—the food's just as good."

"I'd rather go to Biffi's—or some other restaurant," he persisted.

She laughed. "But I'd rather go home."

Emmanuel shrugged his shoulders. "Then dine at home," he said, and turned as if to leave her.

She touched his arm. "Emmanuel—my dear!" Her reproach was half laughter; she was almost amused at his sudden childishness.

He turned back and said with unnatural quietness: "I've told you that I don't wish to dine at the flat or to spend an evening there. Isn't that enough?"

"Not nearly," Juliet said, "but naturally you must dine where you wish. I shall dine at home. Good-bye, Emmanuel."

"Good-bye."

She walked away, and had almost reached her apartment when he overtook her.

"Juliet, Juliet," he said, "forgive me. I don't know what's the matter with me. I'm a fool. I'm worried and I let my wretched worries come into everything, spoil everything. I'll dine where you wish, I'll do anything you wish, only don't let me lose you."

His face was so white and drawn that all the tenderness in her rose in protest. "Emmanuel, you need never lose me. It's all right—over, forgotten. I shall expect you at eight."

253

"You want to dine at home?" His tone was a little regretful.

With a firmness which was foreign to her, Juliet said: "Yes, I think so—tonight, to please me."

"Very well. Eight o'clock. Good-bye, my very dear."

All the rest of the day she heard the humility in his tone and almost hated herself for her firmness.

During dinner he talked amusingly of his day's work; only when they sat over their coffee his animation seemed to evaporate, and Juliet watched his face growing more and more sombre, listened to his voice growing less vital, and knew that his replies to her questions were growing brief and abrupt.

"Emmanuel," she said suddenly, "tell me what is wrong. It's not fair to keep me in the dark."

"Wrong?" he repeated coldly. "Nothing. What could be wrong?"

"That's what I want you to tell me. Are you happy?"

Mechanically, as if repeating a lesson, he said, "I'm with you, that's enough to make me happy."

"You're not in any trouble? Nothing making life difficult?"

"Not more troubles than usually beset the small shopkeeper."

She rose and walked over to the piano, which stood open at the other end of the long room, saying as she did so, "My dear, that kind of sneer at your work is so unworthy of you."

254

She was facing a crisis, and she knew it. She knew too that she was shaking, that her heart was beating heavily, and that she would have given a great deal to have let the matter drop, and to have allowed Emmanuel to emerge from his despondency in his own way and in his own time. But her experience had taught her one thing at least, and that was to do her best to dispel these clouds, and to bridge once and for all the gulf which Emmanuel had allowed to come between them. She knew his sensitive, over-imaginative nature, and understood how a little cloud "no bigger than a man's hand" could grow and swell on his mental horizon until the sunshine was entirely obliterated.

She sat down at the piano and began to play very softly. Her eyes were turned to Emmanuel, who, though he stirred at the sound of the first notes, did not move, but stood staring down at the little wood fire, his face illuminated by the spurts of flame.

Years ago, before Emmanuel was born, Angela had tried to pierce through the armour of Max's misery in much the same fashion. But Angela, being Angela, had tried to effect it by less gentle methods. Juliet remembered how old Emmanuel had once told her, smiling a little, as if poking kindly fun at himself, "I em a melencholy person by nature, please remember. It iss a so small failing of all my r-race, we qvickly become emmersed in chloom. Vonce ve are r-really emmersed, der vaters close offer our heads and ve are drownt in it. Sometimes ve hev dis depression through very small t'ings, emaginary t'ings, or very, very delicate leetle personal metters. Leetle fears, leetle pains—no, a leetle pain I mean, or leetle vorries vich may neffer heppen. R-remember, Juliet, dot to dispel t'ese t'ings reqvires very brafe people. Any great fool can discuss the chence of a men losing his whole fortune, but only very brave peoples ken discuss the r-reason vhy he has indigestion or vhy he don't pay der milk bill."

To the very soft accompaniment of the music she began to speak, knowing that she was facing a crisis in the life of herself and Emmanuel Gollantz.

"It's rather a dreadful thing after all," she said, "to tell anyone—any man that you love him. It gives him such immense power to humiliate you."

She saw Emmanuel's figure stiffen a little, but he did not either turn or reply.

"To put all your cards on the table, to put all your goods in the window, gives such an admirable opportunity to the other person to say that they don't really like them very much."

Without turning, he said harshly, "Has anyone —I suppose that you mean me—have I said that I didn't appreciate everything?"

"In effect. Yes, I think so."

"You're mistaken."

She laughed. "Then I can only say that I don't

appreciate your appreciation!" She paused, then added: "I find it just a little inhuman perhaps."

He made no reply, and she broke into a quicker measure, letting the notes fall into the silence of the room like shooting stars of sound. It was easier to play quickly, it gave her courage, assurance.

"Perhaps I find your appreciation—unsatisfactory."

Emmanuel swung round impulsively. "My God! Do you know what you're saying?"

"Perfectly. There are a dozen men in the world who will lunch with me, dine with me or take me to dine with them, who will amuse me, pay me compliments, even make rather tepid love to me. I didn't want them—I wanted you, I virtually told you so. I wanted more than a pleasant companion, I wanted—" She paused and turned her attention to the keyboard.

"You wanted?" Emmanuel demanded.

"Briefly—a lover."

"I see." His voice was coldly furious. "And you chose me from among your list of applicants. I am honoured."

She was silent, and almost immediately Emmanuel's voice, tinged with anger, went on, "I regret that I am unsatisfactory; I was not in full possession of the facts. I believed that you would and could understand without forcing confessions and admissions from me. We both r-rated each other too highly. Nothing is irr-revo-

257

cable and we can put matters r-right now. Perhaps you will find it in your heart to be gr-rateful that your r-reputation has not suffered through any carelessness of mine. It has been very regrettable, and—"

She lifted her hands from the keys, turned and met his eyes.

"Emmanuel, stop! This is ridiculous. We neither of us can do without the other. Haven't we tried? Do you suppose that I came back to you without a great deal of thought? Do you suppose that I came back before I had decided that I, literally, couldn't live—live without you? You know me well enough to judge how difficult it is for me to speak of these things, but I want a life with you which is complete, not something which is only half living for both of us. What is it all, this repression, this subjection of every natural impulse? We're living unnatural lives. Lives which have no real warmth, lives which are full of watchfulness, guarding, care, lives which will presently grow hideous and later die, frozen to death. Emmanuel, tell me—explain to me! I love you, you love me; don't hide things from me. It's unbearable."

He stood listening, watching her intently, his face heavy with misery. When she ended, he squared his shoulders as she had seen him do a hundred times when faced with a difficulty, and sighed a queer fluttering sigh as if he had been stripped of some garment he had assumed, and stood naked before her.

"I am ashamed," he said, speaking very slowly, as if he chose his words with great care. "I have been ver-ry unworthy of you. I have allowed my own feelings to dominate ever-rything when I ought to have spoken to you fr-reely. I am wr-retched, wr-retched because I love you so much, and want that love to be such a ver-ry perfect thing."

She came to where he stood, and laid her hand on his arm, saying:

"Come and tell me. Here by the fire."

He looked down at her hand, then very gently removed it from his arm and followed her to the tall carved fireplace. Some thought of making it easier for him made Juliet switch off the lights in the big Venetian glass chandelier so that they were in darkness except for the flickering lights of the fire. Emmanuel stood silent and the quietness of the long room was for a moment almost a solid, tangible thing. Then in the distance the sudden hooting of a taxi broke the spell and immediately afterwards he spoke.

"This divorce which is coming pr-resently," he said—"I promised Viva I would make possible when I left England. It was only fair. It was all that I could do to atone for having made such a mistake as to mar-ry a woman I didn't love. How could I r-really love any woman while you lived? While you are in the world, it holds only one woman. I have known that—actually—for many more years than you remember. I have pr-romised to do all that I can, and now comes the news that I must prove technical infidelity. I must go to an hotel with some woman and send the bill to Viva's lawyers.

"Can you r-realize how horrible this is? Can you imagine how it disgusts and nauseates me? Can you imagine how utterly impossible it is that I should—should"—he stumbled and faltered for a moment, his pale face suddenly swept by a wave of scarlet—"be happy with you while this disgusting thing hangs over me? It is necessary, it is what the law demands. They will take for granted that I have no mental, spiritual love for my wife, or she for me; they will accept it as true when she writes and asks me to return, and I write and refuse in a letter which is so unlike me that any child might know that it meant nothing. She writes, 'Please come back to me, and we will try to make a life together again.' She is in love, honestly in love, with Toby Tatten. I answer, 'My dear Viva, what you ask is quite impossible. I have not the slightest intention of r-returning, and you must take whatever steps you wish. I will give you any evidence necessary.' Legally I have deserted my wife. Now I must legally commit adultery!

"I don't need to assure you that whatever happens I could never be unfaithful to you now.

You know that, Juliet, you understand that? Say that you do."

"My dear, of course I do."

"But the horror of it! To spend a night, seated in an hotel bedroom with a woman I don't even know! To face the look of the servants, the porters, the clerks in the cassa! To walk out in the morning with this woman, to give her money —oh, Juliet, until that is over how is it possible for us to—live completely?"

He turned and held out his hands as if showing manacles which bound him, his face drawn and haggard.

"My poor darling," Juliet said softly, "what terrible bugbears you have made, what dreadful bogeys you have allowed to frighten you! There will be no woman whom you don't know. There will only be a woman you know very well and, I believe, you love—me."

"Good God!" His horror was very real. "You think that I'd drag you into this dirt, you think that—"

"You will drag me nowhere," she said calmly. "I shall only be registered as Mrs. Gollantz, and that will be all. Not here in Milano, that would be stupid, not anywhere on Como, but there are other places where no one knows either of us."

Emmanuel shuddered. "Impossible to—to begin our life together in surroundings like that! Juliet, my dear, it would kill something. Going

261

to some little town, some horr-rible hotel, a dingy r-room, to know that—no, no, never!"

Juliet got up, and put her hands on his shoulders, forcing him to look at her. "Listen," she said. "Your grandfather once talked to me about 'that wild lie which men call pride'. You are consenting to that wild lie at this moment. Your pride is hurt, you put your good name, your integrity, above the love which we have for each other. You're allowing what is a very stupid convention to spoil everything. You do love me?"

"Absolutely and entirely, Juliet."

"You know, without the slightest doubt, that I love you?"

"Yes."

"And you think that this love of ours which has survived three years' separation can be spoilt, smeared by one night spent in some wretched little hotel, where no one will either know or care who we are! Rather, because it is conventional, you would scarify yourself by spending a night with some woman you have never seen, and leave me—because in spite of my love for you I am only very human—to imagine all kinds of scenes, all kinds of temptations through which you might be passing. Emmanuel, my dearest, don't be so abominably proud, and oh, my dear, don't be so utterly childish."

"It seems so terr-rible—"

"It is terrible," she agreed; "we're caught in a terrible machine and we can only free ourselves

262

by making an effort. Then, once we are free, we shall find that we are not even scratched by it, certainly never hurt. But let's make the effort together, let's earn freedom—even if it's only legal, technical freedom—together."

He smiled at last, a faint smile which scarcely touched his lips, but which shone from his eyes.

"How good you are to me, Juliet! Why was I such a fool as not to have told you at once? Ever since that letter came, and it came the day after I found you again—"

"I found you," she corrected.

"You found me," he said. "I have worr-ried, and thought, and become more and more miserable. Everything got out of proportion, everything was distorted, and it seemed to me that I was following the only course open to me, to any decent person."

"The conventional idealist," Juliet said. "Darling, what a very ordinary young man you are!"

His misery was dispelled and he was himself again, very tender, and obviously absolutely content to be with her. They sat and talked by the fire, Emmanuel lying at her feet, his arm thrown across her knees, her hand on his shoulder. The old brass and polished steel clock on the high mantelpiece struck twelve. Juliet said mechanically, "Twelve o'clock—my dear, it's late."

Emmanuel twisted round so that he knelt in

front of her. Once again the thought struck her that a man on his knees ought to look ridiculous, and how strange it was that Emmanuel looked so perfectly natural.

"Juliet," he said very softly, "it's twelve, midnight. It's the beginning of a new day; can't we begin it together, and leave all our fears behind us in the day that's over?"

She did not answer, only, leaning forward, took his face between her hands and kissed him.

Book Three

Book Three

1

HIS divorce was over and the law had dissolved the tie between Viva and himself. The Church had bound them, but only the law could set them free. To Emmanuel there was a kind of cynical amusement to be found in that fact; he confided his feeling to Guido. Guido, who, though he might be cynical enough himself over his own religion, was always ready to point its advantages over other Churches, nodded.

"Indeed," he said, "if one considered the permissions of the English over many things one would regard them as the greatest fools in the world. You are all so—beautifully mad. Here is yourself, a Jew, you are married in a church which is Protestant, because it is so nice, so respectable, so pretty to have marriages in old churches! But after a little time you never run to the church and say, 'Loose me, please'; you say, 'Oh, the devil, I must go to law courts and get lawyers to make this freedom for me.' The Church," said Guido piously, "knows and admits of no divorce. That is why there is no divorce in this country."

"Then what if, after you are married, you find

someone you love so dearly that you can't live without them?"

Guido considered for a moment, then said, "One can always live in sin—without the sanction of the Church, of course."

Emmanuel scowled at him for a moment, then said coldly, "I don't much care for that expression, Guido."

Guido opened his eyes very wide and demanded, "Then what is the right expression, if you please, tell me?"

"I didn't mean that," Emmanuel explained, his anger dying down in the face of Guido's evident innocence. "I meant—oh, damn it, you know what it sounded like, don't you?"

Guido considered, then said: "Per Bacco! you mean that I think you live in sin! But so you do! What does it matter, you are very happy? I notice almost all people who live in sin are happy. It is very strange, but quite true. One day," he swaggered a little, "I may be so fortunate myself!"

But Emmanuel could not forget, and gradually the thought grew and flourished in his mind, until he felt that all Italy, all Europe, knew and must think less of Juliet because of it. He had never actually lived at the flat, officially his home was still one of the rooms over the shop, but he was continually there, and he knew that certain people must guess.

Juliet was often away, sometimes for a week,

268

sometimes much longer, but when she was in Milan she entertained a good deal, and many people came to her flat who had names as well known as her own. She loved to be hospitable, and no artist ever came to Milan or passed through it on his way to other towns who could not count on finding Juliet Forbes keeping open house as she had always done.

Emmanuel met musicians there, painters, and composers. All of them treated Juliet with affection and evident admiration. All of them discussed their work with her and listened respectfully, even gratefully, to her advice. What Emmanuel never knew was the amount of money which, from the fortune which Leon Hast had left her, she gave away to people less successful than herself.

While she had never possessed great intellectual powers, she was endowed with great judgment and very sound common sense. She was acknowledged a great artist in her work, and the fact that ever since Hast's death she had arranged most of her own business transactions had given her a very extensive knowledge of the commercial side of an artist's life.

At thirty-nine she was enjoying her powers to their fullest extent. True, her voice had lost something of its youthful freshness; it was possibly a less beautiful instrument than it had been ten years ago; but she was an infinitely greater artist, and her voice had become something which she understood and used superbly.

When she had first met and loved Leon Hast, he had taught her everything. He had instructed her in all the arts which were in a minor degree part of her success. He had taught her the value of beautiful clothes, a complete knowledge of the social side of her work, he had cultivated her taste, an understanding of beauty had been part of her education, and he had shown her the value of being selective in everything, from her choice of songs to her collections of old fans.

So at thirty-nine Emmanuel Gollantz found her lacking in all those small ignorances which had angered Leon Hast so much. She was polished, cultured and cognizant. If the culture and polish were neither of them very deep regarding tangible things such as china, pictures and old manuscripts, there lay beneath them a mind which was essentially beautiful, and a spirit which might lack many things but which never wanted in courage.

Immediately after his divorce, Emmanuel once again asked her to marry him, and, as before, she refused on the old grounds: her age, his future, and the probable dislike of Max and Angela to receive her as a daughter-in-law. Emmanuel repeated Angela's message, and was hurt and disappointed when he found that it had little or no effect.

"How dear of her," Juliet said, "and what's

better still, she means it; but you see that can't alter what I feel, Emmanuel. I've made too many mistakes through not following my own star. I can't bear to tie you to me by any other bonds than those which exist already. I'm a coward at heart, my dearest. I'd rather let you go—if I have to—than watch you break away."

Emmanuel argued, protested and implored, but she remained firm, and gradually he let the matter drop. He was wonderfully happy, his work was growing, and every day he saw the time approaching when his efforts would have made it possible for Louis, Guido and himself to congratulate themselves upon having one of the most successful antique and decorating businesses in Italy.

Louis descended upon them periodically like some gorgeous dragon-fly—his clothes seemed to get more exquisite every time he came to Milan. Once he came accompanied by Olympia, or, more correctly, in the train of that lady. Guido almost prostrated himself, while Emmanuel felt that there was something almost indecent in such effulgence. She was overpowering—generous in figure, pink and white as to complexion, and possessing hair which was a living testimony that art is more successful than nature.

She prided herself upon speaking every European language, and stated that she had always conducted her love affairs in the language of the native land of her lover. Emmanuel decided that the lovers must have wilted from sheer boredom, for her conversation consisted of a series of clichés and comments on the weather. Once they were exhausted she sat silent and a little sulky, polishing her nails assiduously.

"We are in Milano," Louis said, "for this night only. Is it permitted that you, Guido and Miss Forbes dine with us?"

Olympia lifted her heavily mascara'd eyes and said: "Ah, Mees Forrbes! I have heard her sing with voices of an angel. Let us all be boys at the same time this evening."

Louis laughed, a laugh which sounded to Emmanuel to be almost idolatrous. "She means, the silly little one," he said, "that together we will be boys!"

The dinner was not a success. Louis for the first time in his life seemed fatuous, Guido just a rather silly little Italian boy, and Emmanuel's soul revolted at the sight of Olympia's blatantly displayed physical charms. Her bare shoulders, her naked bosom, and the obvious reliance she placed on them both to obtain attention from Louis to the head waiter made him feel sick.

As the dinner progressed, his temper began to get the better of him. It would have been bad enough had he been there alone, but to know that Juliet was with him, listening to the inanities—and, to Emmanuel, vulgar inanities at that—of an overblown one-time dancer, infuriated him. He felt that had Juliet been his wife, Louis would never have given the invitation, and that only because Louis classed Juliet as his mistress did he dare to ask her to meet this objectionable woman. Had her conversation been amusing he might have forgiven her other vulgarities, but she was dull, egotistical, and greedy. When the dinner ended, Louis proposed that they should go and dance; Olympia agreed, and Guido welcomed the suggestion with delight. Juliet, on the ground that she was leaving for Vienna the following day, excused herself, and Emmanuel walked back with her to the flat fuming and seething with anger.

"Juliet," he said abruptly, when they had passed out of the Galleria and were walking down one of the wide quiet streets which led to her flat, "my decree will be made absolute on November the tenth. I want you to marry me on the eleventh."

"My dear, I thought we had talked all this over before."

"Tonight wiped out all that we said, or you said. It's an impossible position. Do you think that, if we were married, Louis would have asked you to meet that horrible piece of blatant vulgarity? Never! My God, Louis will hear from me in the morning! It's insufferable."

Juliet stared at him, frankly astonished. "But —but I didn't dislike her. She's stupid; most dancers—except the highly intellectual ones who are too boring for words—are. Emmanuel, don't be foolish. He evidently adores her, he thinks that she's the centre of the universe, and thinks it's a great honour for anyone to meet her. You're being foolish, my darling, and just a little bit—snobbish."

But Emmanuel had worked himself into a state of acute irritation and was not prepared to listen to reason; he imagined a grievance, and was prepared to defend it.

"Do you think that Louis would ask his sisters to meet her?"

"I think it very likely."

"Juliet, be reasonable—this isn't being snobbish—could you see my father welcoming her at Ordingly?"

"Could you see your father welcoming me there?"

"Certainly, and you know it. Not perhaps as things are at the moment, but if we were married —of course."

She sighed. "Oh, my dearest, why can't you be content to be happy? What does Louis Lara's Olympia matter to us? Aren't we sufficient for each other? One night in the year we've had to dine with them. That's not very dreadful after all."

"Quite dreadful enough that Louis should ask you to meet his damned vulgar mistress!"

"Who was probably just as bored at having to meet yours!"

Emmanuel stopped dead, then caught her arm

and forced her to stand beside him. He was breathing quickly as if he had been running, his eyes were furious, his face very white. Juliet had never seen him so angry.

"I beg your pardon, Emmanuel," she said gently. "I had no right to say that. I'm sorry."

"It was unpardonable," he said very coldly. "I shan't worry you again, Juliet. I've asked you to marry me for the last time. Next time you can tell me that you are willing to marry me. Whenever you wish. I'm sorr-ry that I have been tedious."

"Very well." They walked on in silence, Juliet wondering miserably why he must force these quarrels on her so often, why, if he really loved her—and she knew that he did love her—he could not accept the fact that her refusals were prompted by a sense of justice to him. At the entrance to the flat he stopped and said, "Good night."

Juliet said impulsively. "My dear, don't go like this. Come in and talk to me for half an hour. I can't bear you to go home thinking hard thoughts."

He said nothing, but followed her into the hall and entered the flat with her. It seemed that the atmosphere there soothed him immediately, for his ill temper vanished and he became the man she loved, kind and solicitous. Only when they were seated by the fire did he begin to speak gravely.

"This shall be the last time, Juliet," he said. "I shall never speak of it again. Only let me say that nothing matters except that I shall keep you with me. Age is nothing, you yourself admitted it. It's only one of those bogeys that you r-reproach me for allowing to frighten me. I love Ordingly, but it counts for nothing beside you. My mother loves you, and even if she hated you —and after you I love her more than anyone else in the world—it wouldn't matter. Marriage with you wouldn't be very easy. I'm a poor man, you're a r-rich woman. Because of certain decencies, as I call them, and conventions, as you call them, I should have to learn not to mind that I lived with you in a flat far more expensive than anything I could possibly afford. Besides—dear, beautiful Juliet"—he came closer and took her hand in his—"we don't want to keep all this love to ourselves, do we?"

She met his eyes, looked at him intently, then turned away.

"I—don't know what you mean, Emmanuel."

"I'm a Jew," he said softly, "and all Jews long for children—when they love their wives as I love you. But not to handicap them from the very beginning."

The thought of a child came as something of a shock to her. She had never considered such a possibility, indeed there was so much that was maternal in her love for Emmanuel that she had not felt the need or the wish for children. But

276

now, as she watched his face, handsome, young, and shining with a tenderness that seemed to make it radiant, she knew that she longed for a child of his to make their lives complete.

"You want a child—children so much?" she asked to gain time, for his expression and his tone had given her the answer to her question before she uttered it.

"It would be r-rather nice," Emmanuel said with one of his queer lapses from the ideal to the prosaic form of speech. Juliet smiled—how young he was! One moment angry, then repentant, romantic, and now phrasing his deepest thoughts in the language of a schoolboy. "If that happened, pr-romise that you'd marry me, Juliet. It would only be fair to let all your objections—oh, and such foolish objections—go by the board then, wouldn't it?"

The thought came to her that a child would bind him to her, would make those additional years of no account. She knew him sufficiently well to understand how such a thing would make it impossible for Emmanuel Gollantz to leave her. She would have become something more than his mistress or his wife, she would be part of his family, she would have given that family what counted for most in their scheme of things—a child to carry on their tradition, their name. She realized that already she was thinking of a possible child as a son.

"Objections," she said softly; "yes, I suppose

they would have to be abandoned in favour of Emmanuel the Third."

And as he heard the gentleness in her voice, Emmanuel felt a sudden sense of power and certainty. In his heart, Emmanuel Gollantz was a humble person. Not humble concerning his House, his father's attainments, or even his own small successes, but essentially humble touching his personal affairs. He never knew why Guido should regard him as something of a hero, why Louis should have such an obvious affection for him, and least of all why Juliet Forbes should have given him her love so fully. Always at the back of his mind was the belief that he loved her so much more than he could ever expect her to love him, always the little fear existed that one day she might tire of him and go out of his life or send him out of hers, as she had done once before.

So while she became conscious of the thought that a child might keep him with her—a thought born of her own fear that she might grow old quickly and cease to attract him—Emmanuel through all his tenderness felt a sudden rush of power, that it might be possible to bind her more closely to him. Because she was older and wiser than he, she tried to push the thought from her and tell herself that she must never, never try to hold him should he wish to go.

She left Milan the next day for Vienna, she was to be away for a month, and during that time

Emmanuel was going back to England to take his first holiday for over two years. The thought of seeing his mother and his home again excited him. All the long journey he sat and dreamt of Ordingly, of the great beeches which would be turning scarlet under the fingers of autumn. With those dreams came others, the low mist lying on the fields in the early morning, the cold tang in the air, even the low grey skies seemed pleasant in contemplation after a land where the skies were almost unalterably blue. There were other things, more matter-of-fact—hot toast, crumpets, good English bacon and eggs all white and golden. Theatres, delightful dinners, rather light foolish music, and impossible tenor voices singing choruses. He had not known how much he missed all these things until his mother's letter had come a month ago.

"Surely you can spare time for a holiday. I want to see you so much. Ask Juliet to spare you to me for a little while".

He had read the letter to Juliet, and at that point had looked up from it and said, "I didn't know that Angela knew you were in Milan."

"She's always known," she said. "I told her. Why should I mind her knowing?"

The crossing was bad, the journey to town cold and apparently unending. The Kentish fields looked very bare and unfriendly, but nothing damped Emmanuel's pleasure. He stood at the window as the train drew slowly into Victoria, and only when he saw the spires of Westminster did his face darken a little. Julian was still making a success of his life; he would have to meet him and listen to his list of achievements, having none of his own to proffer in exchange. Bill was waiting for him, Bill with that air of having been newly scrubbed and brushed five minutes previously which always sat on him. Emmanuel knew that his throat ached, and wondered if he was becoming as emotional as Guido. Bill waved, then came forward to the carriage door.

"Hello," he said. "D'you know you're twenty-five minutes after time? Bad crossing?"

It was easy enough to regain his composure. "Rotten," he said, "and the boat crowded."

"Bad luck. The car's waiting. Got much stuff?"

"Couple of suitcases. I've learnt to travel light."

He sat forward, watching the streets eagerly; nothing had changed. The Park, Marble Arch, the long stretch of Edgware Road, on and on until the houses dropped behind and the trees became more frequent. They were out in the open country, nearing Ordingly, before Bill uttered anything more than civilities.

"Jolly nice to have you back. We miss you a lot. Specially Angela. You ought to have her come out and stay with you."

"What, in my room over the shop? I'm a shop-keeper, Bill, and don't forget it."

"No, but when you're married. You're going to get married, aren't you?" Then, without waiting for a reply, he went on. "Viva's going to marry Toby on November the fourteenth. I got a card yesterday. Rather sporting of her to ask me, don't you think?"

Emmanuel nodded. "I suppose so. Viva always was a sporting sort of person."

Bill said, "Nice woman, Viva. She and I are distinctly partial to each other. United in a common dislike of her horrible brother and her scarcely less horrible father. Walter's a tick."

Speaking slowly, because he found it difficult to put his thoughts into words, Emmanuel said, "They didn't all mind very much about the divorce business, did they?"

"I don't think so. The Guv'nor said once that it was undignified and unpleasant, but that was all. In fact, Viva went about telling everyone— in strict confidence—what a grand chap you were, that Charles and I had to warn her not to do so much of it. Positively dangerous! Old King's Proctor and all that, y'know. Nice feller, Toby. Remember him?"

Emmanuel said: "Good Lord, yes! I've only been away just over a year, Bill."

Bill stared at him, then said: "By Jove, so you have! Seems like ages and ages."

For the first time Emmanuel was conscious of

a queer chill. Did he remember Toby Tatten? Bill felt that he'd been away ages and ages. He was not quite au fait with everything; he didn't quite belong any more. The thought gave him a strange little shock, and he sat silent. Bill broke the silence, and again Emmanuel wondered if he felt that he must make conversation.

"Is Miss Forbes quite well?" Then, as if the stiffness of the question communicated itself to Bill as he spoke, he added: "And as lovely as ever?"

Emmanuel said: "She's very fit, thanks. Looking marvellous. She's singing in Monaco tonight."

"Monaco," Bill repeated. "I thought Angela said she was in Germany."

"She is—Monaco—I mean Munich. It's Italian for."

"Oh, I thought you meant the South of France—"

Again that little coldness touched Emmanuel. He had learnt to say "Monaco" because he had lived in Italy—no, he didn't quite belong at the moment. The thought made him feel dreadfully lonely; he felt that he wanted to turn back and get to Monaco—even in his thoughts he called it that—and Juliet.

2

EMMANUEL had been at Ordingly for a week. He had gone everywhere, had met everyone, had been made much of, treated rather like a Prodigal son, and still felt that little chill creep over him at recurring intervals.

Max had taken him down to the Galleries, and there had been a new messenger-boy. Emmanuel had stared at him almost resentfully. He wondered what had happened to "Ginger" Marsden, who had been there before; then in the office he saw "Ginger" occupying the desk of the junior clerk. Max had enlarged the long gallery, had tried out a new scheme of decoration, modern but essentially dignified. But somehow it didn't look like Gollantz and Son, and Emmanuel hated it. Davis fussed into Max's office and said that it seemed years since they had seen Emmanuel; he looked fatter, older, less vital. It seemed that even his father had grown more set in his ideas and methods. He had become so dignified as to convey the smallest touch of pomposity. It never occurred to Emmanuel, youthfully intolerant, that Max was feeling the strain of running the huge business singlehanded, that he felt his years weigh heavily on him, and often longed to have his son with him again to share the burden and heat of the day.

Where to Emmanuel the Italian dealers with their overdone eulogies and their gestures had become ordinary enough, Marcus Arbuthnot, old Augustus Morris and Jacob Lane seemed fantastic and unbelievable They came into the office to see him, making a kind of royal visit of it. Emmanuel wondered if they'd come to see how far he had deteriorated, and became very stiff and answered them coldly.

Arbuthnot, who had once tried to make him join a ring with Peters, the American dealer, had apparently forgotten all about the incident. In his waisted coat, elaborate tie with its huge pin, he looked more out of date than ever.

"And when are we to have the pleasure-ah of having you he-ah again?" he said, with his overdone drawl which he had learnt in the '90's. "Can't find much in Italy I imagine except Sacred Families and slightly worm-eaten furniture-ah, what?"

"I find a good deal more," Emmanuel said; "and worm-eaten furniture has never appealed to me, thanks to my father's training."

Old Lane was easier. His face was more purple, his breath shorter, but his little dark eyes shone as brightly as ever.

"You kom beck," he said, as he sat sipping the brandy-and-water which Max had poured out for him, "but I doan't t'ink for long, eh? Vat are you goin' to do? Merry an Italian girl, and hev a lot of leetle brown-skinned kinder?"

"I don't think so, sir."

Lane chuckled, "T'ink! Neffer t'ink about merriage or you'll never do it. It doan't bear t'inkin' about, young feller. Do it qvick, und any t 'inkin' vot's gotter be done, do it efther ven it's too late to beck out of it."

Augustus Morris, the only dealer except Max who had been given a title, puffed and blew indignantly. His elder son Joseph watched him intently, as if he thought he might die on the spot.

"Vat a yen!" he said. "Time dot de poy was married. Mex, you oughter find him a suitable vife—a Jew girl. Time dot your femily vent back to their own people—there's been too much merrying mit Christians. Giff up dis stoopid Italian business, Emmanuel, und kom home again!"

Lane gave vent to his thick chuckle again. "Mebbe," he said, "he doan't vant a vife, mebbe he's found somet'ing just as goot, mitout no everlasting responsibilities!" Then, turning to Emmanuel, he demanded: "Tell me, is she pretty?"

Curiously, Emmanuel disliked him least of the three. There was a jovial frankness about him which disarmed criticism. It was sufficiently easy to answer that she was very pretty and make some rather poor joke about his life in Milan. Lane

285

laughed, almost choking himself as he did so, and pushed forward his glass for more brandy.

"Dot's der style!" he gurgled. "Doan't take no notice of Joseph und Samson Morris. Beliefe me, they drink barley vater from choice! Und"—with a fresh strangled shout of laughter—"der old fadder lets 'em do it!"

Later, when they had gone, he sat down in his father's office and listened to Max's pleasant, rather tired voice speaking. He was obviously anxious to discuss his business. Private ledgers were sent for; Reuben Davis was asked to come and give details as to this and the next thing. Hannah came bringing a sheaf of private letters concerning some of those dealings with people in exalted positions who offered jewels, pictures and impossibly valuable bric-à-brac to Gollantz and Son.

"You see," Max said slowly, "we are more than antique dealers. We are actually in the confidence of these important people. They would never open negotiations with other dealers, but they come to us with absolute confidence. I like to know that they place their trust in me. It was the aim which my father always kept before him, and —well, one day, Emmanuel, I hope that you'll still keep it before you."

He paused, closed the ledger and locked it, then continued: "Anyone can make a reasonable success, but it needs decency, straight dealing and integrity to gain the confidence of everyone

286

from an exiled king who wants to raise money on his family heirlooms to the little widow in the country who wants to sell a Wedgwood teapot. It is conceivable—I don't know that it is a fact, and believe me I have a great regard for Jacob Lane —that he may have made more money than I have. But he remains Jacob Lane while I am Max Gollantz, Baronet. Oh," very quickly, "don't think that I place any particular value on that title, I don't, and"—with a smile—"it's a very expensive luxury into the bargain, but it is a sort of sign manual that I have managed to carry on what my father began. That title was never really given to me, but really to the House of Gollantz." Then, speaking almost impersonally, reflectively he went on, "I suppose that Bill will marry one day, but his children won't have much interest in all this; Julian may have children—but I confess to you that between ourselves I don't particularly want Julian's children here." He added with sudden bitterness, "Amanda is a pretty fool, and Julian"—he shrugged his shoulders—"is much too clever. I'm rather pinning my hopes on you, Emmanuel."

Emmanuel did not answer. He sat silent, watching his father's thin, kindly face. Max was still good-looking and well preserved, but he looked pallid; his eyes were heavy and there were new lines graven on his face. Emmanuel thought with a sudden sense of panic: "Supposing he died! They'd try to make me come back. Leave Juliet if she won't marry me. I couldn't do it. I won't do it."

Max went on very gently: "You haven't thought of coming back now this horrible divorce is over and done with, have you?"

"No, sir, not seriously."

"I should like you to. It's—it's important to me, Emmanuel."

"There are difficulties—"

"Surely not insuperable ones?"

Emmanuel again felt that sense of panic; they were all conspiring to catch and keep him. Old Lane, Morris, with their talk of marriage, now his father asking him to come home. Surely his father understood?

"I don't know. I want Juliet Forbes to marry me, you know that."

Max nodded. "Yes, I know that. It's very difficult to speak plainly, Emmanuel, difficult not to be hurtful or intrusive. I hate to be either. There is a duty which you owe to me, to your grandfather. We have built this, we have made it, and we look to you to carry it. You can't throw over all your responsibilities lightly."

Emmanuel said coldly: "I have no wish to. I accept them only too willingly."

"You're young, under thirty. What sort of a life is it that you lead in Milan? What home have you? Whom do you meet? What future is there for you in a back-street antique-shop—"

"I made seventeen thousand lire in the last nine

months," Emmanuel said; and when he remembered how hard it had been to earn that sum, how his connection had been made from nothing, he could not entirely keep a ring of pride out of his voice.

"Seventeen thousand lire," Max repeated, and, reaching for a pencil, made a calculation on the pad before him. "Roughly three hundred and ten pounds. Have you forgotten what Gollantz made two years ago?—and this year it is almost double."

It was all said very kindly, but Emmanuel's pride was hurt. He had not attempted to explain to Max how he had striven, what he had done, how he had touted for orders, and yet the fact that his father did not realize what that paltry three hundred and ten pounds stood for hurt him terribly.

"I have learnt not to think in terms of Gollantz and Bond Street since I went to Italy," he said. "My grandfather began in a small house in Camden Hill. You want me to come home, you want me to leave behind my work, the connection which I have made, both very small and unimportant to you, but they're mine! I have other ties in Italy, ties which may one day be even closer than they are now. I want to have children, I want a home, I want to be happy with Juliet—because it's my life and hers, not because I feel that I must provide an heir for Ordingly. Oh, can't you understand? Can't you see that I must live in my own way, work out my own salvation?"

His urgent tone, the sudden demonstration of feeling, reached Max, and the vital difference between them was made apparent. Max was the product of England, of a public school and university, he had superimposed his adopted nation's deals and methods above the natural colourful expressions, the emotion and the passion of his own race. Max was a Jew in spite of the fact that his outlook, his training and his ideas were English; his son remained first and foremost a Jew, capable of ready emotion, of sentiment which he did not fear to evince and passionate love when he gave his affection.

The one Jewish gesture left to Max was his little trick of using his hands to demonstrate bewilderment. He was proud of his race, proud of attributing much of his business acumen and integrity to the tenets imbued in him by his father. No man in England gave more liberally to the charities of his race, and despite the fact that his religious beliefs were ethical rather than dogmatic he was regarded by the Jews in England with affection and admiration.

He looked up at his son, his face betraying astonishment and a slight measure of dismay. Emmanuel stood, his hands stretched out towards his father, begging for understanding. His face was pale, and his eyes shone with the fervour of his speech. To Max he looked almost uncomfortably theatrical and, as such, disturbing.

"My dear boy, of course I understand. I've been young, I know how terribly difficult life is at twenty-nine. You are making a mistake, Emmanuel, and I only want you to realize it before it is too late. You're banishing yourself from England, you are adopting a foreign country —virtually at least—foreign outlook, foreign ideas, you even use Italian phrases in ordinary conversation. It's quite amusing for a time. After all, we're not pure-bred English, and I have never minded admitting it. Now—well and good, but what of the time when you will automatically have to come home and take up the work which is waiting for you? How will you be able to transplant yourself then? Or are you prepared to throw away the birthright which has been made for you by your grandfather and myself? Who else is there? Bill a barrister, Julian a politician. Can you repudiate us like that?"

"There is no question of repudiation," Emmanuel said savagely. "I am only asking to live my own life in my own way."

Max shook his head; he was very tired. He wanted nothing so much as to leave the office, drive to his club and sit quietly until such time as he must drive back to Ordingly for dinner.

"But can any of us—live our own lives?" he asked gently. "I think not, unless we are going to throw overboard such things as duty, affection for one's family, pride in one's ancestors and so on. A year ago, when you came to Aix, I listened and agreed and gave you your head more or less willingly. But now I'm feeling the strain of working alone, your mother misses you terribly and—my dear fellow, why not come home again? Oh"—lifting his hand to check Emmanuel's speech—"I know—I know that you have made ties. Tell me frankly, has Juliet promised to marry you?"

"Under certain conditions, yes."

"And those are that you remain abroad, or that you throw over your work here, give up your heritage. Are those her conditions?"

"No—none of those."

"Then"—and he made his Jewish gesture of bewilderment—"I fail to imagine what those conditions can be. Can't you tell me?"

"It's difficult—you might not understand."

"The whole conversation has been difficult," Max said wearily. "Have I been so dense, so insensitive, that you should credit me with lack of understanding? Come, Emmanuel—"

Emmanuel glanced round desperately. He felt trapped, felt that Max, through his very kindliness, his real wish to understand, was gradually stripping him of his dearest and most secret thoughts. He clenched his hands and made a violent effort.

"No, you've been very kind, you've always been very kind. She'll marr-ry me, she has said

292

so, only on one condition. Not because she does not love me, but because she thinks she is too old, and that it might handicap me. I have said—"

"She's right, you know," Max said.

"I don't believe it, I won't believe it. I know myself and I know her. She's all I want; nothing, nothing, nothing else counts. It's terr-rible to me that she will only marr-ry me if she is going to have a child. Can't you r-realize now—"

Max rose and moved over to the tall carved wardrobe where his hat and coat hung. His face was as white as Emmanuel's own, his expression devoid of all the gentleness which usually characterized it. He glanced at Emmanuel, at his hands which moved incessantly, at his pale face and his general air of youthful emotion.

"I am delighted that she at least consents to legitimize my grandchild," he said, and, turning, opened the great carved door. He turned as he heard the door bang, and found himself alone. Emmanuel had snatched up his hat and coat and rushed out.

He walked rapidly along Bond Street, and only when he had put Gollantz and Son far behind him did he check, hail a taxi and give the address of the chambers where Bill worked with Charles Wilmot. His heart was hammering wildly. He felt that his father had purposely insulted Juliet, and in offering insult to her had virtually struck him over the face. He wanted Bill, with his common sense, his sanity and his essential kindness.

The clerk said that Mr. Gollantz was busy; Emmanuel hesitated and would have turned away had not Charles Wilmot emerged from another door and hailed him.

"Hello! Come to see me, Emmanuel? Come in, have a drink?"

Emmanuel followed him into his room, the room which Charles declared was the only barrister's in London which was kept not only clean and tidy, but allowed to be definitely attractive.

From an old corner cupboard Charles produced two tumblers, rubbed them carefully on a cloth, and proceeded to pour out whisky-and-soda. Emmanuel watched him, apathetic and dull. He was shaken, both by his father's words and his own anger. In his mind disappointment raged. He had looked forward to his home-coming, had thought what fun it was going to be and how much he was going to enjoy it. Instead he had found himself to everyone, except his mother and Bill, almost an outsider.

Charles handed him his glass and smiled. There was something very pleasant about that smile of Charles Wilmot's, it radiated kindliness, good fellowship and seemed to imply intimacy.

"There you are, drink that and you won't feel so rattled."

Half sulky, Emmanuel demanded, "How do you know that I am r-rattled?"

"It's part of my business. It's one of the things

which have gone to make me quite a considerable success—knowing when people were rattled. That's how cases are won—and lost, my lad."

Emmanuel sipped his drink, and gradually his control returned. With it his sense of loneliness became accentuated, and he obeyed a sudden impulse to talk to this handsome, grey-headed man whom he had known all his life.

"Charles," he said, "they're tr-trying to make me come back—make me become part of Gollantz and Son again. I won't do it!"

Charles sat down in his big armchair, and leant back, surveying Emmanuel with steady eyes, his mouth touched by a smile which was so small as to be scarcely noticeable, and which contained no hint of mockery or genuine amusement.

"Oh, you Jews," he said, "with your royal family attitude and call of the blood royal ideas! Poor wretched Emmanuel, the heir apparent! Not much fun, is it? Why can't they leave you alone? You'll have to come back one day. This damned business, that damned great house, the park, the furniture, the pictures and the title will bring you back."

"None of those things," Emmanuel said. "I don't care for any of them sufficiently. My interests, my life, the woman I love, are all out there in Italy. Why should I come home? I'm making my way there, alone. It satisfies me."

Charles pursed his lips, rearranged some

pencils on his desk, and moved an inkpot an inch farther to the right before he spoke.

"Don't allow yourself to get emotional, Emmanuel," he said. "If you do you lose any sympathy that your father, as an Englishman, is ready to give you. He's very English—I doubt if there are any Englishmen so typical as the Anglicized Jews who admire and love the country of their adoption. That's only a little bit of advice for you personally. You see"—he leant back again in his chair, took a cigarette from the box near him, pushed it over to Emmanuel, then continued—"you see, it won't always be what you want. It may be now, but other factors creep in as some factors fall out. No one feels at twenty-nine as they feel at thirty-nine. They can't. I never wanted to be a barrister. I wanted to be a sailor. A very small bit of me still does. But we'd always been in the law, and though I kicked—I hadn't the strength to kick hard enough. And gradually I stopped kicking, probably just as well that I did. Not many naval men can belong to a couple of decent clubs, keep a really admirable car—and—well, I won't bore you with a list of my achievements."

Emmanuel, half startled, and half disturbed, said: "But you never married, did you?"

The response came very quickly, "You're not married?"

"Virtually, yes."

"Ah, virtually!"

296

Immediately Emmanuel's overstrung nerves snapped. "Don't sneer, Charles. I said virtually and meant it. I ought to have realized that nothing short of a ceremony before a couple of bishops is recognized as binding in this country!"

Charles was in no way disturbed. "Pooh! Don't fly off the handle, my lad. Bishops be hanged. I've never seen two bishops at a wedding in my life, never hope to or wish to. Marriage is as binding in this country as in any other. If you saw as much of the results of that binding as I do, you'd begin to think about easier divorce! If only the idiots would make marriage more difficult, and divorce easier! We're not discussing that, however. What I do say is this, that marriage makes cowards of us all. It makes us want—and rightly—to do the best, as we see it, for the woman or the children. That's why I asked if you were married. At the moment you're a free agent. If you marry—when you go through a legal form of marriage, if that pleases you better—touchy fellow you are today, Emmanuel—you'll begin to play with the idea of coming home. It's fate, you can't fight against it. It's all machinery. It's a machine-made age. There's the machine of business, of law, of military position, of politics, even of family. The bigger, the more successful, the family, the stronger the machinery. Certain conditions enforce certain attitudes of mind. The more you love people—your wife, your child— the more you want for them those things which you have been taught are worth while. Take my advice, if you want to stay in your little one-horse place in Milan, don't marry—don't have children. If you do, both she and they will—unwittingly—conspire to bring you back to play the Big Game in Bond Street in the House of Gollantz."

"Do you mean," Emmanuel said slowly, "that I must eventually come back, that I can't help myself?"

Charles nodded. "Practically, yes. It's too strong for you. It's been built by two rather remarkable men—your grandfather and Max—none of you recognize how remarkable Max has been and is, by the way—and you can't fight their influence, plus your very over-developed sense of duty, and your Hebrew love of family. Your"—the pause was almost imperceptible—"wife? Does she want to come back?"

"She would never come back—with me—to Ordingly."

"Then I suppose as long as you remain very much in love, she may manage to keep you away. Her influence is probably stronger, more personal, than your family's. But one day"—he shrugged his shoulders—"forgive me, I perhaps shouldn't say that. Don't let them worry you, Emmanuel. Don't worry yourself. You see, you're all Gollantz, there's nothing of the Drews or the Heriots or the Wilmots in you. You're so astonishingly your grandfather over again, without his certainty. He'll go on ruling the family for years to come. He elected to start that family in England, and only one of his sons managed to get away, and he ended pretty stickily. You may think that you love Italy and sunshine and all the rest of it, but England's in your blood."

He stopped short and said abruptly, "Have another drink?"

"No, thanks, Charles. Not very cheering, are you?"

"On the contrary, most. Showing you that you'll really appreciate the change when it comes!"

"It won't come."

"Tell me that in another ten years' time."

Emmanuel shook his head. "I know myself."

"Fortunate feller, I wish I could say as much. I spend my life realizing that no one surprises me so much or so often as Charles Wilmot. Ah, there's Bill's old Admiral gone. Nasty old bloke, and a horrible old liar! Let's go and rout Bill out, shall we?"

3

EMMANUEL returned to Ordingly that evening stigmatizing Wilmot as a fool and yet wondering, unwillingly, how much truth there might be in his statements. He was sufficiently young to resent them, but sufficiently wise to probe for the germ of truth which he felt might be contained in them.

He was conscious that his love for Juliet had undergone a change. At first he had accepted her love for him and his for her as something which was almost inevitable. He had been passionately happy, yet that utter content had alternated with moods of unhappiness and small fits of irritation. He had even resented her keeping open house as she did for her musical and artistic friends, because those friends had been made and those friendships formed when she had known Leon Hast. It had seemed to him that these people must inevitably compare him with Hast, and among themselves comment upon the fact that Juliet had allowed herself to become attached to a man of no financial standing and no particular artistic attainments. He had been irked when she made the smallest demonstration of her own monetary position and had refused, almost brutally, to allow her to give him any present of value. There had been times when he had sat alone in his room over the shop and wondered if he could face being "the husband of Juliet Forbes".

At other times, when he overcame his moodiness, he had been content only to be with her. He had rejoiced in her beauty, her talent and her popularity, and whenever she had appeared could scarcely rest until he had read what every critic, great or small, had said of her work. An adverse criticism, no matter from what source, had upset him for days, and nothing would restore his good humour except Juliet's laughter that he could take such people seriously.

Now, after a week in England, facing the fact that his marriage with her would be unpopular with his father, and probably looked on with doubt by his father's friends, conscious that his father was trying to influence him to return to England and put Milan and all that it contained behind him, he was able to differentiate between the essential and nonessential in his love for Juliet.

His petty jealousies, his moods of depression caused by some imagined slight or neglect, his hatred of her past, all slipped away, and he saw her for the first time in true perspective. Even his hatred of Leon Hast diminished, and he forced himself to review coldly and calmly all that he had done for Juliet. She was a great artist as well as the possessor of a wonderful voice. Much of her artistry was due—looking at all the facts

Emmanuel could not but admit it—to Hast's training. The best, and only the best, had been good enough for Leon Hast, and he had constituted himself Juliet's most severe critic. More, he had made it possible for her to employ the best teachers in Europe, and he had launched her on her career under the best possible auspices.

Juliet's past was her own, whatever the future held they must share. He need never of necessity be only Juliet Forbes' husband, unless he allowed himself to slip into that role, or except to such people as delighted to put little tickets on things which they did not, and could not, understand.

Seated in his room at Ordingly, at the window which looked out on the wide parklands, where the trees were already touched with red and gold, from which he could see the flaming skies at sunset, and the vivid scarlet, rose and silver of the early mornings, he wrote to her. Letters which were young, impassioned, but which were filled with such love and tenderness as she had never known. Reading them in huge hotels in Germany, Juliet laid her hands over her heart, because the joy of them so nearly caused her pain. To her it seemed that she might enter a life which in its fullness and richness made her previous life seem poor and pale. His letters banished her fears, and for the first time those years which divided them seemed nothing. For the first time her scruples appeared to be the foolish things which Emmanuel had declared them to be.

"It is ten years since I saw you first", he wrote, "and you have only changed to become more beautiful. There is only this difference, that then I loved you with the ineffectual love of a boy, and now I can love you with the passion and adoration of a man. To see you unhappy, lonely, neglected then made me unhappy, now —to see you any of those things would drive me frantic, because I have suffered them all, and know how horrible they are".

And again:

"I love you now because I understand a great deal. Ten years ago I loved you romantically but without understanding anything except your beauty".

After his interview with Max, it seemed to Emmanuel that there was a conspiracy of silence at Ordingly with regard to his future. Max, after their interview in the office, never alluded to Emmanuel's return, Bill seemed to take it for granted that he was only going back to Milan in order to settle his affairs and return to England, and Angela seemed to Emmanuel to watch them all, silently, keenly, and to be drawing her own conclusions, which she confided to no one. The whole atmosphere was getting on Emmanuel's nerves and he knew that he was restless and dissatisfied.

He found that the theatre did not amuse him very much and he did not want to go to night clubs; firstly because there was no one with whom he cared to dance, and secondly because he was obsessed by a fear that he might run into Viva. Dining out with friends of his family, with Davies and Salamans, with Drews and Heriots, he felt that they regarded him as a sort of freak, an eccentric who actually preferred to live abroad in discomfort than to bask in London under the sun of the House of Gollantz.

Once or twice he saw Bill Masters, and to his dismay found him older than he had imagined, set and just a little pernickety in his habits and ideas. His courtesy was just a little overdone, his heartiness just a trifle too obvious, and his references to Juliet in such admirable taste that Emmanuel's teeth were set on edge.

At other times he would reproach himself. He would sit and review the excellent qualities of such people as Bill Masters and decide that their tact, their warmth of heart, and their beautiful manners were entirely satisfactory. He would blame himself for not appreciating these things, and when next he met Masters almost overwhelm him with affectionate inquiries as to his health, with solicitude—if they dined together—concerning what Bill liked best. Julian gave a dinner-party in his honour; Emmanuel wanted to refuse, but Angela persuaded him to go. He disliked Julian's house, the furniture and the vivid paintwork. Amanda seemed to him to be a pleasant half-wit with an American accent, and Julian was developing into a totally unreal person.

His good looks had become intensified, and his success had produced in him a strange insensibility, or so it appeared to Emmanuel. Masters had said that Julian was the spoilt child of his Party and that he was beginning to take advantage of his popularity. However that might be, Julian was certainly, Emmanuel decided, becoming intolerable. In his present highly sensitized state Julian jarred on Emmanuel terribly.

The other guests had gone and Emmanuel and Bill were left talking to Amanda. Bill seemed happy enough, but Emmanuel's eyes turned restlessly from the stippled parchment-coloured walls to the vivid curtains and angular furniture. Amanda watched him and said:

"Like my room, E-manuel? It's restful, and just now—I feel that I warnt my eyes to light on nothing that's not just lovely."

Emmanuel turned from the scarlet and green hangings feeling a little giddy. "No," he said, "I see."

Bill said, grinning cheerfully: "I shouldn't call it lovely or restful. It's the sort of colouring to stab your spirit wide awake, not soothe it."

Amanda, with a slight air of patronage, replied: "That's not the effect it would have on the modern mind, believe me, William."

Then Julian sauntered in, and stood with one

305

hand on the back of his wife's chair and began to talk in a fashion that made Emmanuel long to hit him.

"Amanda's right," Julian said. "Amanda always is right. This room is entirely restful. Rest is only comparative after all. A bench in the park is restful to a navvy after eight hours' work with a pick and shovel. Well, Emmanuel, how are Crucifixions in Milan? Those are your great standby, aren't they?"

"You mean pictures?"

"Of course, unless you are going through a private one of your own?"

"No, I'm quite satisfied with Milan, thanks."

Amanda said: "Now isn't that nice!" and Julian shot a glance at her which made his brother feel a little sick, it was filled with such concentrated dislike and intolerance.

She repeated: "I saay, isn't that just sweet, Julian?"

"Delightful. Possibly the rumour that I heard about your possible marriage has something to do with this content? Is it true?"

Bill said cheerfully: "You bet it's true! I'm going over to be his best man."

Emmanuel wished that sometimes Bill could contrive to be just a little less hearty and hated himself for the thought. Dear Bill, who had only put in an appearance because he felt that his presence would make matters easier for Emmanuel!

Julian's eyebrows lifted slightly, he seemed to

search his memory for a moment, then said: "It's not—I mean is it permitted to ask the lady's name, or rather to have confirmation of the name which Louis Lara gave me when I saw him in Paris? What a little tick he is! Dresses like a poof and behaves like a shopwalker, doesn't he?"

Amanda giggled: "I thought he was just too good to be true!"

Emmanuel knew that his face burned suddenly and that his dislike of Julian threatened to flare into obvious hatred.

"You're right, Amanda," he said steadily, "Louis is almost too good to be true. The miracle is that—his goodness is quite true."

Once again she commented: "Now isn't that nice!"

"Then you are going to marry Juliet Forbes?" Julian asked, as if the idea was incredible.

"I hope so." Then, turning to Bill, "Ready, Bill? I must be getting along. Good night, Amanda, and take care of yourself."

"That's nice of you, E-manuel. Good night."

Julian followed them to the door, saying as he did so: "Oh, she'll take care of herself. I see to that. I think the old man would disinherit me if anything happened to the prospective heir."

"Heir?" Emmanuel said sharply. "To what?"

"Ordingly and Gollantz and Son"—blandly. "To say nothing of the Van der Hoyt money."

Bill blustered suddenly, turning with his coat on his arm, his fresh face scarlet. "I shouldn't

307

count too much on that! You heard what Emmanuel said tonight. After all, he's the present heir, not you. Or are you trying as usual to be offensive?"

They stood in the black and orange hall, where black and orange tiles winked up at them from the floor, Emmanuel suddenly coldly furious, Bill hot and angry, and Julian—immaculate and cool —turned back from fiddling with the lock of the front door, his face mystified and astonished.

"Good Lord," he said, "have I hurt someone? This is dreadful. I do beg your pardon, Emmanuel. But, rather naturally, it never occurred to me that you would marry Juliet Forbes with the idea of having children in your mind. I'm sorry if I've hurt you."

Emmanuel said very coldly, "Does the idea seem so fantastic or so improbable, then?"

Julian uttered a short embarrassed laugh. "Since you press me, both improbable and fantastic, and"—with sudden gravity—"just a little hard on my father should such a thing happen."

As he spoke the words, Emmanuel's hands flew upwards and caught him by the shoulders; he held him like a vice and spoke very softly, but with more concentrated hatred in his voice than Bill had ever heard.

"It's just a little late to consider what is hard on my father, isn't it?" he said. "Might I r-remind you why I went to Italy the first time?

308

Could you take your mind back so far? Wasn't that little indiscretion of yours just a little hard on him? Listen to me, Julian, you have tri-ied to spoil things for me pretty often, and I suppose you'll continue to do so, but this is the first time you've dared to be impertinent to my face. Let me have no more of it. You hear—this may help you to remember!" And with his gloves he slapped Julian smartly across the face, then turned and said: "Now, Bill, if you're ready."

They walked to the nearest car-park in silence, Emmanuel with his hands deep in his pockets, his head bent, Bill making various attempts to whistle and giving them all up after the first couple of bars.

As they climbed into the car, Bill said, "Sorry you did that."

"Why?"

"He'll never forgive you."

"Does that matter very much?"

"I think so. He's such an unpleasant chap when he gets nasty. You never know what he's going to do next." Then reflectively, "I damn well won't go there again. God! What infernal cheek!"

Emmanuel said easily: "As I said—impertinence." He took his gloves from his pocket, looked at them attentively for a moment, then, leaning forward, threw them out of the window of the car. Bill, the tension broken, laughed. "How like you! Quite a good pair of gloves too.

You might have sent them to the cleaners, y'know."

"No, no," Emmanuel said earnestly, "they might have reminded me when I looked at them how desper-rately I hate that br-rother of mine. Let's forget it all, Bill. It wasn't ver-ry pleasant for me."

"Oh, rot," Bill said with stubborn cheerfulness. "Who cares what he says? I fell desperately in love with her when I met her. She's charming. I wish that I had half your luck. I think she's—well, I think she's grand!"

Only as they turned in at the big gates at Ordingly did Bill refer to it again. "But don't give Julian a handle," he said, "for if you do he'll twist it, and you, like a shot."

Emmanuel's anger had died down and left only a cold hatred of his brother. He tried to dismiss it from his mind, but again and again his words returned, "improbable and fantastic", and every time they flashed through his mind they stung more sharply. That night he determined to leave England. He was tired of it, and not even Angela's love could make it worth while staying in a country where he felt so entirely out of the picture. He sat down at his writing-table and wrote a long letter to Juliet, feeling that every declaration of his love and devotion for her served to obliterate partially those horrible words—"improbable and fantastic".

He was still writing when Angela knocked and

entered. She had been dining at a house some miles away with Max, and entered in all the glory of diamonds and soft velvet. Emmanuel swung round in his chair, then rose and went towards her, his hands outstretched.

"Darling, the one person in the world I wanted most."

She smiled, a little quizzical smile. "The one person?"

"At this moment, yes. Sit down. A cigarette? A very little drink just before you go to bed?"

"A cigarette—yes. A drink—well, just a very little one. No, less than that, Emmanuel, you have that one. It's only to keep you company. Now talk to me, tell me."

He laughed. "'Talk to me—tell me', you've said that as long as I can remember! I feel that I'm a very small boy again."

"So you are, you get so muddled over things. Wasn't it nice at Julian's?"

"Is it ever—nice—at Julian's? Not for me, I'm afraid. It's no use, I just dislike him and that's all there is to it. He loathes me, and—"

"Because he's under an obligation to you," Angela said quickly. "It takes a bigger man than Julian to forgive benefits. Don't hate him, Emmanuel, hate is such a limiting thing. It absorbs such a lot of energy too. Dismiss him, if you want to, but don't hate him."

Inconsequently he said. "He talked about providing an heir for the family—would you hate the idea of my doing that?"

She knocked the ash off her cigarette carefully, then said with a little smile: "It would depend a great deal upon whom you got to—to co-operate with you in the providing. Don't get into that very unpleasant habit—lots of men do—of believing that they provide the children and their wives merely accept the opportunity to experience maternity through their kindness. It's so irritating to women to hear a man talk about 'my son' and 'my daughter'. No, why should I hate the idea? I should like it—I think."

With his back to her, his foot on the rail of the fender, he said: "There could only be one woman. You wouldn't mind her?"

"One half of me, my nasty, snobby little soul half, would hate it," she said promptly, "the other half, the nicest half, would be delighted, because you were such a very nice baby, and so I imagine was she. Anyway, you're both terribly nice people."

"You, at least, wouldn't regard it as fantastic."

"Why should I?" Then after a pause, "But don't forget, my dear, that quite a number of people probably would. Still, that's your business. After all, you're rather a fantastic young man, you always have been with your little side-whiskers and stocks and your general air of having been left behind by the tide of the Regency. Lots of people said years ago that I was crazy to marry the son of an Austrian Jew—admittedly most of them knew even less of Austrians than they knew of Jews! But it's worked very well. I never let Max know, it would have hurt him dreadfully, poor sweet. It would still; anyway, I believe that he has forgotten that he is half Austrian. He reads 'The Times', sighs and says, 'If only those unfortunate Austrians could understand this or that or the next thing,' exactly like an Englishman. Darling, I must go. Max will wonder what has become of me."

Emmanuel turned from the fire. "Wait," he begged, "just one more minute. I want you to let me go, will you?"

"You mean back to Italy?"

"To Germany first. My sweet, I don't belong here any more, I don't fit in. Max gets hurt and angry with me, and I get angry in return. Julian makes me hate him, I'm out of touch with everyone except you and Bill. The solidity, the completeness, the well-trained servants here all frighten me. I don't like restaurants, the waiters seem so much more sophisticated than I am. I don't want to go to night clubs, or dance. Let me go, dearest. I want to get on with my own life, and it's not here any longer."

He stood looking down at her, very serious

and intent. Angela Gollantz thought: "I must like Juliet very much, or how I should hate her!" Aloud she said: "If you must. You've only been here ten days."

"I know. I have tried awfully hard."

"Has it been so beastly?"

"Not beastly, only horribly lonely—except when I was with you."

Then her control broke down. She loved him, he was her eldest son, the son who had never disappointed her, who had so obviously given her all that was best of himself. Once Julian had been her companion, now she scarcely ever saw him. Bill was immersed in his own affairs, and he had never given her affection as Emmanuel had done. Bill was not the type to remember small things. In an emergency Bill was dependable, but emergencies didn't occur every day. "Bill's love for me," Angela thought, "is all invested capital, but he has no use for handfuls of small change."

"Emmanuel," she cried, her arms round him, "You'll come back, you promise that you'll come back—one day?"

"To stay for ever?" The blankness in his voice hurt her. "I'll come back. I shall want to see you. You'll come and see me too, won't you? Come and see—us, perhaps?"

"Yes," she said eagerly, almost too eagerly, "of course. I must not be selfish. I mustn't try to force you, it's wrong of me. I do understand. I

314

do want you to be happy—always I want that. There, I must go. Good night, my darling, and God bless you."

SUNDAY luncheon at Ordingly was looked forward to by Max Gollantz as the most pleasant meal of the week. Every other day he ate in Town, and dinner each evening was usually eaten either in the presence of guests or in the houses of other people. Sunday luncheon was reserved by tacit consent for their own family.

He had wandered round hot-houses, listened to eulogies concerning fruit and flowers, for which he cared nothing except that they should please Angela; he had walked round the stables, glanced at Bill's new hunter, Angela's mare and his own cob. He had listened to Martin's implied scorn of the chauffeur, and to the chauffeur's more than implied scorn of Martin. Max liked routine and enjoyed his visit of inspection each Sunday; he returned to the house soothed and content. For the last three days Emmanuel's display of temper had rankled in his mind. He considered his own remark which preceded it, and by mentally repeating it in an entirely different tone from the one which he had originally used had convinced himself that there had been nothing offensive in it. Unwise, a little— but only to a very small extent—discourteous, but nothing to warrant Emmanuel flinging out in a passion. It was obvious that the boy ought to come home, his duty was to his father and his father's business. One day when he had to take it over, he'd be all at sea after years of haggling and peddling in a back street in Milan. Max looked back on the past year and decided that he had behaved very decently. Emmanuel had wanted to leave his wife, or they had wanted to leave each other. The whole thing was ridiculous, and distasteful. He had agreed to everything, though it had hurt his pride to hear that Emmanuel had given the necessary grounds for divorce. Charles Wilmot had said: "Frightfully badly they make out their bills in these foreign hotels. I saw Emmanuel's 'proof' bill today, place called Trento. Is that Trent of the old Council of Trent, d'you know?"

Now the divorce was over, absolute, or would be in a few days, and Emmanuel ought to come home. All very well for Angela to protest that he wanted to marry Juliet Forbes. Max always longed to reply that he had no right to want to marry her, but he never opposed Angela openly. Only yesterday Julian had walked into the office, very cock-a-hoop, very full of Amanda and a baby due in the New Year. Seemed to think that it was an achievement peculiar to Julian Gollantz! Julian was getting objectionably puffy under the eyes, putting on weight too. Working too hard—or playing too hard.

Charles spoke well of Bill. Bill was solid through and through. Good boy, Bill; nice, decent feller. But all Drew; not a scrap Gollantz; neither was Julian for that matter. Fair, like his own brother Algernon had been. Emmanuel was the only real Gollantz, and Emmanuel wanted to marry a singer who had been another man's wife and Leon Hast's mistress; whose divorce had only come after Hast's death. Old enough to be his mother. Max checked his thoughts. No, damn it, that wasn't fair; still, ten years when the woman was the other side of thirty was a devil of a long time.

Then, because it was a fine cold morning, because he stood on the wide steps before his house and looked down at the sloping park and the fields beyond, because the trees still held fast to a few bright red and gold leaves and he had spent a very pleasant hour in viewing his property, Max's fears lost some of their keenness. Of course Emmanuel would come home and settle down; get over this nonsense of Juliet Forbes and take his part in the business. Of course, no real need to worry.

He went in to luncheon feeling almost tenderly towards Emmanuel, determined to be additionally nice to the lad and not show the slightest trace of resentment.

As a matter of fact, Max, being a bad actor, rather overdid the brightness and kindliness.

"Oranges look wonderful," Max said. "I

suppose you get them for little or nothing in Milan, Emmanuel?"

"Very cheap and very good—except peaches, I think they're the best fruit we do get."

"Peaches were wonderful here last year—this year, I mean. Woodcock did marvels, didn't he, Angela?"

"Except that he hated me to ask for any, yes."

"Oh," Max continued, his hand going to his inner pocket, "Jacob Lane sent this over this morning. Wants us all to dine there on Friday next—it's little Rachel's eighteenth birthday."

Angela nodded. "Jacob is a wonderful man for giving superb parties. I tell him that he ought to have been in the catering business. His food's the best I know. Manage it, Bill?"

Bill, busy with his diary, nodded. "Yes, with a bit of luck."

Max turned to his eldest son. "Emmanuel?"

Angela said very quickly: "He won't be here. He's going back tomorrow to—going back abroad."

Max frowned. "You don't mean that, Emmanuel? You'll have been here under two weeks!"

"I'm afraid that I must," Emmanuel said in that new constrained voice which Angela scarcely knew. "I must get back."

"To Milan?"

"I shall make a call on the way . . ."

Making a great effort to control his annoyance,

319

Max said: "Cut out the call on the way and stay for Jacob's dinner. That's a good suggestion. What do you say?"

"I'm afraid that it's impossible. I can't."

Max stared at him for a moment, then said coldly: "Very well, if it is impossible, there is no more to be said."

Angela, watching them, wondered why two people who in reality loved each other dearly— more, the two people she loved best in the world —should find it so impossible to bridge the chasm which was between them. They had both got to that point in their relationship when mutual understanding was impossible.

"Only one thing might save them," Angela thought, "and that would be an infernal row, when they'd lose all this dignity and coldness, when they'd shout and rave and throw things at each other and emerge—friends again. As it is, Emmanuel can't open his mouth without hurting Max, and Max can't speak ten words without rubbing Emmanuel's fur the wrong way. It's awful!"

The next day he went to his mother's sitting-room to have tea with her for the last time. He had always loved the room, with its two wide windows, its comfortable simplicity, bright chintzes and masses of flowers. Woodcock might grudge his peaches to Lady Gollantz, Emmanuel reflected, but he certainly did not spare his flowers.

320

As she poured out tea Angela said: "I'm always saying good-bye to you in this room. I shall grow to hate it very soon."

Emmanuel took the cup from her and inhaled the fragrance of the China tea luxuriously. He loved his mother's tea, and its delicacy appealed to his fastidious taste.

"Lovely smell!" he said. "Well, say the next goodbye in my room in Milan!"

She leant back, relieved that his voice had lost it cold aloofness and that he seemed himself again.

"What is it like, this room of yours?"

"Smallish, rather dark. The window looks out over some rather attractive roofs and other windows where I can sometimes see people. There is a girl who does her hair at one, a tailor who stops work and comes to the window to stare at her by way of relaxation; there is a very old woman who shakes two very small and horribly filthy mats from another, and two little girls who sing in high piercing voices from their window every morning when they are getting ready for school. They sing 'Lacrimae Rosae'. It's very sad and drawling and they love it."

"That's not your room, that's what you see from your window," she objected.

"Oh, far more interesting, believe me. I doubt if my room is even very clean. It never smells as if it were. It may be because all the furniture is old. Come and see it for yourself."

"Perhaps." Then suddenly: "You'll call and see Max on your way to the station, won't you?"

Immediately she heard the coldness of his tone, he had ceased to be the Emmanuel she knew and became this new creature who was almost a stranger.

"If you wish it, certainly."

"He'll wish it. Max is very devoted to you, Emmanuel."

"And to demonstrate his devotion he tries to make me conform to his ideas, no matter where my happiness lies. I see! He treats me like a child, he behaves as if all my affairs, my hopes and my future were things which could be swept on one side to oblige the head of Gollantz and Son. Can't he realize that I'm not a child?"

"No, I doubt if he'll ever realize that completely. Max is developing into a patriarch, and patriarchs always look on the rest of the tribe as their children. He's a tired man who wants your help, he's a lonely man in his business and he wants your companionship. Oh, it can't be helped, you are as much to blame as he is. You each play-act before the other, and pretend and assume queer cold voices and keep stiff upper lips and a great deal more nonsense of that kind. After all, Max is my husband as well as your father and I'm still rather in love with him. I hate to see him miserable, in fact I won't allow him to be miserable long! There is only one thing which comes within a hundred miles of being as hurtful to me as to see Max unhappy and worried—that's to see you unhappy and worried."

"But," Emmanuel objected more gently, "I must live my own life."

"Of course you must," she agreed. "but when that life is quite different from what Max planned, you can't expect him to like it much. After all, it's only a recent idea that children must and can and ought to do as they like, and though it's easy enough for you to support it, it's not nearly so easy for pre-war people like Max."

"Don't you think it's right, though?"

"Me?" she demanded in surprise. "Certainly I do, but then, as you've often told me, and anyway I knew it already, I'm a very remarkable woman. My dear, it's one thing knowing that a thing is right and another thing liking it. I should have liked to keep all of you at home, firmly attached to my apron-strings, and you know it." She sighed. "What nice people you'd all have been, too! There, that's enough of meandering. Certain sign that I'm growing old. Tell me, you've got plenty of money, plenty of clothes, or shall I send you some out there? Where is it you're going to first? Dresden? That's a nice place. Give my love to Juliet and tell her not to keep you dangling at the end of a string. She's either to marry you or send you back to me quickly. I won't have this shilly-shallying. Tell her that and see what she says! Oh dear, I do like her so much, it would be so much easier if I cordially disliked her."

Emmanuel smiled. "Could anyone do that?"

"Idiot!" Angela jeered. "Of course they could. Probably a great many people have. Come and kiss me and promise to be sensible, and not work too hard and be happy. Oh, darling, I do so want you to be happy." Holding his face between her hands she kissed him on the lips, then held his face so that she could look into his eyes. "How I hate your going!" she said passionately. "I wanted this to be such a lovely holiday for you, and you and Max have managed to spoil it between you. Never forget that this is your home, darling, and never forget that you can come home at any time." She caught her breath in a little strangled sob. "I'll see to that. No one shall—shall bully you. God bless you, my most loved, and take care of you for me."

It was typical of her, Emmanuel reflected, that she did not attempt to come downstairs to see him go. She remained in her own room, and if she watched him from the window as he drove away, she did it in such a way that he could not see her. He watched the house disappearing, hidden by the trees, caught one last glimpse of it as the car drove along the high road, dignified, immense, splendid, and shrugged his shoulders. The house, the car in which he drove, the long row of glasshouses, meant nothing. He was happy again because he had set his face towards the town where Juliet waited for him.

He determined to try to heal the breach

between himself and his father, and Max responded at once. Max Gollantz might be rigid, he might even tend to be narrow-minded, but there was nothing mean or petty about the man, and on that November afternoon Emmanuel thought that he had never liked or loved him so much.

"I thought that I'd come in to say good-bye, father," Emmanuel said as he entered the office, "and Angela gave me a note for you."

Max nodded, held out his hand and cut the envelope with the big silver paper-cutter which had lain on his and his father's desk for nearly sixty years.

"Excuse me," he said softly, his eyes already on the written words. As he read, his smile widened, and when he finished he held out the sheet of paper to his son. "I don't often allow anyone to read Angela's letters to me," he said, "but—read that."

Emmanuel took the paper and read:

"Max dearest Emmanuel is coming to say good-bye. Please be yourself, no one in the world is nicer. You have both behaved very stupidly and made me very angry. I hate and loathe being angry with either of you. Don't come home to dinner. Take me somewhere amusing and let's do a show. I'll call for you at the club at half-past seven. Tails—I want to make a festa of it! A."

Max took the letter as Emmanuel handed it back, folded it and put it in his pocket, smiling as he did so. He looked suddenly younger, less tired.

"When you realize that I've been married thirty years," he said, "and that a note like this still makes me feel like a schoolboy, you'll be able to understand why divorce seems such a queer, impossible thing to me. However—that's only one of my many limitations. You're off—why don't you drive down to Dover? Much better than the train. Take the car."

For a second Emmanuel hesitated, then said: "I'm not going by Dover. I'm going from Harwich to Flushing. I'm going to meet Juliet in Dresden tomorrow night."

"I see." A hint of the old coldness crept into Max's voice, but he mastered it valiantly. "Then you don't leave Liverpool Street until quite late. Dine with us somewhere, won't you?"

"Will you think me an ungrateful fool if I say that I'd rather dine alone, sir?"

Max looked at him steadily, then his eyes softened and his lips lost their hard line. "Neither ungrateful nor a fool," he said, "in fact I rather applaud you for it." Then less seriously: "Have a pint of champagne, it will do you good. There, be off with you, and here's something to oil the wheels of the train for you. Don't be a fool, of course you'll take it! Unless that precious business of yours and Louis Lara's earns enough to make a couple of tenners look ridiculous. And"— Emmanuel waited almost apprehensively—"give my regards to Miss Forbes."

Liverpool Street, most gloomy of stations, looked almost attractive to Emmanuel. The hotel seemed friendly in spite of its vast spaces and melancholy waiters. He sent off telegrams, bought his ticket, and settled down to an early and solitary dinner feeling as if his holidays had begun. He had practically started on his journey back, and the end of that journey would mean that he would find Juliet again. It seemed impossible that he had been away less than two weeks, he felt that he must of necessity find Milan changed out of all knowledge, his shop demolished to make room for new buildings, and Guido elderly and staid waiting for him after many years.

He found the long, dark railway journey in a second-class carriage almost amusing, decided that no boats were so clean, so comfortable or so admirably run, and as he stood on the deck and watched the lights of Harwich recede he knew that his heart was lighter than it had been since he left Italy. Even the dreary and uninteresting German plain seemed full of interest, and when night fell he leant back in his corner and tried to keep his excitement within bounds. Leipzig— and another Englishman told him that he ought to get out and look at the station, which he said

327

was the finest in the whole world. "The new station at Milan isn't really a patch on it," he declared. "These Germans know how to build, I will say that for 'em."

Emmanuel shook his head. "I don't think I will, thanks. You see, I find Milano the most attr-ractive station possible. I live there, it's my home."

"Oh, I beg your pardon. I took you for an Englishman."

Then a river, spires and domes against the dark sky, looking as if they had been drawn in Indian ink. Emmanuel said to the English traveller: "Dr-resden?" and wished that his voice didn't shake so.

"That's right. Not this first station, though. Another few minutes." He spoke rather loudly and very distinctly in a manner which he obviously felt was correct to use when addressing foreigners.

"Here you are," he said later. "This is Dresden. Got a good hotel? That's right. Good night."

The air was clear and very cold. To Emmanuel after hours in a hot railway train it tasted like wine. He carried his own suitcases, rejoicing in his strength and enjoying the pull on his muscles. It was fine to be young! He would have walked to the hotel, but a sudden panic that Juliet might be waiting for him made him fling his bags into a taxi. It seemed an impossibly short drive, and he was standing beneath the glass portico of the hotel, his hands shaking so that he could scarcely find the money for the driver without dropping it.

His lips were dry, and he had to lick them before he could speak to the porter.

"Miss Forbes? Is she in yet?"

"Miss For-rbez," the man repeated, as if he was offering a correction. "Not yet. At any moment. Will you wait, please?"

Emmanuel nodded. "Yes, here," and knew that his hands were shaking dreadfully. Perhaps the fellow would think that he was tight and throw him out. He sat down in one of the big armchairs, and felt as if its padded arms and back were a rack. His eyes were fixed on the revolving doors, and people who entered glanced curiously at the good-looking young man with the white face.

Each time the doors revolved Emmanuel gripped the arms of his chair. The intensity of his longing was so great that he resented it, almost wondered if he wanted to see Juliet at all. A stout German, in an overcoat made apparently of carpet felt, entered, stood staring and walked away to the lift. Two women pushed the doors round, laughing because they both tried to walk out together and jostled each other against the frame. One of the diminutive pages came in with a rush, puffing and blowing on his cold hands. Emmanuel wondered who had sent him out and for what reason. He saw a car drive up, half started from his seat and sank back, a feeling of physical weakness overcoming him. A man and woman came into the hall, talking and smiling at each other. They glanced at him and the thought struck Emmanuel that he must look both dirty and untidy. He sprang up, asked the way to the wash-place, washed feverishly and brushed his hair. Wondered if he had time to get a clean collar out of his bag, and decided against it. Flicked dust from his coat, cleaned his nails, was certain that he heard Juliet's voice and rushed back to the hall, colliding with a very stout German who muttered his annoyance. Back in his chair his eyes sought the door once more, his heart beating heavily, every pulse in his body throbbing. This waiting was intolerable. Suppose that Juliet was supping at a restaurant, suppose she had not got his telegram, and did not expect him! What if she had been taken ill on the platform? He saw headings in the morning's papers, "Famous Singer Seriously Ill", and shivered. Two more cars discharged their cargoes, and just as Emmanuel had given up all hope, and felt himself abandoned and deserted by the whole world, he heard Gilly's voice, high and thin as always, speaking. "No, I'll get back. Tomorrow then, at half past ten. Good night." Through the glass doors he could see her, turning to say a last word to little Gilbert. Half stupidly Emmanuel wondered if Gilbert was in love with her and pitied him. He rose and stood waiting for Juliet to enter the hall. The porter gave them a twist and a second later she stood before him.

"Emmanuel! Have you been waiting long?"

"Not r-really. How are you?"

"Very well"; then more softly, "Very glad to see you."

She turned to one of the men in uniform who stood near. "Is my maid back? She is. Then we'll go up, Emmanuel. You've booked your room? No? Gustav, a room for Mr. Gollantz. Come along. . . ."

In the lift he wondered how they could utter ordinary words, make everyday comments, wondered how he could bring himself to ask evenly if the concert had been a success, and add that the critics had been almost satisfactory during the whole of the tour. The long corridor seemed endless, he felt as if he had walked along that thick pile carpet for hours before Juliet stopped and opened the door of a room.

"There!" She pointed to the supper-table for two, lit by shaded candles. "You're hungry?"

He shook his head. "Not for those things. Oh, Juliet, it's wonderful to be with you again. Let me look at you! How dare you grow so beautiful when I was away fr-rom you?"

"Have I?" she said. "My dear, romantic Emmanuel."

331

5

TWO days with her were all that he would allow himself, then she departed for Berlin, The Hague, Amsterdam, Stockholm, and Oslo. After Oslo, she told him, she too would set her face homeward towards Italy, Paris, Lyons, and then Cannes, Mentone, and the rest of the pleasant places where people would have congregated, hoping to find sunshine.

Emmanuel grumbled: "Horrible! How long will all this dr-readful tour take?"

"A month, no longer—yes, I'm wrong, five weeks. There are two additional dates, one in France—a private engagement. I mean not in a concert hall, in a huge and quite dreadful house, for people who are equally huge and dreadful. Then home for ages and ages. Gilly says that I ought to go to America again, but I don't want to. Not this time of year. Will you be patient for five weeks?"

He smiled. "Needs must. Especially when the devil who does the dr-riving is—you!"

Two wonderful days were what he had to look back upon as the train carried him over the Brenner Pass down into Italy again, where the sight of the tumbledown peasant cottages warmed his heart. He was tired of well-kept, beautifully tended cottages; these patched and repaired—or not even patched or repaired—hovels delighted him. At Verona, where he arrived in the early morning, he stood at the window and looked out over the town. The Verona of Romeo and Juliet. He smiled, and then the smile died as he remembered that Bill Masters had told him that it was here Juliet had first met not only Vernon Seyre, but Leon Hast.

The recollection started a train of thought which occupied him until he reached Milan. He found, in some strange way, that his intense hatred of Hast had died, and that the thought of Vernon Seyre was far more detestable to him. Hast had given her so much, and some extra sense, some new understanding, told Emmanuel that in all probability Juliet's life with Hast had been the happiest she had ever known.

"The past," he thought, "must have been wonderful. Even the pain she suffered couldn't rob her of that. It belonged to him, to Hast, but the future shall be just as beautiful, and the future belongs only to her and to me."

Milan was lonely without her. This was the longest tour she had made since he had come to Italy, and the days dragged only less than the long dark evenings when he sat alone, or wandered through the streets to make himself sufficiently physically tired to ensure sleep. Guido was absorbed with a countess, and apt to be a little boring concerning her. He wanted to discuss her at every opportunity and contrived to shock Emmanuel considerably.

"Good God," he burst out one evening when Guido's confidences had become particularly personal, "you mustn't tell me those things!"

"Why not? They are my own experiences, you are my friend!"

"She wouldn't like you to tell me."

"She tells all her friends. I know because their lovers tell me."

Emmanuel said: "Well. I'm damned!"

Guido polished his finger-nails, watching him like an attentive monkey, then said: "You would never tell your experiences with Mees Forbez?"

Emmanuel glared at him: "How dare you! You little brute!" Then very coldly: "In any case, I have no experiences to recount."

Guido gasped his admiration: "Oh, my beloved friend, how beautiful is the outgaze for the English! They not only never open their tongues, but they lie with conviction should one make suggestions. Never again will I discuss a lady who does me the honour to sleep with me. I swear it! Rather I will declare that she is like a sister to me. That is the right phrase, no?"

"It will serve," Emmanuel said shortly.

"I shall not forget," Guido said meekly but with gratitude.

Once again his work absorbed most of his waking hours. His one wish was to make money. Not for himself, for his tastes were very simple, but so that he might stand on an equal financial footing with Juliet. More than once she had assured him that she never spent a penny of Leon Hast's money on her apartment, her clothes or the small presents which were all Emmanuel could be persuaded to accept from her; but the fact that she, through her own efforts, was a rich woman, and that he, in spite of his, was a poor man, worried and disturbed him.

The thing was beginning to affect his outlook, and all his joy at some sale, some new commission, vanished when he remembered that his earnings in a month did not equal what Juliet could make in a single evening. It would have been easy to apply to Max for help, and Emmanuel knew how gladly Max would have financed his business, given him the benefit of his experience, his influence, and his name. But he could not bring himself to accept help.

Then, one afternoon, when the rain splashed down and the streets were cold, wet, and horribly depressing, when Emmanuel entered, wet from head to foot, his portfolio under his arm, the rain dripping from the brim of his rather shabby hat, Guido looked up smiling and said: "You are wanted quicker than at once at the Europa. The name is a fruit—I have forgotten it, if indeed I ever heard it correctly."

Emmanuel flung down his portfolio. He had listened to an elderly contessa declaiming on art for over an hour, and he was both cross and tired.

335

"You must have got the name," he protested. "I can't go and ask for a man with a name like a fruit, damn it!"

Guido smiled. "No, indeed," he agreed, "but I will telephone to them and ask who is the man with such an imbecile name."

Emmanuel sat down, stared at the toes of his wet and splashed shoes and wondered if his others had come back from the cobbler's. He hitched up the knees of his trousers and surveyed the damp ends of them gravely. There was no doubt about it, he was shabby. One of these days, when the winter was over and the Italian spring sun shone brightly and rather cruelly, Juliet would notice just how shabby he was and would try to offer him new clothes. He sighed. That would mean a hell of a row! He would be hurt and angry, she would never understand, and would say that if he loved her nothing could be impossible. Oh, how damned difficult it all was, especially when so often her flat was filled with successful young musicians who dressed superbly. And once upon a time, Emmanuel remembered, he had been something of an exquisite!

Guido was gushing over the telephone: "Thank you a thousand times, I was foolish indeed. Good-bye. Yes, I have it perfectly now."

"The name," he said, turning to Emmanuel with his wide, beautiful smile, "is Jaffa! Like oranges, as I said. Jaffa, no, again I am mistooken. Not Jaffa, Jaffe—Simeon Jaffe."

"Simeon Jaffe," Emmanuel repeated; "he's a cousin of my father's—no, a second cousin. He was my grandfather's cousin. I wonder what he wants. All right, I'll get along."

He rose, and Guido screamed: "Emmanuel, I beg, change your shoes and put on another hat!"

"Change nothing!" Emmanuel said. "I shan't melt."

He was taken up in the lift, and it was evident that Simeon Jaffe was a person of some importance, such was the deference shown to him by implication when the staff spoke of him. His suite was on the first floor, and Emmanuel was ushered into a sitting-room where a fire roared and blazed in the hearth, and by it sat one of the most fantastic-looking old men he had ever seen.

He remembered that Rupert Jaffe, a younger brother, had come to old Emmanuel's funeral, but he had never seen this man before.

He sat swathed in a purple velvet dressing-gown, a skyblue smoking-cap embroidered with gold leaves on his head, his feet encased in red leather slippers with curved toes, his large white hands heavy with rings, his hair rather long, and his moustaches curled in the manner of a past age. It was evident that his hair was parted down the back of his head, huge locks being brought forward and curving round his ears almost in the manner of side-whiskers.

He glanced up, his small dark eyes looking out of puffs of flesh, his great handsome Jewish nose and full lips which showed under his moustache making his face one of the most remarkable Emmanuel had ever seen.

"You are young Emmanuel, eh?" His voice was deep and rather thick.

"Emmanuel Gollantz, sir."

"Dot is vot I said. Emmanuel bar Mex bar Emmanuel. Sit down, if you please. I am your gr-reat cousin, Simeon Jaffe, und I veesit Milano for der express purpose dot I see you."

Emmanuel sat down and felt the pleasant heat of the blazing fire against his damp trouser-legs. Simeon Jaffe said nothing, but watched him attentively out of those twinkling, pouched eyes.

After a long silence, Jaffe said: "I am eighty-four years of age."

Emmanuel made a polite noise indicative of delighted surprise.

Again there was a long silence. Emmanuel reflected that it was as well he had plenty of time to spare.

"Your trousers are vet, and your shoes take in vater."

Emmanuel laughed: "You can't keep your trousers dry or the wet out of your shoes on a day like this."

"You should vear overshoes—rubber vons."

"I don't like them, thank you, sir."

"Den you ought ter hev a motor-car."

338

"I agree! Only—I can't afford one."

Jaffe gave vent to a huge, gusty sigh, as if he had reached the point he desired: "R-ring der leetle pell on dot table," he ordered.

The door of another room opened and a man, who looked to Emmanuel to be the most obvious type of stage valet, entered and stood, his heels together, bowing slightly. He was very pallid, with sleek dark hair, and a tall, thin figure clothed entirely in black clothes which were only relieved by the startling white of his collar and cravat.

"Cigars," Jaffe said, "und brendy." Then as the man bowed and turned to go, he shouted: "Vait! Listen! Bring two lemons, sugar, und a leetle kettle of hot water. Be qvick und shut der door, der vind blows down my neck." When the valet returned he continued: "Here is der brandy. For me, plain, Valter, for Her Gollant, mit hot vater, a leetle sugar und lemon. Vat do you mean you don't like it? You hev it or you hev a bed cold. Do as you are told if you please. Now," as the door closed behind Walter again, "ve shall talk. I am mooch displeased mit you."

Emmanuel sipped his brandy-and-hot water, and found it soothing.

"With me?" he said. "I am sorry. Why are you displeased?"

Simeon Jaffe puffed out his immense chest, so that the silk frogs of his magnificent dressing-gown were strained to the utmost, and made a gesture with his huge white hand, so that the light

339

of the fire caught the stones in his rings and made them glint and glimmer like electric sparks.

"I tell you," he said, "I em engry because you are very shabby. You liff in a Christian country und are shabby. Dot is bed business. To be shabby is to argue yourself unsuccessful, and no Christian r-respects an unsuccessful Jew. He may tr-rust him but he don't r-respect him. It is evident dot you hev very leetle money. I esk here at this hotel about you. T'ey t'ink dot t'ey hev heard of you, but t'ey aren't sure! Louis Lara tells me dot you are megnificent. Vot a vord! Megnificent! I find you a nice-looking poy, in vet trousers, boots vot let in der vater, und a very bed het! Dot is not megnificent! I—Simeon Jaffe —am megnificent! Dot is vhy I am so very r-rich. In Vienna every people is poor—but neffer Jaffe. Every people is shabby—Jaffe is alvays vonderfully dressed. Every people is hungry and t'in, Jaffe is vell fed and fet! In Von Vord"—he said it in capitals—"Jaffe is successful!"

Emmanuel set down his glass and rose. He towered above Simeon Jaffe, tall, thin, and shabby. His eyes shone with anger, but when he spoke his voice was very soft, dangerously pleasant.

"I am indebted to you, sir," he said, "for a ver-ry instructive lecture. I r-regret that my clothes displease you, but I reserve to myself the right to wear what I please, and further to conduct my life and my business as I please. I have the honour to wish you a very good afternoon."

Jaffe wagged a fat white forefinger at him.

"Dot empresses me," he said heavily. "Dot takes me beck to Vienna fifty years ago, ven I spoke mit annuder young Emmanuel. I offer you my apologies. I vas r-rude possibly, ven I get engry I frequently get r-rude. It is offer, ve are friends vonce more. Sit down. I hev propositions to make mit you for der penefit of us both. Giff me some more brendy, und take some more for yourself. So!"

Emmanuel's anger never lasted very long, and the sight of this fantastic old man amused and interested him. He smiled, took his glass and poured out more brandy, then sat down, saying: "I shall be very much inter-rested in what you have to say, sir."

Jaffe talked solidly for an hour. He told a story which was a saga in itself, filled with a wealth of detail and masses of information regarding himself and his kinsmen. It appeared that at the age of twenty he had fallen in love with a girl who had the bad taste to prefer his brother Adolphus; but in spite of the fact that she married Adolphus, Simeon continued to love her for the rest of her life. Adolphus had died ten years before, his wife had followed him a year later. They had left no children. Simeon's younger brother, Rupert, had two sons, one a mining

341

engineer, the other a dealer in gold, silver, and precious stones, living in Amsterdam.

"So," Jaffe concluded, "I am left in Vienna, old and very lonely. My peoples are dead or gone away, und Vienna is dr-dreadful now, a city of the dead who only valk about because funerals cost too much. I talk mit Louis—Louis is very alive, effen t'ough he heng alvays after dot terrible voman Olympeeia. I say, 'Louis, here I em, mit dis gr-reat pusiness vich is a pusiness no longer. I keep open my gelleries but no persons puy. I em too young, too ective to r-retire fr-rom pusiness. Vot is eighty-four? Not'ing to Simeon Jaffe!' I hev offered Louis Lara five t'ousand marks for his pusiness in Milan, und I kom now to talk mit you and see if you vill accept dot sum. Either you ken hev five t'ousand marks und go, or take on a new partner und stay. Your selery is two huntret und fifty lire a veek mit a room. Der odder poy get two huntret lire a veek. Und a room. I hev seen der premises dis morning. No damn goot! I hev seen odders very damn goot. Now—tell me, vot vill you do?"

Emmanuel pushed back his hair, frowned, and tried to think what chance this old man offered him. New premises, additional capital, obviously the old man would have very little interest in the actual work, and equally obviously he would have considerable stock to bring from his galleries in Vienna. Emmanuel remembered how Max had

342

always quoted Simeon Jaffe as being the finest expert in Europe.

"I am good," Max admitted, "I am even more than—just good, but Simeon Jaffe has a flair which is uncanny. He says, and others say of him, that he can see an old master under ten layers of paint."

Emmanuel said: "For many reasons I should like to stay. But I could never stay at my present salary. Whatever this business is worth, I have built it. Originally it was nothing, now I can show you that though the profits are small—yet there are profits. I have trebled them in just over a year. I have clients who rely on my judgement, who allow me a more or less free hand in decorating. I must be left with that freedom. I could never work under anyone else. Louis has never bothered me so long as I have sent him accounts from time to time. I should want at least six hundred lire a week and commission to remain in the business if it was enlarged. More, I have come to rely upon and understand Guido. He may seem unbusinesslike, but he is definitely an asset. His Italian is perfect, his manners admirable. Under any new scheme—I can speak for him—he would certainly demand and have a right to expect at least four hundred lire a week. How does that affect you, sir?"

Simeon blinked his eyes, swallowed hard, then asked: "Vot commission?"

"For myself?"

343

"God of my Fadders!" Simeon shouted suddenly. "I don't giff der odder poy no commission! Ven I looket t'rough der vindow all he vas doin' vas cleanin' his nails mit an old tagger!"

"Be thankful that he cleans them at all! Let's get back to the question of my commission, shall we?"

For an hour they debated and argued, and Emmanuel watching the heavy old face could tell nothing. It was impossible to judge if Simeon Jaffe wanted or did not want the business; it was equally impossible to decide whether he really wanted Emmanuel Gollantz to remain in that business or not. Finally, after haggling over introductions, new customers, old clients, buying, pricing stock, and a hundred other things, the old man said, as if in desperation:

"T'ere is no doubt dot at der age of eighty-four I shell be ruined! But hev it your own vay. Ondly, I don't vant der poy vot cleans his nails mit taggers! He ken go in a veek."

Emmanuel smiled pleasantly: "Very well, then I shall go with him. He and I can start in another shop, and remember I take my customers with me—so does he."

Simeon shrugged his huge shoulders: "Oh, dis is demnation!" he said. "Vot a poy you are for archuing, neffer setisfied. Your name ought to be Shylock, not Emmanuel! Very well, hev it your own vay."

As Emmanuel was leaving half an hour later, Jaff held his hand enveloped in his own immense fist, and patted it with the other, saying as he did so: "Hed you let der little nail-poy go, I would soon hev let you go! Ve shell make a gr-reat success of t'ings. In der morning I vill take you to look at new premises, mit r-room to sving many cats. Vot time? Vell—shell ve say two o'clock?"

"You said—morning," Emmanuel reminded him.

"No chentlemen effer appears in der streets until efter midday," Jaffe returned with dignity. "Please call here for me at fife minutes to two o'clock. Good-bye."

Emmanuel walked back to the shop, his heart singing. It seemed as if, with the coming of this queer old eccentric Simeon Jaffe, all his worries had vanished. True, even six hundred lire a week was not a fortune. He had made more in his father's galleries two years ago. That did not affect his happiness. He had made a move forward. He had entered into a partnership with a man who obviously possessed capital, who loved his business and who, even at the age of eighty-four, found himself unable to live without the stimulus which it gave him. Where previously he had been cramped, fearful to accept any large orders for decoration because the initial outlay frightened him, now there would be room for expansion. In another two, three, four years, who could tell? He was suddenly nearer to Juliet than he had ever been. He would be able to tell her that he, at least, had a future, that he was not going to drudge on with his little orders here and his small purchases there. He could once again enter the ring with real buyers and meet them on their own ground. No longer must he confine himself to small unknown pictures, or at best buy those which were "attributed to"—real masters were within his reach if he could find them.

He entered the shop shouting: "Guido, Guido, come here! I've got news, marvellous, wonderful news—" Then stopped short, for Juliet Forbes rose from the big carved chair and came towards him.

"Juliet," he cried, "you're back!"

"Yes—I couldn't face the South and those towns full of smart people."

He leant forward, looking at her face intently: "My dearest, you're not ill? Tell me—you're not ill?"

She moved back to the chair, still holding his hand in hers.

"No, I'm not ill—I saw a doctor in Paris. He says I'm very well. Oh, Emmanuel, it's dreadfully difficult—"

He put his arms round her, and bent his head so that his cheek rested against hers; then in a voice made very gentle, so that his little Jewish inflections became more evident than usual, he said: "I once said that nothing would ever make

346

me say this again. I was wr-rong—I am so pr-roud to say it now. My beloved, my wonderful Juliet, will you marr-ry me?"

6

EMMANUEL said: "It was a dull sort of business, wasn't it? For the first time I realize what it feels like to be regarded only as a sort of attribute of yours. I'm Miss Juliet Forbes' husband now, and don't dare to r-remind me of it. I feel that I am going to be ter-ribly sensitive over it!"

Juliet held out her hand, and he took it and held it.

"Your nice old Simeon Jaffe puffed so loudly that I could scarcely hear my own name," she said. "He's rather a dear. Like old Emmanuel, with all the fine lines a little blurred."

"Guido wept this morning," Emmanuel said reflectively. "I only persuaded him to stop because I told him that it would ruin his complexion. He wanted to attend wearing a morning coat and a white waistcoat-slip. Dear little Guido!"

They had been married before the Consul that morning. It had been a cold and rather dreary affair, and Emmanuel had sighed with relief when it was over. He was very tired, physically and emotionally. For the past week he had been at Simeon Jaffe's beck and call, and it remained a marvel to him that at eighty-four the old man

348

seemed apparently tireless. In addition he had been attacked by fears which had shaken him.

Juliet's return, her news, and the fact that they must be married immediately had come as a shock to nerves which were already strung far too tightly. His visit to England had disturbed him more than he realized; he had worked tremendously hard since his return and had tried his level best to adjust himself to the conditions of life which Juliet had imposed upon him. He had tried to dismiss the idea of marriage because it was contrary to her wishes, and had overcome his natural desire for it out of his affection to her. Because he was young and fluid, he had adapted his mind to these conditions and had come to look forward to a future in which he would remain Juliet's devoted lover, and in all probability never her husband. The sudden readjustment had been too sudden. Marriage, home, and a child instead of the life which he had come to accept.

His first excitement and joy had lasted only so long as he had been with her, but that night when he returned to his own room, that rather shabby and not overclean little room of which he had spoken to Angela, his mind had turned traitor to him and all that he knew of himself. It had been as if one Emmanuel Gollantz who loved Juliet Forbes passionately and with intense devotion had been forced to listen to the arguments of another Emmanuel Gollantz, who disliked changing his present mode of existence. He had lain there and heard the voice of one uttering arguments which the other was too weary, too exhausted, to refute.

It seemed that he knew the answers to all these arguments, but that his brain was too weary to offer them. Snatches of conversations with his father, with Angela, and even with Charles Wilmot, came back to him, came back reproduced so faithfully that he could recollect every tone, every inflection. All night he had lain awake and listened and hated it all, loathing himself because he felt that he was being unfaithful to a woman who loved and trusted him. All the old arguments—Juliet's age—all very well now, but in ten years he would be thirty-nine and she would be nearly fifty. A man at thirty-nine was still young. No woman was really young at fifty. Money—she was rich, and, though he had what might reasonably be called prospects, he was far from being affluent. To live in the house of a rich woman, when he could not possibly contribute his equal share towards all expenses, was degrading. Other people would eye him, exchange glances, smile and, in private, call him—oh, horrible! "Thank her for agreeing to legalize my grandchildren"—that had stung him, and now Max might say it, or think it, again. "After all, she only married him because it was necessary." Julian, too. Emmanuel shivered and lay in his chilly bed biting his nails in angry irritation.

Julian with his serene face, his success, and his quiet confidence that his children would be the heirs of Ordingly. Julian would make calculations, and smile, rather bitterly, and say damnable things. Emmanuel turned restlessly and, as the light began to filter through the curtains, rose and dressed, walking out in to the dim streets and striding along trying to leave his bogeys and fears behind him.

That evening he had gone to dine with Juliet, fictitiously gay and light-hearted. She had watched him gravely, and finally, when he stood in his favourite attitude by the fire, sipping his coffee, she had spoken.

"You're tired, Emmanuel."

"A little. I didn't sleep."

"Neither did I. Bodies came and sat on the end of my bed and grimaced at me until I was too afraid to sleep. Horrible things."

"You?" Emmanuel said, rather blankly. "You had—bogeys?"

She nodded and smiled. "Dozens of them—all with tickets hung round their necks. Almost the ugliest was ticketed 'Twenty-nine years old', and the others weren't very attractive either. They were 'Money' and 'Ordingly', 'Duty', 'The conventional right thing'. That was a very unpleasant-looking fellow who muttered, 'Caught, by Jove!' under his breath. Oh, my dear, I was so glad when morning came and I could ring for tea and a hot bath to restore my self-

351

respect. I felt such—such a cad towards you."
She laughed. "Say that you forgive me. I almost
made up my mind to send for you this morning
and tell you that I wouldn't marry you. Would
you have minded very much?"

He said gravely, "At what time would that
have been—I mean when would you have sent
for me?"

"About eight o'clock."

"I should have minded ver-ry, ver-ry much at
that time, but at half past five I believe that I
should have been very r-relieved. You see, I had
all those fears too, Juliet."

They had sat on very late, by her big open log
fire, with the shadows leaping against the walls,
and the big room very quiet, and talked of all
those things which had frightened them both.
It had required all Juliet's wisdom and innate
simplicity to kill them for ever, and the effort left
her, she felt, drained and weak. But it had been
worth it when Emmanuel knelt before her, lifted
her arms and laid them round his neck, saying in
that low, tender voice which she loved, "They're
dead, those ridiculous fears—and you have killed
them for us both, and for ever. If you can r-risk
marriage with me, knowing me for what I am,
then there can be no r-risks for me. My content
and happiness are assured with you. Oh, Juliet,
we'll make each other happy, won't we?"

It had ended in the marriage before the Consul,
when old Simeon, attired in clothes which were

fantastic in their magnificence, and Guido, who looked like a weeping cherub in a fur-collared coat, had attracted more attention, Emmanuel said, than the bridegroom. Juliet, entering with little Gilbert, had known that her heart went out to the tall, grave young Jew who stood waiting for her. He scarcely smiled, but she had met his eyes and seen in them a depth of love and understanding which gave her confidence. This was the end of her waiting for happiness. It had come to her very completely, and filled with essential beauty.

"My dear young man," Gilbert had said when it was over, looking moist about the eyes, and speaking in a voice which shook a little, "we were late, did you notice it? Juliet said it was only five minutes; I said"—and he paused for a moment to regain command of his voice—"that she was nearly five years late. This ceremony ought to have taken place at Como years ago!"

The winter passed. Gradually the stalls in the streets were filled with spring flowers once again, and Emmanuel would come home carrying bunches of violets and sprays of mimosa to prove that spring was knocking at the door. On Sundays, as he said "in a manner befitting a good tradesman", he drove her into the country, and together they explored valleys which were already turning to the brilliant young green of the first season of the year.

"I have never been so utterly happy," he said.

353

"Oh, what am I saying? I have never been r-really happy before in all my life." He never alluded to the child, and Juliet never allowed anything to remind him of it. She sensed that he was pushing the thought of it from him, and that its birth was the one fear left to him.

Julian's son was born in March, and as Emmanuel read his mother's letter telling him of its arrival, Juliet watched the sudden convulsive movement of his hands which crushed the paper as he read. She did not speak, and presently Emmanuel laid down the letter and said:

"Julian's wife has a son. Born a week ago. Angela says that it was announced in 'The Times'. Did you see it? I never r-read 'The Times'. I dislike seeing my brother's name in the Parliamentary news!"

"Yes," she said, "I saw it."

"Why didn't you tell me?" he asked sharply.

"I don't quite know," Juliet said slowly, "I just thought it better not to—"

"To what?" He rapped out the words.

"To remind you," she said.

He threw back his head and gave a short laugh.

"Remind me! You think that I need an announcement in 'The Times' to—remind me! God, how ver-ry funny you are, Juliet!" Then as if something in his mind had been released, he began to speak very quickly, the words pouring from him in a torrent, the sweat standing on his forehead as he talked: "R-remind me! Don't you

354

know that I'm terrified, don't you r-realize that this is the one fear left to me, and that with each day it gr-rows, and gr-rows, gets more and more dr-readful? Do you know that sometimes I dare scarcely look at you for fear something, some little change in you, should make this more than I can bear? I adore you, I worship you, you've given me ever-rything, I am yours—body, soul, spir-rit. I tell you that I can't face it. It's too much. It's too long to wait, and know and imagine. I tell you this, too, that if it were poss-ible"—he dropped his voice to a whisper which shocked her in its intensity—"that this need not happen, if anything could be done to pr-revent it, I should welcome it, welcome it, welcome it!"

"Emmanuel, my dearest, don't—don't talk like that!"

He stared at her, shaking his head as if to clear his mental vision, then answered in a voice from which all colour was drained, a voice which was old and very tired.

"I'm sorr-y, Juliet. I was half cr-razy. I don't know quite all I said. Forgive me. I—I get worried. I love you too much. There, it's over, forget all I said."

She rose and came round to where he sat, putting her arm round his shoulder, pressing him to her, feeling his body quiver again as if his fears still mastered him.

"Emmanuel," she said softly, "you mustn't,

you mustn't—because you love me. It's not quite fair to me."

Instantly he was repentant, so full of remorse that she almost blamed herself for having made use of such a weapon. A moment ago he had seemed like a boy, a frightened child; with almost disturbing swiftness he became a man, strong and confident.

Going about his work all day, for with the new premises, with additional capital and with the knowledge and experience of old Jaffe the business was increasing, Emmanuel's mind went back to the time when, as a little boy, he had suffered so acutely because Angela lay ill. Again he remembered after his grandfather's death, when Meyer Bernstein had walked in and out very softly as if each additional noise might make her fight with death more difficult. All that he had suffered then seemed reproduced again during the spring and summer of this year in Milan.

He had no personal knowledge of either physical pain or illness. They had all been strong as children, and since they had grown up Emmanuel could not remember that he or his two brothers had ever suffered from anything worse than a heavy cold. Therefore his imagination had full rein, and where another man who had suffered himself could have checked those imaginings, Emmanuel's knew no limit.

Both Max and Angela had written to him, kindly letters in which they expressed their delight at the coming of Simeon Jaffe, and their content at Emmanuel's happiness. Their letters soothed him a little, made him feel less as if the world held only himself and Juliet, but there were times when he would have given almost all he had for his mother's gay companionship, and that quality of hers which had the power to banish fears.

Old Jaffe watched him anxiously. The fellow was growing too thin, he worked feverishly, never ceasing to drive himself from hour to hour. Jaffe shook his massive head and wondered what could be done.

"You don't hev to vork so hard, Emmanuel," he said one day, when he drove down to the galleries in his outsize car, which shimmered with glossy paintwork and silver plate. "Der koms a time ven a vise men allows odders to vork, vhile he sits und dir-rects."

"I can't work that way," Emmanuel said. "I like to see things done."

"You'll see yourself done von of dese days, I vouldn't vonder," the old man snapped. "D'you t'ink dot your vife likes to see you get home looking like a dead r-rat?"

"My wife knows that I have to work, she understands."

Jaffe sniffed loudly, "Der first voman who effer did, then!"

Guido, who had blossomed into magnificence since the opening of the new premises and

357

peacocked about the rooms in a morning coat, striped trousers, and huge tie, ventured to speak to his hero.

"Do not allow yourself to be overdone," he said. "People now understand that you are not a little fellow in a dirty little shop. You are a mister, and they understand that you can keep them waiting if you wish. Only this morning I said to Signor Luzzato, 'Patience, if you don't mind a lot. The Master'—I always refer to you in this way—"

Emmanuel said, "I wish to God you'd stop it too!"

Guido continued without a pause: "'—is much occupied. He will come when it pleases him. Did Leonardo complete his works in two minutes? Did Dante write the 'Commédia' in a week? Let me tell you that now I add—can Gollantz complete his designs, form his ideas, in a few days?' He said no more."

"Struck dumb by your impudence!"

"Dearest of friends," Guido said impressively, "you are breaking my heart in small pieces. I see you thinner and thinner. I say that I cannot bear it. Either you work less harder, or I must go and speak, in my person, with The Forbez."

"Do," Emmanuel advised, "and I'll break you in small pieces. Let me alone, Guido, I'm all right."

In May, Max and Angela came to Milan. Max left her there while he went on to Rome, Naples, and Venice. Max dignified, but very kind, greeting Juliet with just a shade more affection than he had shown her previously.

"I think the boy's very happy," he said tentatively, one evening when Emmanuel sat talking and laughing with his mother, while Max stood by the piano as Juliet played.

"You think that he looks well? I fancied that he was working too hard. Simeon is generous, but he likes to know that profits are coming in for all his grandiloquent manner."

Max turned and looked at Emmanuel, then said: "Perhaps he is a little—apprehensive." Then he added very gently, "Will you remember —that Angela and I would be very honoured to have you at Ordingly?"

She looked up and smiled. "Then you have decided to forgive me?"

Max spread his hands wide, and made a little grimace as if excusing himself. "I have been stupid very often in my life," he said, "and I ought to have asked that question of you, Juliet."

"In July," Emmanuel was saying, "I shall have a holiday. No one will be in Milan during that month. Juliet will go to the Lakes—to Como perhaps. I think perhaps Menaggio."

Angela said: "Where Max first fell in love with me! Perhaps Bill might come out then for his holidays—eh?"

She saw Emmanuel's quick nervous frown, saw his hand which held a match for his cigarette shake suddenly, and thought, "The boy is crazy with fear and hates to think that Bill might notice it."

She added, "Unless he goes to America with Charles."

Emmanuel nodded, "Oh yes, he told me that Charles might go."

They talked trivialities, and she watched Emmanuel's eyes always sliding back to where Juliet sat at the piano, and wondered why they neither of them dared be frank with each other, wondered why she could not speak to him out of her experience, and why he could not bring himself to ask the questions which were so vital to him.

At last she said: "Listen! I want to be driven round Milan. I love towns at night. Find a little horse carriage and take me."

Emmanuel frowned. "It's late—for Juliet."

"I don't want Juliet," Angela responded, "I want you and Milan. Juliet has you all day and every day. Damn it, I have some rights—or are they only privileges now?"

As they drove round the town past the grim fortress of the Sforzas, through the park with its triumphal arch, she laid her hand on his and said suddenly, "You're frightened, my baby, aren't you?"

Emmanuel, startled out of his control, turned a white face to her and said thickly: "Horribly—it's unbearable. Even now, with you here, and I love to be with you again—I'm aching to get back to her."

"Why?" Angela asked coolly. "What could happen to her?"

"I don't know." She felt his whole body shaking. "I don't know—it's this not knowing. It's—hell."

"My angel," she said, and congratulated herself that she could even produce a passable imitation of a laugh in the face of his misery, "what an idiot you are! You might consider the fact that your mother, who is sitting here beside you, perfectly well and safe and sane and all the rest of it, went through this without turning a hair—or almost. Not once, but on three separate occasions—almost four if your father hadn't chosen that moment to be hit by a German bullet."

Emmanuel drew a deep breath, and said in the "little boy" voice which always made his mother's heart contract a little: "Did you?"

"Max junior, that was what he was to have been called, you, Julian, and Bill. Audit that and find it correct, please." Then, drawing his arm through hers, she talked to him very sanely, very calmly, and with a quiet serenity which drove his fears away far more than any protestations could have done. She felt his tense muscles relax, knew that his breath came more evenly, and ended by saying: "And so you see, my angel, all you're doing is making yourself not only profoundly miserable, but making yourself the most frightful idiot. If I were in Juliet's shoes I should take a tour in America in sheer self-defence."

He laughed a little shakily. "Have I made an awful fool of myself? You see, if anything happened to her, well, I couldn't go on. She's everything to me—everything."

The grasp of her hand on his tightened. "Never talk like that," she said, "it's stupid. No one— listen, Emmanuel—no one is everything to anyone else. Possibly they would like to be, possibly they believe that they are, but they never are, you know. They may be a great deal, almost everything, but completely everything, never!"

He turned and stared at her. "You really believe that?"

"I know it! I've proved it."

Emmanuel shook his head. "There is a saying about exceptions proving the—"

"Good heavens," Angela said, "don't tell me that you're developing into the type of man who hurls tags of that sort at one! I couldn't bear it. Exceptions don't prove rules, they only prove that there may be exceptions to those rules. Anyway, you're not one of them, and nothing is going to happen to Juliet. She's a perfectly healthy, normal young woman, who has taken great care of herself for years, who has a very nice husband and is going to have a very beautiful baby. Now let's talk about something else, for although I love

362

you, and have a great affection for Juliet, I'm beginning to find you both just a little boring."

7

HE had left Juliet at Menaggio, and driven back to Milan in the new car which bore no resemblance to the old one, which had been half car, half traveller's van. The heat in Milan seemed unbearable, the roads and pavements quivered in the heat, and the air was heavy and oppressive. It was almost impossible to believe that four hours previously he had been swimming in Como, coming out to sit wrapped in a bath-robe, to drink coffee and eat new crisp rolls with Juliet on the terrace of the villa. The galleries in spite of electric fans and shaded windows were airless, and even Guido, who loved the heat, wandered about listlessly, mopping his face from time to time with a silk handkerchief of "almost Oriental splendour". Tempers were short, and often Emmanuel found himself speaking more sharply to this or that workman than he intended. Were people, he wondered, additionally stupid in very hot weather, or did it affect him so that he was incapable of making his orders sufficiently clear?

Guido, too, seemed to take a devilish delight in making difficulties and retailing foolish little bits of gossip. The Contessa had said this, Signor Luzetto had said the other, Simeon Jaffe had declared that he disliked the arrangement of the china in the long room.

"Listen," Emmanuel said, half seriously, half joking, so far as anyone could joke in such a temperature. "Let the Contessa say what she likes, let old Luzetto yarn as much as it pleases him, and whatever Simeon Jaffe dislikes, let him damned well come and see me, and not make bullets and leave you to fire them, my dear Guido."

"Indeed," Guido said readily, "you are right as always. Have you seen the new picture? It is a Moroni, and very fine and large. There! The subject is Joseph sold by his brethren."

"We should be as sold as he was," Emmanuel said, "if we bought that thing as a Moroni. Who wants to sell it?"

"An English milord—or nearly a milord. He is a Kolonel, and an Honourable."

"Not much honour about him," Emmanuel commented, "unless he is a born fool. Has Jaffe seen it? No? He'll have a fit when he does. Send it back to the Kolonel for heaven's sake, it makes me feel bilious, that blue! My hat!"

"I thought it quite pretty," Guido said, shrugging his shoulders, "and the Kolonel is charming! Quite the English gent."

"Splendid! You spend a pleasant half-hour with him when he calls, then. I don't want to see him, it's too damned hot."

"You work too damned hard, it is too bloody

365

silly of you," Guido said, smiling. "That is a new expression for me."

Emmanuel grinned. "Try using it to him to describe the Moroni, then," he said. "Take it from me, it won't make much of a success."

He went into his office and sat down, taking off his coat to work. The window was open, and the orange sunblind made the light which filtered in very pleasant. Emmanuel felt happy and light-hearted. Juliet was well, they had spent a wonderful week-end and his mind was filled with great content. Angela's visit, her acceptance of Juliet's condition as something entirely common-place, had done much to soothe his fears. He sorted the papers on his desk, whistling softly as he did so. Only five days and he would be with her again. They would sit by the blue lake, watch the changing ribbons of colour which wandered over the water, listen to the soft lap-lapping of tiny waves against the low wall, see the stars come out and hang suspended in a wide velvet sky and see the little sickle moon creep up over the mountains, making a silver path on the water. Resolutely he turned to his papers, making his estimates carefully and exactly, occasionally checking a figure on his writing-pad to ensure its correctness. While he worked a little smile hovered on his lips, as if even when he was immersed in his business he could not entirely forget his happiness.

He finished his work, shuffled the sheets

366

together, and his smile widened as he looked at the total. Things were moving towards them, people liked their work, believed in them, and had Emmanuel realized it—which he never did —liked best of all the young, good-looking Englishman who spoke fluent but incorrect Italian and never tried to trick his customers into spending more than they could afford.

Men respected him, and women found him slightly romantic. The story of his marriage was known, and it was considered that he had—through it—added to the romantic aura which surrounded him. True, it was evident that Juliet was older than he, but she was successful, rich, and beautiful, and Emmanuel was the envy of all right-thinking young men in Milan. In addition, he was on the high road to success, and it was rumoured that he was Simeon Jaffe's heir.

As Jaffe entered the galleries that morning, the first sound that Jaffe heard was Emmanuel's low whistling. He turned, puffing and blowing with the effort of mounting the four wide marble steps, to the man who followed him, smiling and nodding.

"Vait," he said, "ve giff him a gr-reat surprise. Dis is a ver' excellent good poy."

The man who followed him looked whimsically dubious. "I don't know that he'll be too pleased to see me," he said. "The last time we met— well, it ended in a very nasty row. 'Pon my word, I still don't know what it was all about. He's a

367

good fellow, but terribly touchy, y'know. Still, I'd love to see him again."

Jaffe wagged his fat white forefinger. "Say not'ing," he said. "Brudders hev got to be friends! Dot vas vhy I vas so pleased vhen I heard you vas at der hotel. Now, vait here, und let's giff der goot poy a surprise." He padded forward to the door of the office, still holding up his finger to Guido as he passed, demanding silence. Julian stood leaning on his stick, a smile on his lips, as if he waited with pleasurable expectation the result of Jaffe's announcement.

He heard Emmanuel's voice speaking: "Good morning, sir. You're just in time to sign these estimates for me, if you will."

Then a confused sound of old Jaffe's broken English like a great bee humming in the distance, and once more Emmanuel's voice very clear and cold: "I refuse to meet my brother Julian, sir." Again Jaffe's voice, and then the door closed and the murmur died away. Julian, meeting Guido's frankly admiring gaze, laughed gently.

"The old gentleman's plan for reconciliation hasn't come off," he said pleasantly. "My brother won't see me."

"Indeed?" Guido said. "I did not hear. I have taught myself how rude it is to over-listen to conversations. I spiritually close my ear-holes."

Without abating any of the friendliness of his tone, Julian asked: "Have you learnt that kind of rudeness from my brother, I wonder? I hope you

368

—what was your expression?—close your ear-holes to what people say of him in Milan. I hear that he's the laughing-stock of the place."

Guido frowned, looking like a Murillo cherub grown angry. "What is laughing-stock, if you please?" he asked.

"What my brother is, apparently, in Milan! The respectable married man. I hear they're going to start a family."

Guido's English was apt to betray him at moments when he was a little confused. He could not understand this man who spoke so pleasantly, who smiled, and whose voice held no trace of annoyance. He felt certain that he was being unkind about Emmanuel, but after all there was nothing wrong in saying that a man was either respectable or married. As for that other expression—laughing stork—or stook—what did it mean?

"Yes, indeed," Guido said eagerly, delighted to shower praise on his beloved Emmanuel, "he and she are both most respectable. And the family —it will not be a family, only one, of course. We hope to have its arrival next month, August, I believe me."

Julian's smile widened. Guido thought what beautiful teeth he had. "When were they married? I forget!"

"In January—the date I forget—perhaps the third week."

"Ah!"

369

Something seemed to catch Guido by his warm, olive-skinned throat. He had been so pleased to talk with Emmanuel's brother, he had felt that he was very much the confidential friend of Emmanuel Gollantz, he had been proud and had inflated his chest, and held his delightful curly head very high. Now—it was as if chilly fingers had caught him and a cold wind blown over his warm young heart. He stopped, rather like some startled animal confronted with something it cannot understand. He licked his lips because they were uncomfortably dry.

"Please why did you say 'Ah'?" he asked.

Julian shrugged his shoulders. "Emmanuel was always lucky," he said. "After all, what do dates matter?"

"No, no," Guido agreed. "What are dates when two people love?"

"Quite—and being Emmanuel, of course he did the decent thing."

"He could do nothing but very decent things," Guido said warmly. He was feeling happier, the cold sensation was slowly leaving him. This handsome, fair Englishman loved Emmanuel, and even if they had quarrelled, he had come to make friends. What a splendid thing it would be to walk through the Galleria with a Gollantz on each side of him, and know that people whispered: "There goes Guido, with two Englishmen whose father is a milord"!

"You will never know what he has taught me!

All that is good and best and cleanliness. One day when I marry I shall bring my sweetheart to Emmanuel for his confirmation—more, I would let him choose one for me!"

Julian yawned. He was a little tired of this round-faced little Italian with his eulogies of Emmanuel. He had waited long enough for Emmanuel to make up his mind. It was annoying, because he had honestly wanted to make friends both with his brother and old Jaffe. Money was horribly tight at the moment and a trip to the Lido, which, Amanda decided, was the only place in the world she wanted to visit, was going to be damned expensive. Amanda was rich, but old Van der Hoyt was getting a little tired of sending additional drafts across the Atlantic.

"See that he chooses a rich woman for you," he said. "If possible, one who earns her own living, and possesses a large income left to her by a former lover. If a fellow doesn't mind living on a woman, it must be remarkably pleasant—if you don't catch what people say about you."

The cold hand closed again on Guido's throat. His heart was hammering suddenly against his ribs. He felt breathless and rather frightened. More, he did not see quite plainly; it was as if the Englishman's face stared at him out of a red fog.

"To live upon a woman . . ." he said, stammering a little. "Is it you who says this of my friend? What peoples say? Please make it possible for me to hear what they say. Damned horrible bestia you are!" Scarcely knowing what he did in his blind rage, the tears starting to his eyes, he made a dart towards Julian.

"Pig and worse than a thousand pigs!" he screamed. "Let me kill you!"

Julian's stick swung up, his face was distorted with anger and astonishment. He had thought this little poof too stupid to understand more than half of what he said, and it had amused him to insult Emmanuel and hear the little fool agree with him. Now suddenly he was screaming with rage, his hands were curved like a cat's claws, the tears were dropping from his eyes, his mouth was open as infants' mouths open when they cry.

He stepped back, his foot went through the reputed Moroni which Guido ought to have moved and had left there because he thought it "very pretty" and liked to look at it. He cursed, and tried to recover his balance, to bring his stick down on the shoulders of this ridiculous Italian boy who was still coming towards him. The light rug was treacherous and slipped from under him, hurling him against a heavy marble column on which stood one of the huge bronzes which no one would ever buy, but which Simeon Jaffe had brought with him from Vienna. He struggled, and for one delicious second felt that he had saved himself, then the column caught him, and the bronze came hurtling down and pinned him where he lay.

Then thick darkness, pierced only by Guido's screams, enveloped him, and he sank into a pit where nothing existed but stabbing pain. After an eternity, voices reached him: old Jaffe's thick and heavy, the chatter of an Italian—no, several Italians—and once, Emmanuel's saying, "He must have caught his foot and fallen against the column." He tried to shout to them that it was the fault of the damned Italian boy, but, though he felt his lips move, no words came. Hands were touching him, moving him, lifting him; he screamed, shrieking that they were killing him with pain, then darkness enveloped him again and consciousness left him.

Hours later, after interviews with doctors, with officials, with people who seemed to arrive for no reason and demand answers to questions for no particular reason and with no particular right or authority, Emmanuel went back into the office and laid his hands on Guido's shoulders. Guido lifted a face ashen-white, pathetically tear-stained, his mouth quivering, and asked:

"Is he dead? Will they put me in prison for ever?"

"He's not dead," Emmanuel said gently, "and no one shall touch you. It was an accident. I have told them so, so has Simeon Jaffe. Now, tell me what happened. No, don't cry, tell me sensibly."

Guido was beyond speaking sensibly, he told his story with sobs and tears, he held Emmanuel's hand as if it were the only stable thing in a shiv-

373

ering world. From a disjointed welter of sentences Emmanuel caught bits of the information he sought.

"I was pleased—talked so nicely to me—and you—I mean of you. My Master—I was proud to be able to say when you were married—and show I knew of the bambino—dates didn't matter, he said. Then it went wronger—no, I don't know how—I got very cold—then a rich wife, and money, and finished with lovers who were rich—and you—oh, Emmanuel—you—I cannot speak it—I went mad. I said, 'I shall kill you.' I wept with rage and he stepped into the Moroni—I mean the one which is not a Moroni —and the marble and the bronze fell on him, and that is all. Tell me, am I a murderer?"

"No," Emmanuel said, "you're nothing of the sort, you poor, dear little devil. You've got to keep that loyalty of yours in check, my lad, it doesn't pay. My brother won't die, and by God, if he did, it's got nothing to do with you. How dared he! To you—why, he didn't know you!" He paced up and down the little room, pausing to lay his hand on Guido's shoulder. "Listen! Never again, whatever people say about me, lose your temper. This time it's all right, next time— it might not be so simple. Poor little Guido!"

Guido clutched at his hand and carried it on to his lips. Emmanuel promptly dragged it away. "Don't do that! Now, pull yourself together. There's going to be a devil of a row about that

374

wretched Moroni fake. Tell your Kolonel that we'll either have it repaired or he can do so—we'll pay for any damage, but—damn it, Guido, do listen—not as damage done to a genuine Moroni. Have you got that right? I must get along to the clinic where they have taken my brother."

Guido sniffed: "I heard, only I am overturned today, and my nerves are not themselves. Make no mistake, I shall send the Kolonel very quickly packed up."

Emmanuel went back to the clinic, where the doctors were still making their examination. They came out to talk to him and Simeon Jaffe. They were cold, impersonal and not encouraging. The damage done was to the nerves of the spine; it was doubtful if Julian would ever walk again. There would be little or no pain; he would probably live for years—as a cripple. One of them asked, still in that queer uninterested fashion, if Julian did any work.

"He is a Member of Parliament—a Deputy—is that what you call them?"

The doctor smiled frostily: "In Italy we have them no longer. The system is abolished. There is only one party—Fascism. It serves very well indeed."

Jaffe puffed and blew and said: "Ah! Dot is bed!" Suddenly his old puffy eyes met Emmanuel's, and he stretched out his immense white hand and laid it on Emmanuel's arm: "It

375

hes not'ing to do mit you," he said earnestly. "Not'ing, not'ing, not'ing."

"What has nothing to do with me?" Emmanuel asked, surprised.

"Not'ing of dis. Listen, here I beg mit all der sincherity of vich I em capable—do not let it touch you, neffer, neffer, neffer." He might have said more had not the doctor moved impatiently, and indicated that he wished to get back to his work. At that moment Amanda burst into the little, clean, over-light room. Her fair hair was disarranged, her blue eyes were wide with terror; she rushed to Emmanuel and clutched his arm.

"Have you seen him?" she demanded. "He's lying there for all the world like a statue. My Julian, they tell me that he'll never move again. Oh, say, it's terrible, it's unbelievable! Can't you do anything? Can't you make them have an operation or something? I'm half out of my mind. Thank God we left Max at home, poor little soul! What's going to happen to him, I wonder! Oh, say, Emmanuel, it's just fierce!"

The rest of the week was a nightmare to Emmanuel. He spent his time rushing backwards and forwards between his work and the clinic. He soothed Amanda, he despatched telegrams, he attended to Julian's business as well as his own. Max and Angela arrived from England, Angela white-faced but serene, Max looking older and more worn than Emmanuel had ever seen him. He explained matters to them, gave them the verdict of the doctors, and did his best to mitigate the gravity of the situation.

"Have you seen him?" Max asked.

"Of course he has," Angela interjected.

"No," Emmanuel said, "I haven't seen him." He paused, then added with an effort, "I don't want to see him."

Max lifted his hands with a gesture of despair: "More trouble! I thought all this was over! I can't face these hatreds and resentments any longer."

"There are no hatreds, no resentments," Emmanuel said, "only—I will not see my brother. If he were dying I should say the same, and believe me he is very far from dying."

"It appals me to hear you speak so," Max said, "it's—it's terrible—unbelievable!"

Angela rose, slipped her hand in his arm and led him towards the door. "Come," she said, "let us go and see him, shall we, Max? Will you be here when we get back, Emmanuel?"

"No," he said, speaking roughly to her for the first time in his life. "I'm going back to work. I've done nothing all this week, and tomorrow I want to get away."

Max turned sharply. "Away," he said, "with your brother so ill? With your mother and me in Milan? Where are you going?"

With a sudden return of ease which gave a certain insolence to his reply, Emmanuel said, "To Menaggio—to my wife."

"Couldn't Juliet come to Milan?" Angela asked gently.

"No—Juliet cannot come to Milan!" Emmanuel blazed. "Juliet will come to Milan when Julian Gollantz is out of it! She shan't breathe the same air, she shan't walk the same streets where he has walked! God knows what he will tell you—oh, listen to him, I beg of you! Whatever Julian says has always been worth hearing, and I don't suppose that his tongue has lost its cunning! Let him tell you what story he likes, only—and please remember this—that if he dares to say one word against my wife I'll kill him, brother or no brother, cripple or no cripple."

Max said, speaking very steadily: "Emmanuel, I'm ashamed of you."

"Not for the first time!" Emmanuel retorted, beside himself with passion. "For the first time in my life I realize that there is a sense of Justice." He looked at Angela, who stood silent, white-faced and weary after her long journey, and his heart softened. "I beg your pardon, darling," he said. "I ought to have been less frank. I ought to have pretended—only I have always tried to be honest with you both. I'll come in this evening, unless you care to come to the galleries after you leave the clinic."

378

8

THEY drove in silence to the clinic, and Max did not speak until they entered the room where Julian lay. He looked very beautiful, his white face and fair hair giving him the appearance of spirituality which he had lacked before his illness. He lay perfectly flat, his hands folded outside the sheet, his eyes cold, hard and defiant.

"My poor darling," Angela said, taking his hand in hers and stooping to kiss him. "My poor sweet. We've come to take you home."

Max stood beside the bed, his lips working convulsively, his eyes full of tears. The beauty of this young man—his own son, lying there, his career cut short, his life ruined—hurt Max unbearably.

Julian's voice was unmoved and steady. "Hello," he said. "It's very nice to see you. I'm sick of Italians who can only jabber their own language. It's boring, and Amanda weeps all the time she's here. As for Emmanuel—the one person who might be useful—he stays away. Amusing when I remember that I went round to his shop or whatever it is, with that old elephant Jaffe, to make things up with him! This is all the thanks I get—a smashed back!"

He stopped and looked from one to the other. "You heard how it happened, of course?"

Angela said: "Don't talk about it, Julian. When we get back to England—you never know—or German surgeons—perhaps these men aren't the very best."

"But I want to talk about it," he persisted obstinately. "Hasn't my archangel of a brother told you anything?"

"That you slipped and that a marble column fell on you," Max said. "That's enough, Julian, don't distress yourself."

He moved his head impatiently, then said: "Have you got a decent cigarette? These Italian things are frightful. Oh, that's good!'—as Max held out his case. "Thank God for a decent smoke!" He drew a long breath and sent a cloud of smoke down his finely cut nostrils with evident enjoyment. "It doesn't distress me, it almost amuses me. Emmanuel keeps a little pet poof there—no, no. I'm imputing nothing wrong, only wait until you see the little worm. In England he wouldn't be tolerated for a second among decent people! He's the most obvious specimen of— well, let it go at that. I went there all full of brotherly love, anxious to kiss and be friends. While Emmanuel is approached—there's no word for it—by this old grampus, Jaffe, I am left with this pretty boy. It's evident that he is horribly jealous of Juliet Forbes—does this disgust you, mother darling? It's only amusing—but you

380

might give Emmanuel a hint. Pity for me to have a broken back for nothing, eh? He told me that they had only been married in January, towards the end, he said. That she was going to have a baby immediately and a good deal more. I—stupid of me—lost my temper, said that Emmanuel appeared to be very happy, that she was charming and very rich, and that if the things which he had been saying were typical of Milan gossip, I only trusted that my brother would never hear them. That infuriated this little brute, who made a rush for me. I stepped back, tripped —and that was the Death of Poor Cock Robin! It's an amusing story, only the sequel is a little tragic for me! Well, when are you going to take me home? I long to get back among you all—Ordingly, the gardens, the big trees—everything."

Angela leant forward. "Julian," she said gravely, "tell me, on your word, is that story true?"

"On my word! Why on earth should I make it up?" His face showed nothing but astonishment at her question.

"But Emmanuel wasn't to blame, was he?" she urged.

"Only for making friends with such people," Max said.

Julian laughed. "Or for allowing them to get unbearably jealous. It's his fatal charm, I suppose. Emmanuel does like queer people—I always thought Louis Lara a rum card, didn't you, father?"

Max turned away and walked over to the window. He stood there looking down over the roofs. His old feeling of antagonism against Emmanuel bubbled and seethed. He had always tried to be fair and even in the face of what he regarded as Emmanuel's brutal treatment of his brother; he was going to make an effort to be fair now. He turned and walked back to the bedside, and stood, his arms folded, his fine, rather care-worn face serious and perplexed.

"Look here, Julian," he said, "whether you mean it or not, you're making implications against your brother and I can't allow it. Oh, I'll admit that you have reason to be bitter, every reason—except that bitterness never did anyone any good—but you mustn't say things which are damaging to Emmanuel without good and solid proof. It's very hard that you went there to make friends, that you should have met this objectionable youth, but it must end there."

For the fraction of a second Julian's blue eyes blazed hate at his father, then the hate died and he lay there looking at Max surprised and hurt.

"I'm sorry," Julian said, "I was only trying to be amusing. I impute nothing, never intended to. It's just a little hard to be taken wrongly, like this—especially today."

Max said gravely: "I beg your pardon if I was mistaken."

Julian sighed: "I believe I'm tired, that's why I'm getting touchy," and gave a little rather pathetic laugh. "Perhaps I'd better try to rest. You'll come in tomorrow, won't you? There'll be a lot to arrange. The Chiltern Hundreds, my affairs, because I shan't be able to do much writing for a bit at any rate, and that's most of my income gone! Julian Gollantz, MP, is one thing, but Julian Gollantz—nothing—won't be such a catch for the papers. Money—my God, where it's going to come from, heaven only knows! Old Van der Hoyt's a good old fellow, but he can't do—"

Angela laid her finger-tips on his lips. "Hush," she said. "You're not to worry. Max will see to everything. You've never found him ungenerous, have you? Ordingly will take you and Amanda and little Max—there's the suite on the first floor; it looks over the park. That big room with the two windows will make a lovely study for you, won't it?"

"Ordingly," Julian said softly, "how heavenly! I might have that big room that was my grandfather's, eh? I'd like that best, I think." Watching her as he spoke, Julian saw a quick movement of her lips, as if she closed them to prevent herself answering him. He decided then that the only room he wanted at Ordingly was the great room where old Emmanuel had held his salon. It was beautiful, spacious and dignified. Yes, that would do for him very well. "Of course," he added quickly, "I shall be only too grateful for whatever rooms you can spare me—you're both very good to me."

As they drove round to the galleries, Angela leant back and closed her eyes, her hand sought Max's and he held it tightly. Once she said, her eyes still closed: "Oh, Max, how horrible for him, my poor Julian! It's too terrible. We must be very good to him, my darling."

Max said: "Trust me. I'll see that he has all he can possibly want. You do trust me, don't you?"

She opened her eyes and smiled at him. "I've trusted you in everything for over thirty years— ever since I first knew you, Max."

"You make me very proud," he said.

Guido, wearing a tussore silk suit with a lavender silk shirt, met them. He was nervous and excited, his English became rather more eccentric than usual.

"Milord and milady Gollantz," he said. "This is the top notch of our honouredness to have you veesit us. For the present Emmanuel is engaged in the little gallery with a very old and plain trout, but the Padrone—Signor Jaffe—awaits you in the office. My name is Guido, I am the friend of Emmanuel."

Max glanced at him coldly. "Will you tell Mr. Jaffe that we are here, please?"

Guido smiled brilliantly. "I fly on wings," he said.

Max turned to Angela as his small, neat figure

384

departed down the gallery. "I admit that I share Julian's dislike," he said.

Jaffe, wearing a linen suit, which his bulk and weight had crumpled to such an extent that it looked as if he had slept in it, advanced swinging a great purple handkerchief in his hand with which he mopped his head from time to time.

"Der heat," he said, "is tremendous! I take a leetle trip to hell to find coolness, I t'ink. How is der poor poy? Lest night I saw him, und he seem not too bed. He don't like me very mooch. Perhaps I am too fet, perhaps I blow too loudly. Vill you sit here? It is cooler den der office und I vould like to spik mit you." He turned to the waiting Guido: "Leetle poy, is it possible dot you make tea und bring it here? Proper tea, not Italian?"

Guido slid forward, his face ecstatic. "Indeed I can. Who has instructed me but Emmanuel, who makes the best tea in the world!"

Jaffe grinned. "Is there anything dot he do vot ain't der pest in der vorld? You und Emmanuel, you leetle fool!"

Jaffe leant back, his hands folded on his stomach, his purple handkerchief hanging down almost to the floor between his fat fingers.

"Dot leetle poy," he said, "iss full of loff und gretitude to your son. Emmanuel found him a leetle gigolo, but he vill leaf him a leetle goot poy. Now, Mex, Enchela, listen, ef you please, for I vish to speak privately. For dis eccident not von person vas to plame, only your son Julian. No, do not interrupt me. I hev forced Guido to speak mit me, und—let us be very kind—say dot your son was foolish und not very sympathetic. Ve will leaf it ut that. Now, vot is more important, der qvestion off Emmanuel."

Max said: "But surely there is no question concerning him?"

"At der moment, none," Simeon Jaffe agreed, "but alvays I look vorvarts to der future, und t'en t'ere may be. Emmanuel is vot der first Emmanuel vos, mit somet'ing gained und somet'ing lecking. Der first Emmanuel was romantic und at der same time loffed pisiness. Emmanuel is all romanticism—vot a vord!—and only ven his surroundings is romantic does he loff pisiness. Here, he hes a peautiful vife, und a very dear vife, und soon vill hev a very nice papy, I t'ink. She is vot he hes vantet for all his life—ondly he didn't know it. Now I beg, mit all der earnestness of vich I am capable, leaf him here."

He spoke impressively, his great pale face with its heavy folds of flesh flushed for the moment over the cheekbones with the intensity of his feelings. His big hands trembled a little, and he pursed his mouth as if he was going to whistle, emitting only a long deep breath.

Angela watched him, and saw under the mass of flesh something which reminded her vividly of old Emmanuel. Jaffe might be bulky, he might dress eccentrically, he might even be slightly offensive to the eye and ear, but there remained a great dignity, the heritage of a line of ancestors who had reached the highest pinnacle of their chosen profession, who had made themselves more than mere art dealers and who had left their impress upon the minds of the people with whom they had come in contact.

"You mean that he ought to stay here always," she said; "you mean that he ought to be left in Italy, away from his own people?"

"I mean dot v'ere he is now, dere is his own peoples."

He paused, turned his huge body to watch Guido approaching with a tea-tray, and waited until it was set before Angela. Guido stood in an attitude of respectful attention until she had poured out the first cup. It was black, and a number of tea-leaves floated on the top of the liquid.

"Is it pleasing to you?" he asked.

Angela met his eyes, and the anxiety in them touched her. He might be all that Julian had said, but at that moment her heart went out to him because of his gentle solicitude.

"It is quite perfect, thank you."

Jaffe said: "Run away, Guido. I am verry pisy. Tell Emmanuel dot his fadder und mudder is here. Now"—he turned again to Max—"tell me vot is peoples? Vot is dis country or dat? My country is v'ere I am happiest. I do not t'ink dot Emmanuel vas verry happy in England—for many reasons vot don't metter now. He is von of dose stoopid peoples who vill alvays make sacrifices. I beg you neffer let him again." He stopped, then added with astonishing intensity: "Der Gott of my Fadders knows dot he hes made more t'an enough!"

Max took his cup of tea from Angela, glanced at the dark liquid and set the cup down untouched. His tall figure was rigid, his lips set, and his whole bearing argued lack of sympathy with all that Jaffe had said.

"It would appear," he said, "that Emmanuel has obtained all the pity for himself, and left none for his unfortunate brother. Has Emmanuel been whining to you, then? Telling you his fears, apprehensions?"

"Max, my dear—" Angela said softly.

Jaffe's face took on a deeper tinge. "Vhine— he don't vhine!" he retorted. "Don't I hev eyes, ears, please? I know vot is vot."

"And you are asking me," Max went on, "to make no appeal to my eldest son, you are telling me that I have no right to ask him to make sacrifices for his brother, for his family, possibly for his mother, should anything happen to me. In short, you want me to allow him to live an utterly selfish, self-centred life in Italy even though the business which his grandfather and I have built up needs him very badly. Is that the upshot of all you have said, Cousin Simeon?"

Simeon Jaffe spread his hands wide, leant back

in his big chair and puffed out his massive cheeks, then said, speaking very slowly and with tremendous weight: "Listen—vot is femilies? Yes, und I em a Jew! Vot is pisinesses? Yes, und I em a Jew! Are ve gods—knowing good and efil—dot ken demand sacrifices from one for annuder? I tell you dot you are like der fadder in dot very cleffer parable—oh yes, I hev read all of t'em— who vas der most stoopid men dot effer vas. Vot hes your odder son effer done for you?—not'ing. But now he come home mit a beck vot is hurt, und you vill contemplate to make der goot poy, der hard-vorking son, vait on him, vork for him, giff up his life for him. You haff not done it, but I know you und I know dot you vill. More I know dot dis Emmanuel vill kom—and somet'ing in him vill die! I hev said all d'ere is to say. I hev done. I em an old man und I am tired."

He heaved himself to his feet, and said in an entirely different tone: "Enchela, my tear, vill you kom and see some of der pretty t'ings vich Emmanuel and I hev bought?"

He held out his hand to her, and she was about to take it when Max interrupted. "No," he said, "don't go yet. I want this explained to me; at the moment—"

Jaffe smiled a wide, fleshy smile. "At der moment," he said, "I vant to show a lady some pretty t'ings, if you please."

Max shrugged his shoulders. "Very well."

That night Emmanuel dined with his father

389

and mother. The dinner was difficult, for Max
scarcely spoke, and even Angela's efforts to make
conversation were not markedly successful. At
the end of dinner Max rose and stood by the long
open window, facing his son.

"Are you still determined to leave Milan
tomorrow?"

Emmanuel said: "Quite determined. I can't
disappoint my wife."

"But surely she knows the facts of the case,
knows that your brother is ill, that we need you?"

"She knows nothing—and"—slowly—"she is
not going to know."

Max made a little stiff bow. "Very well," he
said; "that, I suppose, settles the matter. I am
going to write some letters—will you excuse me?
Don't wait if you want to go, Emmanuel, I may
be some time. Good night."

The door closed behind him, and Angela
turned to her son.

"Aren't you a little cruel?"

"Hasn't he been more than a little cruel?"

"Isn't he paying for it now?"

"Paying!" Emmanuel echoed. "Paying who?
Paying what? Not, assuredly, paying me! I don't
want him to pay anything, I want him to let me
alone. I've got my work, my home, my wife. I
want nothing else, no one else"; then a little smile
touched his lips, "except you, darling. Listen to
me for a moment. All my life Julian has tried to
hurt me. Even back in the old days when I first

390

wanted to marry Viva. He tried to turn my father against me—and succeeded. He tried to ruin everything for me when I first met Juliet again in London. Now he comes and tries to speak ill of her to a boy who is my friend. Isn't that a sufficient indictment? And," he laughed, "God only knows what he tried to tell you about Guido, but whatever it was, I can assure you that it wasn't true. Oh, I know my dear brother! Now he's ill, a cripple, and I'm afraid of what he may be able to do. Make no mistake, Julian won't suffer. Julian will be very happy, very luxurious, very much admired for his courage—and he'll use, use, use everyone who comes in contact with him. You, Max, Amanda, Bill—even me, if he can."

Angela shivered. "I hate to hear you talk like this! It's so unlike you—as I know you, Emmanuel."

"Is it?" he asked, rather wistfully. "Or is it that for the first time in my life I am trying to make a bid for being happy? Until now I've been what you and Max and Viva wanted me to be— yes, even you, my dear. You liked me to be gentle, hard-working, ready to shoulder things for other people, and I was all those things to please you, because I wanted to stand well in your eyes. Max wanted me to be a good man of business, knowledgeable, to cultivate a flair, to understand wood and paint and the cost of every-thing. Very well. I wanted to stand well in his eyes and I became those things. Then Viva, who liked me to be rather out of date, a penny plain tuppence coloured imitation of the first Emmanuel Gollantz. Something of a figure—heaven help me!—in London society. I did all those things until Juliet came back, and I knew what a sham I'd been for years."

He came a little nearer to where Angela sat, and pulled up a chair beside hers; his voice dropped, and he sat with his hands clasped loosely before him as if he spoke rather to himself than to her.

"Juliet is a very real person, you know. She's so real that at times it's—almost painful. She loves me very dearly, very tenderly, and she thinks—she thinks—that she loves me with her whole heart. It's a very large, splendid heart too, my Juliet's. She doesn't really. Leon Hast still has a great deal of it, and there are times when she would—very nearly—like me to speak as he used to, when she would welcome some of his caustic comments and his sarcasm. I think"—he paused and drew a deep breath, "—I think that when Juliet dies, if she should die before me, her regret at leaving me will be softened by her pleasure at possibly finding him again. Oh, I don't mind. I love her, love her unbearably, and I love her for what she is; and, after all, Leon Hast helped to make her what she is now. I used to hate him, I used to suffer agonies of jealousy, I used to resent the fact that through him Juliet was a very rich woman. I don't mind now. That's all an accident, and she is all that matters. Oh, my lovely, lovely Juliet!"

Angela said, very softly. "You're very happy?"

He turned and smiled at her—a smile so confident, so lacking in reservation, that he became once again the son she knew. His bitterness had gone, the hard lines round his lips vanished, and he seemed to have thrown off years.

"Happy!" he said. "Happy! I've been away from her for five days, I've spoken to her every evening over the telephone, I've written to her every morning, and now, because I shall see her again tomorrow, I feel like a schoolboy after a long, dreary winter term when he remembers that he goes home in twenty-four hours!"

"And out of all that happiness," Angela said, "you have nothing but hate left for poor bankrupt Julian!"

Emmanuel threw back his head and laughed. "Bankrupt!" he said. "My angel, never! I have sunk all my capital in my life with Juliet. Max—in you. Bill—I don't quite know, his ability to work and work well at his job. But Julian has never put all his eggs in one basket, and he'll find consolations in plenty. He'll build up a Julian who will be the admiration of everyone with whom he comes in contact. He'll be the beau ideal of what a gallant cripple ought to be. He'll be gay, wistful, a little sad, intellectual, and slightly cynical by turns. Don't be hurt with me, Angela. I'm only speaking what I know is the truth. Take him home, then I can bring Juliet back to Milano. Give him everything, give him Ordingly itself if you wish, spend all the money in Gollantz and Son on him, but—don't ask me to meet him, because I have nothing to say to him, now or at any time."

9

JULIET said: "I wish you'd go out, darling. Take the car, take Simeon or Guido and stay out until it's all over. You mind so much more than I do, you know."

Emmanuel stopped his pacing up and down the long room and stood, his forehead puckered into a frown, beside her.

"You beloved fool," he said. "You don't know what you're talking about. I wish I was a Catholic, it must be very comforting to believe that all the Company of Heaven take a keen and personal interest in one's affairs, mustn't it?"

"How do you know that they don't?"

"I don't—I only don't know with any certainty that they do." He resumed his restless pacing, only ceasing for a moment when Juliet moved in her chair by the big stone mantelpiece. Then he stopped abruptly, looking at her with an almost painful intensity as if he tried to gauge the extent of her pain.

Juliet looked at the clock. Three in the afternoon. She must give him something to do, something to occupy him and prevent him tearing his nerves to pieces.

"Emmanuel—"

He was at her side in an instant. "Yes—what is it? You're not worse?"

"My dear, no—I'm wonderful, only I do want some tea! Don't let Maria make it. She makes it abominably. You make it—and wouldn't some toast be nice?"

The sudden relief on his face was pathetic. He was glad to have something to do, something to distract his mind.

"Yes, yes," he said eagerly; "I'll make it, and real buttery toast! You'll like that?"

"Love it!"

Juliet watched the heavy door close behind him, and lay back in her big chair a little exhausted. It was an effort to hide everything from him; impossible not to make an effort to do so when the slightest exclamation from her made Emmanuel's face turn white. As she lay back, her eyes closed, she wondered what Leon would have done, said, how Leon would have behaved. Somehow she couldn't see Leon rushing away to make tea and buttery toast. It didn't fit in.

She supposed that at the moment she was more than usually susceptible to her thoughts, perhaps having a child made one less mistress of oneself —only now her thoughts seemed to be beyond her control, and again and again turned to Leon Hast. If Leon had been here—if this had been Leon's child—if Leon had not died. She loved Emmanuel, and every day found new reasons for that love, but now she wondered how much of it was intense maternity. He was so young, so pathetically in love with her; she was all he had, and she knew it. Her life with Leon had never been peaceful, she had never had so much and such intense love showered upon her. She was Emmanuel's life—she had only been one of the interests in Leon's. He had loved so many things: his pictures, his china, his old furniture. He had loved beauty, colour, knowledge. He had loved her—among other things. Not, she had always felt, among other women. Even Morrie Wilmot —Morrie Gollantz she had been afterwards—had not really mattered to him. She moved restlessly, shutting her lips tightly, waiting for the pain to pass. The pain came between her and her thoughts. Leon had hated pain, that was why he had pretended to laugh at it. Romance he had sneered at, classing it as nothing more than senti-mentality dressed in a swinging cloak and wearing a dagger on its hip! If Leon could come in now, she wondered what he would do. Come to her, stoop down, and kiss her lightly, glance unwill-ingly at her figure, perhaps not even trying to hide a little grimace.

"My lovely Juliet, what have they done to you?"

He would have moved away, stood with one arm along the high shelf of the mantelpiece, one foot on the wide steel fender-rail. He would have talked of ivories he had bought, of some picture he had sold because he had decided that it was not really the best of its school. "I only want the best, in everything." That was what he had always boasted. "The second-rate never appeals to me." And then perhaps immediately, with a queer, cruel little twist of his eyebrows: "Oh, that reminds me, how is your voice?"

Perhaps after all these years she might have gained sufficient courage to answer him: "Still the best of its kind in Europe—some people say in the world." That would please him. He would throw back his head and laugh softly. "Not perhaps so typical of my lovely Juliet, but very clever!" She could hear it all—when the pain didn't disturb her thoughts. She resented it. She wanted to sit and listen to Leon, no matter what he said.

It was over, she could hear him again.

"This—this infant—won't hurt your voice?"

"It might even improve it."

"You have just told me that it was the best in the world! And it—won't spoil your loveliness, lovely Juliet?"

"No, my dear." She would dare to say "my dear" because his voice had sounded almost tender as he spoke.

"I couldn't bear that. I think"—she remembered how his words used to come very slowly when he was being kind—"that—I almost resent —this—infant."

She caught her breath, for a sob had risen, and she realized that her eyes were wet. A terrible sense of loneliness swept over her; she wanted Leon, no one but Leon, with his bitter tongue, his adorable lovemaking, his cynicism, and his tremendous certainty.

"Leon," she whispered, "don't go—stay with me. I could be so brave if you were here."

She sat upright and, with a sudden almost convulsive movement, switched on the light at her side. She was light-headed, she was allowing herself to be fanciful, to imagine things. She had Emmanuel, her perfect husband, her devoted lover, she wanted no one else—ever. . . . Her hand flew to her mouth, and her teeth were pressed into the flesh. It was unbearable. Her back ached—she wanted nothing, no one, except to lie down and press the palms of her hands against her back to stop the aching. She fumbled for the bell, rang it, and when the servant entered said that she would have the tea which Signor Gollantz was preparing in her room.

Impassive except for the widening of his eyes, the man said:

"Si, signora, si."

The nurse, trained in an English clinic in Rome, was kind but impersonal.

"Yes, go to bed if you like, Mrs. Gollantz—there's no need to unless you really want to."

"I do—I'm tired."

Wonderful to lie down, to feel the pillows very soft and cool beneath her head. The room very quiet, the sun shut out and only the whirr of an

399

electric fan to break the stillness. She felt that if she lay quite still, if the pain did not interrupt her, Leon might come back. She imagined him entering the room, closing the door very softly, and walking over to where she lay with that silent, almost catlike tread. A new Leon, very tender and solicitous, whose voice was almost a caress. Not only watching her, not only asking how she felt, if there was anything he could do, but talking of other things, amusingly, lightly, with sudden blazes of colour in his words.

". . . A Book of Hours, which has been lying tucked away in some worm-eaten chest for years. Illuminated with bits of bluest sky, with gold which can only have been found in some sunbeam without any motes in it!—I shan't read it, neither will you, but you shall look at it, and press your fingers on the smooth gold. For sheer sensual pleasure there is nothing to equal the sensation of touching gold, unless—perhaps your arm, Juliet, just inside the elbow. . . ."

Or, "Lane is in treaty for it. I must have it. The owner? An impoverished and very aristocratic lady. No, I can't go and buy it myself, Lane must go. He's used to unpleasant things, and elderly, impoverished, and highly aristocratic ladies always smell so stuffy! You're not highly aristocratic, Juliet, are you? You're certainly not elderly, and I'll take good care that you are never impoverished, so you will never have the slightest excuse for smelling stuffy!"

She lay with her eyes closed, because she could see and hear Leon better that way. His voice came very clearly, and once she thought that she felt his cool, firm lips brush her forehead, smelt the faint odour of eau-de-Cologne which hung about him, so faint as to be negligible, except to her. To her, eau-de-Cologne always meant Leon. She hadn't used it, hadn't had any near her for years, because it made recollections too vivid— too painful.

The nurse's voice interrupted her thoughts, and a wave of hot resentment swept over her. How dared she! Leon hated interruptions. She could hear his sudden nervous whisper: "Damn the woman! I wanted to tell you . . ."

"That last song . . . the new one . . . it's not good enough. . . . It's . . . it's pretty. I won't have you singing pretty stuff . . . it's not worthy of you. They don't like Bach and Brahms! Then they must learn to like them. I won't have your talent butchered to make a British public enjoy itself in a welter of sentiment. Next time . . . I must go through your programme carefully. . . . Gilbert has no real taste, and yours"—she heard his little half-suppressed laugh—"is deplorable. You've got a great deal to learn, lovely Juliet. Never mind, it's fortunate that I can teach you—"

"Mr. Gollantz has brought the tea you wanted. Do you think you'd like a cup?"

She opened her eyes, conscious that she felt

401

resentful. These interruptions were unbearable! Emmanuel stood by the bed, with a tray in his hands, his eyes anxious and very tender. Dear Emmanuel—she smiled. Leon would never have made tea and toast for her. Leon would have abducted the finest cook in Milan, paid him a salary like a Prime Minister's, and ordered him to make it his masterpiece!

"It's really—buttery," Emmanuel said, and smiled down at her.

She sat up, the pain in her back was better— or wasn't it? She didn't know, she wanted them all to go away and leave her with Leon. But she couldn't hurt Emmanuel, because she loved him so much.

"Kind Emmanuel," she said, "it looks lovely and smells too wonderful. How clever of you! Yes, pour it out for me."

He set down the tray and poured out the tea with grave concentration, frowning a little because he wanted to get it just as she liked it. Milk—for she hated cream—no sugar, and the tea only coming up to the little orange-and-gold rim near the top of the cup. Months ago she had said, said only once, that she hated cups full to the brim. But Emmanuel had remembered.

"There!" He handed her the cup.

"And you too," Juliet said. "You've got to help to eat the toast as well."

He nodded, and said: "You know, I believe

you're better. You look better, really. That's good, isn't it?"

"I'm a very fine healthy woman," she told him, "and everything is going to be terribly easy, and you're not to worry. Oh, this tea is good—lend me your handkerchief, the butter is running down my chin. You're extravagant with butter, my lamb, aren't you?"

His hands were very deft, large, with long fingers, and well-kept nails. She watched them with a sense of satisfaction. Emmanuel was so very pleasant to look at. People said that Julian was the best-looking of the three, but she'd never thought so. Emmanuel had a most satisfactory line which ran from his ear to his chin. His nose was well formed, just a little melancholy, with beautiful nostrils, very sensitive. His mouth was tender, but the lips were firm and sufficiently full to be generous.

"Oh, my dear," Juliet whispered, "I do love you!"

She watched his lips part in a smile. "Bless you," he said softly. "Get well again quickly. I can't bear the thought of your being ill. Never, never again!"

"Only children aren't the most satisfactory," she teased him.

"He'll have you and me—we shall have to suffice."

"You've quite decided that he is to be a him!"

"I don't care. My dear, is it bad?"

She said: "Take this cup! Oh, my God . . ." She caught the corner of his coat and twisted it in her hands because it was firm and felt strong. Things, sounds, took on new aspects. The nurse's voice wasn't loud, it was cold. ". . . Better go, Mr. Gollantz." Emmanuel's voice was warm, and it moved up and down. It was his "little boy" voice again. "Oh . . . must I? I mean, would you like me to stay, Juliet?"

"No," she said, very roughly and far more loudly than she intended. "For God's sake go away—now—quickly!"

"Yes . . . yes . . . I will—yes. . . ." His voice faded away. She decided that his voice was blue, nurse's was pale green, her own was deep yellow, Leon's was—how much longer was Emmanuel going to stand there saying "Yes, yes, yes"?

He picked up the tray and tiptoed out of the room, closing the door very quietly behind him.

He went back to the long room, still holding the tray, and set it down by the fire. It was too hot for a fire really, but Juliet had said that she felt chilly, in spite of the heat. It was a very small fire, nothing more than a few twigs and a couple of handfuls of pine-cones—she liked the smell of them. A telephone rang in the hall; the nurse's voice speaking in Italian reached him. Silence. He sat down and tried to read a book. Flung it down and said in a loud, distinct voice what he thought of it; used a very vulgar, schoolboy word, and wondered what on earth made him say it just

404

then. He saw something white lying on the floor, stooped and found that it was Juliet's handkerchief twisted into a little rope. Very carefully he smoothed it out, folded it, and put it in his pocket.

Mario came and asked if he would like dinner there.

Emmanuel said: "Dinner! It's only five o'clock."

Mario smiled, "It is almost eight o'clock, signor."

"I don't want any dinner. I'll have"—his voice was shaking, and he tried to steady it "—I'll have a whisky-and-soda and a dry biscuit. Why hasn't the doctor come?"

"He is here for more than an hour, signor."

"I see."

It seemed that Mario was away for hours, then came back bringing not only biscuits, but pâté and fruit and some caviar. He put it on a little table and pushed it nearer to Emmanuel. Guido came in, and said that he felt certain that everything was going wonderfully. Emmanuel told him not to be a fool, and what the devil did he know about it, anyway! Guido looked meek, and said: "How right you are! What, indeed, could I know? Nothing at all."

Emmanuel tried to pour out some whisky and spilt it all over the carpet. Guido took the bottle from him, and said that he applauded such sensitiveness, it was commendable, worthy, and a

405

great many more dignified attributes. He then chattered about what had happened at the galleries during the day, and what Jaffe had said and what he had answered. Emmanuel didn't listen, but he liked the sound of Guido's voice, it was companionable. Guido asked him to eat something.

"It would choke me! I don't want anything."

Guido with great care spread a biscuit with pâté, and nibbled it.

"You are right to have none," he said, with his mouth full; "this pâté is stinkingly horrible. it must be very old—like the trouts."

"Rubbish, it's fresh! I got it myself yesterday for Juliet."

Guido shrugged his shoulders. "Neverthemore, it is bad."

Emmanuel spread a biscuit, crammed it into his mouth, and said:

"You're cracked, it's damned good!"

"I am a very fine actor," Guido giggled. "Please to eat another."

The room was growing dark. Emmanuel got up and walked restlessly up and down; once he went to the door and opened it, standing there listening. The door of Juliet's room opened and the doctor came out. He was half English, and Emmanuel thought that he looked wholly Italian. He shut the door very quickly behind him.

"Is—is it—over?" Emmanuel said, and wished that he didn't stammer so.

"No—over! No! Going on very nicely. Could I have a drink, d'you think? Perhaps a bite to eat?"

He sipped a glass of soda-water, and ate a surprising number of biscuits spread with caviar, while Emmanuel tried to regain control of his voice in order to ask questions. Guido said, with slightly overdone dignity: "Is Missus Emmanuel Gollantz very all right, if you please, signor dottor?"

The doctor nodded, his mouth full, and mumbled: "Ye' . . . very well."

"Could I—I mean would it be possible for me to speak to her?" Emmanuel asked.

"Better not—probably distress her and do you no good. I'll get back. Nothing to worry about."

They sat silent after he left them; even Guido's brave attempt at cheerfulness had died, and Emmanuel sat huddled in the big chair, his fingers twitching, his eyes staring at the dead ashes in the grate. Once he looked up, and saw that Guido had fallen asleep, his head nodded uncomfortably, his mouth was a little open. Emmanuel shivered. The room felt very cold. Far away a clock struck one.

He remembered that people said there was a sudden chill when anyone died. He wiped the sweat from his forehead and wondered if it really was a help if one prayed. He couldn't think of any prayers which seemed suitable. Anyway, if Juliet was dead, it was too late to pray now. If

Juliet was dead he would kill himself. Guido moved, almost fell off his chair, opened his eyes, and said, "What time is it?"

"Half past one—my God, this is horrible, Guido!"

Guido said: "Very much horrible. Courage!" and fell asleep again.

Emmanuel decided that he hated Guido, and that he would tell him so when he woke again. He got up, opened the door and stood there, his nerves quivering with apprehension, sniffing a scent which seemed sinister and dreadful. Then he heard a cat mewing, and looked round, snapping his fingers and whispering gently, "Puss—puss," but, remembering that of course it would be an Italian cat, he changed it to, "Gatto—gatto—" But the animal did not appear, and in a moment the mewing ceased. He leant against the door-post feeling exhausted and sick, his eyes closed, his body shaking. He wanted to rush across the landing, fling open the door, and see for himself that Juliet was safe. The cat mewed again, and, listening intently, Emmanuel realized that the sound came from Juliet's room. His anger flared suddenly. How dare they let a cat be in there! A nice thing! He was shut out, but the damned cat might walk in and kick up that horrible row when it liked; it was . . . His whole body stiffened, for the door opened and the doctor, blinking and red-eyed, came out.

"Hello," he said; "that's over. He's a nice little

fellow, with a marvellous pair of lungs. Did you hear him?"

Emmanuel shook his head. "No—I mean—is Juliet—you know—"

"Very well, splendid. Plucky wife you've got!"

"Could I see her—now?"

"In ten minutes. Come back and have a drink, you look as if you need it."

He felt light-headed, as he had felt once after having gas at a dentist's. He sipped his whisky and thought it tasted more horrible than anything he had ever drunk. He kept looking at his watch to see when the ten minutes was up. The doctor chattered, and Guido woke up and said: "It is over? I have prayed to every saint in the calendar."

"You!" Emmanuel said. "You slept. Not even the yowling cat woke you. How did it get into my wife's r-room, Doctor?"

"Cat? I heard no cat. In her room? Good God, man, that wasn't a cat, that was your son and heir making himself heard! That's funny! And then they talk about parental instinct! I'll go and see if you can go in for a minute, then I'm off home. It's half past two."

When Emmanuel walked into Juliet's room a moment later, his legs felt boneless and his breath kept catching in his throat. He felt that he had been separated from her for years—years during which he had grown very old and terribly tired.

He stood beside the bed and whispered hoarsely, "Oh, my beautiful Juliet . . ." then bent and kissed the hand which lay on the sheet.

"And you thought he was a cat," she said softly. "Oh, how could you? He's here. Don't you want to see him?"

"Tonight—this morning—I can only see you," he said. "Tomorr-row I may be able to r-realize that he is important. Now—there is only you in all the world. Good morning, beloved; sleep quietly." Then, as he stooped again and kissed her, he whispered: "And the God of my fathers have you in His keeping, now and always."

Book Four

1

EMMANUEL waggled his finger at the baby and tried to believe that the baby responded. He certainly smiled; but before, when in his ignorance he had exclaimed, "Look, he's laughing his head off!" the nurse had replied, "I'm afraid that's only a touch of wind, Mr. Gollantz." How on earth did they know when it stopped being wind and really became amusement?

Juliet stood with her hand on his shoulder looking down at the baby. "Emmanuel Simeon really is rather a delightful person," she said. "I like him more every day! Six months old, and never a moment's worry."

"Why should he worry anyone?" Emmanuel said. "He's well, he's happy—like his father and mother. If everyone was happy, I believe the doctors could all shut up shop."

"I wonder when he grows up," Juliet said reflectively, "if he'll pronounce worry with ten r's in it, like you do. I rather hope that he will."

"Will you hate leaving him dreadfully?" Emmanuel said.

"I shan't like it any more than I shall like leaving you. But it's time I made a start again. People soon forget. I don't want to be forgotten."

It never occurred to Emmanuel to try to persuade her to give up her work and stay at home with the youngest Emmanuel. He had come to regard her work as part of her life, as something which was necessary to her; and his sense of justice prevented his ever attempting to keep her at home. Juliet without her work would have seemed to him a Juliet lacking some integral part. In addition, though his work increased month by month, though his prospects were good, he was not in a position to maintain Juliet as he felt she had a right to be maintained. Until he could provide for her those luxuries to which she had become accustomed, his sense of justice forbade him even to hint that he would have liked her to relinquish her work.

Not that the difference in their financial positions had made difficulties. True, at first Emmanuel had fretted and worried, but he had come to understand how little Juliet cared for money. She was content that he should work and work hard, but it did not affect her opinion of him whether he was able to pay for the apartment and its upkeep or not.

"Don't you see," she had said once, after Emmanuel had put his dissatisfaction into words, "that it doesn't matter whether you make a hundred lire or a thousand lire a week? I have enough for us both. It would matter horribly if you didn't work; it might even matter if you were content with a hundred lire a week, but you're not. The only thing that matters—really and truly—is that you honestly hope to earn more, and that the moment you earn sufficient, you will take everything out of my hands. You'll probably manage much better than I do!"

So when Gilbert began to suggest that she might work again and when Juliet seemed to want to do so, Emmanuel agreed, and felt that in doing so he was doing no more than she might reasonably expect of him. Only once he said rather wistfully: "It won't be America or Australia, will it? That would be so dreadfully long without you."

"I won't go to either America or Australia until you come with me," she said, and he was able to smile again.

He felt that since the birth of their son Juliet had changed in many ways. She was, he thought, more beautiful, and he fancied that there was a new depth, a new content, in her eyes. There was a serenity about her, a kind of conscious fulfilment, as if she had achieved that for which she had always longed. He believed, too, that, if it were possible, they had drawn closer to each other and the last link in the chain which held them together had been forged.

Gilbert declared that her voice was fuller, richer in colour, and possessed of greater flexibility; and old Jaffe, listening to her sing, said, "It iss ass

415

eff all der anchels in heaffen vaited mit der poor leetle songs to listen to yours!"

To Emmanuel she was still the great force in his life, the reason for everything he did, the one person who filled his world completely. He loved his little son, and would stare at him, trying to find some likeness to Juliet in his small, puckered face. That he should be like her, mentally and physically, seemed to Emmanuel the greatest good fortune that could befall him.

And Juliet, after that day when she had longed for Leon, when she had listened for his voice and believed that she felt his lips on her face, had never ached for him again. It was as if Leon Hast had slipped into his right place in her scheme of things. She would always love him, very often she would long for his help, his advice, and his comments on everything which affected her, but the desperate longing which had been almost physical pain had gone.

Emmanuel's tenderness towards her during her convalescence had touched her, and his invariable consideration for her wishes, his anxiety to do everything possible for her pleasure or comfort, had shown her how deep his love was. But it was not only these things which appealed to her, there was something deeper in Emmanuel's than mere love and tenderness. She had come to realize that there was a quiet strength in him, that he possessed a depth of character which she had scarcely suspected. Again and again she found

416

proofs that he possessed the same integrity, the same sense of justice and straight dealing, and that essential dislike of anything which was mean or second-rate which had made his grandfather such a great personality. Men liked him, women found him sympathetic, and Simeon Jaffe said frankly, "In my galleries I hev many t'ings, t'ings vich are assets, but der greatest asset is der keracter und der popularity of my partner, young Emmanuel."

So Juliet took up her work again, and Emmanuel was left alone in the big Milan apartment with his son and a highly efficient and very capable nurse to minister to the child's needs. Emmanuel did not admit even to himself how terrible the parting from Juliet had been. He had stood on the long platform in Milan station and watched the trans-continental express draw slowly out, under the vaulted roof, feeling that it carried his heart with it. He returned home, repeating that a month was no time at all, and that the joy of meeting Juliet again would atone for the pain of losing her. Meanwhile, four long weeks stretched their length before him and seemed like an eternity.

During the second week Bill Gollantz passed through Milan and stayed a couple of days with his brother. They had always been very attached to each other, though Emmanuel had never understood Bill particularly well, and had probably underestimated his capabilities—which were

417

of a type so entirely different from his own. Bill, on the other hand, admired Emmanuel whole-heartedly, and understood his sensitive temperament far better than Emmanuel ever guessed.

Bill had been in Tyrol for winter sports, and had only managed to return home through Milan by something of an effort. He was bronzed, very fit, and had broadened considerably. There was nothing of the Gollantz about Bill; he was pure Drew stock, with their fair skin, blue eyes, and rather stocky figure.

He was interested in the apartment, in the galleries, and in Emmanuel Simeon. He noticed everything, and decided that the antique trade must be a good deal better in Italy than it was in England. He was charmingly deferential to old Jaffe, he treated Guido delightfully and insisted on giving him luncheon at Savini's.

He bought a shagreen box for his mother, a seventeenth-century inkstand for his father, and a large piece of malachite for a paperweight for Charles Wilmot. It amused him that Emmanuel refused to allow him anything less than the price which he first quoted, but that after a few moments' consideration he said:

"Pay me. I'll buy them, you see, then I can take thirty-three and a third off for you."

Bill grinned. "Just as easy to give me thirty-three and a third off the price, isn't it?"

Emmanuel shook his head, saying: "It

418

wouldn't be business. You see, there is no valid reason why you should have any discount."

That evening when they sat together after what Bill decided had been a remarkably good dinner, Emmanuel began to speak about London.

"How are things—I mean, particularly with—us?"

"I gather that they're pretty rotten," Bill replied. "It's hard on Max. He's sixty, and that's a bad time for a chap to adjust himself to new conditions. You heard, of course, that old Van der Hoyt had lost everything in one of the Wall Street busts? That means that Julian, Amanda, and the little boy are entirely dependent on the Guv'nor. And, believe me, Julian is an expensive amusement."

Emmanuel's sensitive face changed; his lips took on a new and harder line, his eyes lost some of their kindliness. His voice when he spoke was very cold.

"I know nothing about Julian," he said.

Bill settled himself more comfortably in the big chair and pulled hard at his pipe. His cheerful face was very grave, and he spoke with deliberate temperance.

"You look like having to know a good deal about Julian in the future," he said. "Julian is making a great success of being an invalid. You see, he can walk—oh, let's be fair and admit that he walks slowly and can't walk very far, but he's got no pain; and old Meyer Bernstein told Max frankly that if Julian liked he could do a job of work with the next man, provided that it wasn't too strenuous. Believe me, Max almost threw Bernstein out of the place, and they've been friends for years!"

Emmanuel's mouth twisted suddenly. "Julian always made a success of everything he touched," he said grimly. "Go on, Bill."

"They took him to some big man in Germany, who suggested treatment. Apparently it was doing wonders—did wonders. He could walk, and there was even some talk about his going back into politics. One evening Charles spoke to Julian about it, after he got back home. Charles was dining there. Julian yawned in his face and said that he'd come to the conclusion that politics bored him. Mind you, I don't want to be too hard on the fellow. He'll never be able to—well—go hurdling, or swim or hunt. But, damn it, he never wanted to do any of those things, did he? He decided that the Stock Exchange was the only real interest in life. 'The only one which I have left,' he said one evening, with a sickening self-pitying smirk. That did it. He must be allowed to have his—interest. What he makes or loses I have no idea. I know that he lives rent free, free board and lodging for himself, Amanda, and the boy. Nice little boy, he is. Has old Emmanuel's big room for himself, and three others for himself and Amanda and a couple for the boy. She has a car, so has he. She belongs to every swell nightclub, he goes everywhere, leaning on a gold-headed cane. He walks slowly, looks thin, drinks a good bit more than is good for him, dresses magnificently, and pulls out the pathetic stop every time there's a row."

"Rows!" Emmanuel said. "That doesn't sound like Ordingly."

Bill shrugged his broad shoulders. "Now and then they crop up. Money, I fancy. Max hears about it all right when he loses any. Last thing was racing, if you please. He bought a couple of horses, and has 'em training down near Wantage. Had a winner the other day—not the other day, about four months ago. 'Chasing. Bought Max a new desk lamp and Angela a fur foot-muff for the car. Max didn't want the lamp, Angela had three foot-muffs already; but they were both frightfully touched about it! Believe me, Emmanuel, our celebrated tick of a brother is going to be a first-class old man of the sea to us all before he's finished."

Emmanuel rose, and held his hands towards the fire, rubbing them as if he suddenly felt the cold.

"Not to me," he said. "I have my place here and nothing is going to move me."

"No?" Bill frowned, then said: "I remember Viva once saying to me that we always stressed our Jewish blood and the 'here have we no abiding city' attitude. I remember saying that I wasn't sure. That every now and then something

421

cropped up that made one realize how definitely you and Julian, at least, were Jews. I should hate to think that he was typical, but I do believe that he's a type. One of the types that has made us hated and feared by other nations, and I don't blame 'em either! But you—you're different. You're all the best of the breed. You're a good chap, Emmanuel, and for God's sake don't let that very goodness betray you into doing something you'll regret all your life."

Emmanuel spoke loudly as if he wished Bill to hear very distinctly what he said.

"I tell you, Bill, I have my own place here. My wife and my son. My br-rother Julian means nothing, nothing, nothing to me and never will. He and you can divide Ordingly between you. I don't want it."

"By the time Comrade Julian's done, there may not be much of it to divide," Bill said cheerfully.

"You're not doing too badly, Bill?"

"Not too badly, but I might do a devil of a lot better. It's a slow game, though—the law. Even old Charles isn't exactly a millionaire. Oh, don't let me worry you, old man. I've no doubt that things will pan out right in the end, only at the moment both Max and Angela feel sentimental about Julian, and Julian knows it. It never seems to strike them that Julian might very well have remained a reasonably successful private Member all his days. They see him as a poor crippled bloke robbed by a cruel fate of his chance to be a P.M. And he encourages 'em too! So they entertain less; they do with one car between them —which is damned hard on 'em both!—they go abroad less, and so on. Oh, they don't suffer from poverty; any Socialist would tell you that they live very luxurious lives, but it's all a question of degree. They've been used to extreme comfort all their lives, and it's damned hard to have to cut down when Max is on the shady side of sixty and Angela isn't as young as she once was."

Emmanuel made his little gesture of refutation. "They have the son they admire and love," he said. "No doubt there is a gr-reat deal of satisfaction in that for them both."

But Bill's statement had shaken him, and when he was alone again his mind—that imaginative, sensitive mind of the Jew—kept going back again and again over all Bill had said. Things were bad in England, the country was going through a stage of acute depression. Max was growing old, and was fighting single-handed against heavy odds. Angela must hate to see him worn and worried. Money was tight everywhere. This was no time to embark on racing studs and wild speculations. Suppose . . .

At that point he would get up and walk into the nursery where his son lay, and stand looking down at him, his face very grave, his eyes sombre; then after a few moments square his shoulders and return to his letters, his figures, costs, and estimates with the grim expression still in his eyes and on his lips.

The month passed. March had begun, and here and there the spring flowers appeared in the shop windows. Emmanuel, seeing them, felt his heart beat more quickly. The spring always affected him, always sent his spirits soaring and filled him with fresh hope and energy. Three days and Juliet would be home, two days, one day—and suddenly he found himself standing on the platform waiting for the long black snake of a train to wind itself in over the curving lines, under the domed roof to where he stood. What did anything matter, what did he care for increasingly hard work, for business worries, for—anything? Juliet was home!

Driving home again, he held her hands in his. "You're cold."

She shivered suddenly. "It's nothing. I caught cold in Paris. I have caught cold in Paris with the most abominable regularity for years." She laughed. "That shivering is partly excitement."

"You're glad to be home?"

"I didn't know that I could be so glad about anything. You—and the boy, but"—softly—"you first, Emmanuel."

"I believe that he's grown. He looks tremendous. Guido calls him the younger brother of Carnera."

Wonderful to sit near her while she drank the soup which Mario had prepared for her, and crumbled bits of toast, and sipped some of the wine which Simeon Jaffe had sent round as his welcome, with many directions as to "taking the chill off", pouring and so forth. There were violets in a great bowl at her elbow, and from time to time she bent and inhaled their perfume. There was, to Emmanuel, something so gracious about her, something so ineffably beautiful and so radiant that he caught his breath as he watched her. She turned and smiled, saying, "Oh, my dear, how I've missed you!"

"I r-really make you happy?"

"Entirely—and so utterly content."

"Then at least I am not a failure!"

"If making a woman happy is the criterion of success, then you are the world's shining example."

"You make fun of me!"

"Only when you indulge that nice Jewish trait of yours, only when you grow all grandiloquent, and—lay yourself open to be teased. No one teases people they don't love."

That night he woke and heard her coughing— a little, dry cough, and stretched out his hand and laid it on hers, asking if he could get her anything to ease it.

"I hoped you wouldn't wake. Poor Emmanuel, what a shame! Yes, give me a drink—just water."

"You wouldn't like me to make you some tea?"

She laughed in the darkness. "I always adore you to make tea for me. Do you remember the day the boy was born? You made tea and very buttery toast. How good it was!"

He made tea on the electric stove in his dressing-room, brought it, and sat on the edge of the bed while she sipped it. He thought how bright her eyes were, and how well she looked despite her cough. Her cheeks, he told her, were like "r-red r-roses and cream". She laughed at his simile. "What a horrible mixture!"

In the morning he begged her to stay in bed, and to please him she promised to send for the doctor—who was half English and looked entirely Italian. He telephoned from his work, and she answered him from her bedroom.

"I'm furious! I've brought nothing from Paris with me but influenza! I can't even see the boy because it's supposed to be infectious. Perhaps you'd better not come near me!"

"If that is an order," he said, "I shall disregard it. If it's a suggestion, then it's a very silly one."

That night she was better, and grumbled because the doctor insisted that she should not sit upright because it was a strain on the heart. "I have a heart like an ox," she declared.

Emmanuel said: "Did he say that it was weak? Tell me—quickly. Let me make him bring a specialist in the morning. Let me—"

"Beloved idiot! In future I shall tell you exactly nothing. No, no, and no! This is merely a precautionary measure, because this foul germ apparently makes a dead set at everyone's heart, and must be circumvented in its evil designs. Now are you content?"

The next morning he waited to see the doctor, who laughed at him and told him that he was a scaremonger, and that Juliet had told him the exact state of affairs. "I have twenty cases of influenza on my hands at the moment. I say the same to every one of them. The wise ones obey me, the fools only argue!"

Emmanuel said obstinately: "At least, I want a nurse. Don't say that there is no need. I insist —for my own peace of mind. Send one immediately, please."

The nurse was dressed entirely, Emmanuel thought, in starched clothes, and crackled as she walked. She moved things in the bedroom and said that a huge photograph of Emmanuel and another of his grandfather on the bed-table were in the way. Juliet laughed. saying: "Then you must have a larger table. I won't have them moved. My temperature will rise in protest if they are not there where I can see them."

She was very happy that evening, and Emmanuel was delighted.

"She's better, isn't she?" he said to the nurse as they sat at dinner. "After all, influenza isn't very serious, is it?"

"All illness is serious, Mr. Gollantz," she returned primly.

He gave Juliet an imitation of her clipped

speech as he sat on the edge of her bed, but even in his imitation he could not manage to say the word "serious" in any way but his own.

"How did she say 'serious'?" Juliet asked.

"Ser-rious," he repeated. "And she doesn't think people ought to sit on the edge of beds."

Juliet said: "I don't think that you ought to sit on the edge of anyone's except mine! Oh, I do want it to be tomorrow. I may get up tomorrow, and nurse will bring the boy just to the door for me to see him from a distance." She coughed and said: "Give me a drink, darling. Lift me up a little, I can't drink lying down. That's lovely! I do like your arms, they're so . . ." She gave a little shudder and sighed, while he stood holding the glass to her lips.

He said: "There you are, sweetheart, dr-rink slowly." Then realizing how heavily she lay on his arm, he put down the glass and held her more closely, saying, "Juliet, Juliet."

She did not speak, the weight on his arm grew heavier; he laid her down and stood staring down at her, whispering, "Juliet, it's not true, it's not true!"

The nurse, sipping her coffee by the fire, started as she heard his voice, half wail, half scream, ring through the house.

2

GUIDO said: "I cannot bear it. He is the best man I have ever dreamed of, and to see him suffer breaks my heart. If only he would speak to me of—of things which hurt him. He says nothing, only 'Yes' and 'No' and 'Thank you, Guido'. I would die for him, and I am quite helpless."

Simeon Jaffe turned his pouched, rather bloodshot eyes to the little man who stood twisting his hands together, his face a little distorted with the effort he was making not to cry.

"Learn this, Guido," he said; "alvays for der peoples one loffs best, von vould die; but neffer, neffer is one aple to do anyt'ing but vatch and suffer mit dem. It is, I t'ink, der hardest t'ing in der vorld."

Guido made a gesture of despair. In any other but an Italian it would have been theatrical and unreal; in him it was very pathetic, terribly sincere.

"I understand," he said, "I shall try my very damnedest."

Both of these two men, one very old, the other very young, loved Emmanuel Gollantz; and because of his suffering, they suffered too. They had tried to offer sympathy, and it had been met with a dreadful stolidity. He had been courteous, his words had been adequate, but his face had betrayed nothing—he might have been wearing a mask.

"T'ank God," Jaffe had said, "dot you heff left to you your leetle son!"

Emmanuel had smiled—a terribly difficult, mechanical smile, and had answered: "Yes, indeed—God has been more than good to me, hasn't He?"

Guido, his beautiful eyes streaming with tears, had spoken to him about Juliet, spoken very simply and kindly. Emmanuel had stared at him as if he resented an impertinence. He had listened attentively, politely, then laid his hand on Guido's shoulder and said:

"You're very kind. But please don't talk about —my wife again."

The morning after the funeral—that ghastly ceremony when it seemed that musicians had come from all parts of Europe to pay tribute to the woman they had not only admired but loved —Emmanuel arrived at the galleries. He had gone straight to the office, and there Simeon Jaffe had found him.

Jaffe stood and stared at the white, strained face, and noted the new lines engraved there. Emmanuel had looked up and said:

"Good morning, Simeon. I don't think that this new man, Vigano, is as good as the chap we had previously. What was his name? Grossi. He's

430

more expensive, and less attentive. We might do worse than go back to Grossi, I think."

Jaffe, panting in his big chair, had stared and said, "I didn't t'ink dot you'd be here dis morning. I t'ought dot you might like to hev a few days at home to arrange—"

Emmanuel laughed. Jaffe always remembered that sudden laugh as one of the most painful things he had ever heard.

"Why should I?" he asked pleasantly. "There is nothing to keep me at home, and there is a great deal of work to be done here."

Only when he went back to the apartment after his work was finished for the day did Emmanuel allow himself to let the mask drop, allow himself to become natural, and let fall the elaborate defences which he had built for use during the day.

He had known what loneliness meant, or he had believed that he did, but this was loneliness intensified a thousand times. For more than a year he had lived in a close, warm companionship. Every day had shown him more clearly what happiness meant. He had lived for Juliet, in Juliet, and through Juliet, and now he felt as if he had ceased to live, and only the shell of what had once been Emmanuel Gollantz continued to walk, work, think, and try to sleep.

Angela had been unable to come to him because Max was ill. She had written and said, "My darling, I do understand." Emmanuel had read the letter and laughed, and wondered at her assumption that she could possibly understand! Bill had been briefed for an important case, and only Bill Masters had come from London. Bill Masters, growing old, and anxious to tell stories which began, "I remember . . ."

Emmanuel had been glad when he left, when he was at liberty to sit and think his own thoughts, speaking to no one, answering in monosyllables and seeing no one except the people who were necessary to his work.

He sat, his chin on his hand, staring at nothing, seeing pictures which were for himself alone, finding no comfort in them, but a painful satisfaction that he remembered so clearly.

He saw Juliet, years ago, when Angela and he had gone down to Seyre's house. That long drive through the night, when he had driven her to—what they had believed then to be—Leon Hast's death-bed. The time when she had come to his grandfather's funeral with Bill Masters. He could still hear his father saying, "This is very kind of you, Juliet. My father will be glad to know that you're here." The first day she had come into the little shop, when she had worn a tight, close-fitting hat, and had looked at old brocades. That wonderful summer when he had raced down to Menaggio each week-end, when they had been happy, heedless, and utterly content. Their parting, their next meeting in London, when she had looked up and met his eyes and he had known that then, and for all time, she was the only woman in the world for him. Meetings, partings, and at last their marriage before the Consul. The day Simeon was born, when she said, "And you thought he was a cat!" On and on, torture, pain, the rack, the mental thumbscrew, picture after picture, scene after scene, until the last picture of all, when he had stood looking down at her and known that it was all finished and done with and that he was alone except for the boy.

People told him that the boy would atone for everything, and he had tried to believe it. But the boy didn't seem to mean anything—seemed scarcely to affect him at all. He liked him, he loved him because he was handsome, and intelligent, and because he could never forget that he was Juliet's son, but he didn't seem to matter a great deal. If anything, he intensified the loneliness because when he laughed, or made queer noises which might mean that he was trying to talk, there was no Juliet to listen, to watch and to speculate with him.

Once again he flung himself into his work, nervous, impatient of delay in the carrying out of his orders, anxious to obtain every order possible, and attending to the execution of those orders with a calm, detached attention which seemed to Simeon Jaffe almost inhuman. Weeks became months, and after six months Emmanuel still maintained an aloofness which puzzled both Jaffe and Guido.

"He is so calm," Guido said, "sometimes I wonder if he has forget everything."

"He is so calm," Jaffe said, "because he remembers everyt'ing, I t'ink dot his heart is broken, dot poor goot poy."

"But," Guido persisted, "from the very first I have never seen him cry. I cried, I still cry when I think of Juliet—The Forbez—you cried, Signor Jaffe, but Emmanuel never one tear."

Jaffe waggled a thick forefinger at him, blew heavily and said:

"Let me tell you vot is der vorst tears. Dose vot is shed inside. Dose ven der heart drops tears vot is blood. Dose tears neffer show, und der blood goes on dropping, dropping, dropping."

Emmanuel would enter and find them talking, and they would start, and he would look at them coldly, as if he knew that they had talked of him and resented it. Immediately he would plunge into business matters, ordering Guido to do this, asking why he had not done that and, having sent him away, would turn to Jaffe and demand his attention, arguing over figures and prices until Jaffe's face grew congested with weariness.

At Christmas Guido and Jaffe insisted upon planning gaieties for little Simeon. Guido spent far more than he could afford, and old Jaffe brought toys to the flat and wonderful cakes and sweets which he had sent for from Vienna, where he believed the only cakes fit to eat were made. Simeon at eighteen months was strong and full of vitality. Emmanuel, watching him playing with Guido, admitted that he was beautiful. His thick, light hair, his blue eyes with their dark lashes, were unlike Emmanuel's own people. He was Juliet's son, in every way, so far as his looks went. From time to time he would turn and meet his father's sombre eyes, hold them for a moment, then laugh delightedly. On Christmas night, after Guido and Jaffe had dined with him, both working hard to make the evening a success, Emmanuel sat down by the fire and thanked God that it was all over.

"Tomorrow I can work again," he thought. "This inaction kills me, I can't bear it."

Early in the New Year he was walking down the long gallery, noting various pieces of furniture which had been selected by a rich young manufacturer for his new house, when Guido hurried up to him. His eyes were shining, and Emmanuel looked at him half amused, half contemptuous. "A particularly good-looking woman," he decided. "Nothing else makes Guido look so wildly happy."

"A lady," Guido said, his voice ecstatic, "to see you. She is smartness, very chic, her clothes are very expensive, and she smells of Paris."

"What does she want? Can't you attend to her? Lovely ladies are more in your line than mine."

"She wishes to see you. Her card"—Guido flourished the bit of pasteboard—"says that she is Mrs. T. W. F. Tatten."

For a second Emmanuel hesitated. He did not particularly want to see Viva, not because meeting her would affect him, but because she would bring back those last days in London, when he met Juliet again. Then, shrugging his shoulders, in walked down the gallery.

What did anything matter? It was all over—finished. Viva, exquisite, beautifully groomed, blonde, with a skin that shone with health, came forward, her hand outstretched.

"Emmanuel! Tell me that this is in very bad taste, if you like. I don't care. I wanted to see you. Toby knows that I've come here, and—oh, my poor sweet, how thin you are!"

Emmanuel said, "The result of several summers spent in Milan."

She glanced round the gallery, then said impulsively: "Isn't there anywhere for me to talk to you? One might as well be in Trafalgar Square!"

"Do you want to talk to me?"

"Obviously. What do you think I've come for?"

"Very well—there is my office. It's not particularly comfortable. You must excuse that."

She sat down, and Emmanuel leant against the table. She felt that he wanted to make it clear that he was not prepared to allow the interview to be prolonged indefinitely. She looked at his tall, spare figure, the hair which was white at the temples and thickly sprinkled with grey, at his sunken eyes, and unhappy mouth. He was much

436

older, miserable and lonely. Poor Emmanuel, he hadn't had much of a deal from Fate.

"Sit down," Viva said. "I shan't keep you longer than I need. That's better." She went on speaking very rapidly, purposely keeping any emotion out of her voice. "Years ago I told you that I believed that there was something between us, some bond that would last as long as we did. I thought then that it might be something which would bring us together again. I was wrong. I'm very, very happy with Toby, and you were happy, too happy to ever want to put up with second-best again."

"Shall we take all that for granted?" Emmanuel said coldly.

"Yes, I had to say that to clear the decks—don't rattle me. God knows that it's sufficiently difficult. Oh, don't, don't behave as though I were an enemy, my dear. I'm not; I do understand and I do so desperately want to help."

"It is more than kind of you—but I don't think that I want help."

"Then, my sweet, if you don't, I never saw anyone who did! Look here, Emmanuel, you've got to go back to England, back home again."

"My home is here."

"Nothing of the kind. That's a pose, and you know it. Listen, face facts. You can't live in the past, you can't live here alone with a little boy, for ever looking backwards. It's impossible. You're wretched, and what sort of a life can you plan for that child of yours?"

He rose, and said with sudden fury: "I've told you I won't discuss this. It's intolerable! My life is my own. I live it in my own way. How dare you come here talking to me as if you had some rights over me, some claim on me! Please go, Viva."

She leant back, took out her cigarette-case and said: "Give me a match, please, and don't lose your head. I'm here and you are going to listen to me if I have to follow you all down this street shouting after you. Emmanuel, sit down. Don't mistake decent kindness for impertinence, don't push away people who like you—love you. It's not fair either to them or to yourself."

"I beg your pardon. It's—it's"—he stumbled a little as he spoke—"all ver-ry painful and difficult for me. I can't bear to hear—her spoken of, even indir-rectly."

Viva nodded, smoked in silence, pushing her case across the table to Emmanuel. Absentmindedly he took a cigarette and lit it, and some of the strain seemed to disappear from his face.

"Max has been ill," Viva said. "Pretty ill, too. He's always been lame, ever since I can remember, but not much. Now he limps badly. He's carrying too much weight, and he's riding for a fall. I go about a good deal—Toby's a popular feller. Where everyone used to want Gollantz to decorate for them . . ." She shook her head. "Candidly, Gollantz are out of the running. Antiques—well, who buys them in these days? Everyone wants to sell, not buy. Look here, Emmanuel, there is a good deal more money running out of the business than is running in."

"Where is it r-running to?"

"Need you ask? Julian lives like a duke—or, more exactly, he lives as dukes used to live in the good old days of melodrama. Poor devils, they find it a pretty hard struggle now to get a bit of butter for their bread! Julian's lame, but so is Max. But Max believes that he owes a duty to Julian, and Julian exacts payment to the last farthing. Angela watches, gets worried, and only hopes that Max is happy. Ordingly isn't Ordingly any more. It's Julian's country house, and he kindly allows Max to pay the bills."

Emmanuel rubbed out his cigarette on an old bronze paper-weight.

"And what," he asked, "has this to do with me, please?"

"Everything," she returned—"everything. It's time that you went home, Emmanuel. The place is crying out for you. You're a man, and you're young. Max is getting old, he's sentimental about Julian, who I'll admit is a superb actor. Whenever there's a row, Julian takes to his bed with agonizing pains in his back. He's brave and gallant, and smiles through the pain. Max weakens, and thinks of Julian's lost career. Then out comes the cheque-book, and Julian's better again. Oh, my dear, go home, go home and look after your own job. What's Milan to you? Ordingly's yours—it's your boy's. Go and look after it. Go and do the decent thing, and take that look of worry from Angela's face. It's—oh, damn it, it's your job!"

Emmanuel's mouth twisted suddenly. "And play second fiddle to my brother? Work so that I may help to earn money for those cheques for Julian to spend? No, thank you, Viva, the pr-prospect does not attr-ract me."

"Play second fiddle—nothing!" she returned. "Go home and bargain, go home and make terms. Take over everything. Limit Julian to a reasonable income, and if he wants horses and dogs and cars—let him damn' well work for them. He can if he has to, only he likes this role so much that unless someone kicks him out of it he'll occupy it for the rest of his life—the tick!"

There was a long silence; Viva watched his face and waited for him to speak. She watched the look of indecision gather and fade, and at last he looked up and smiled at her.

"It has been ver-ry kind of you to come," he said. "I am very gr-rateful, but, you see, I don't care sufficiently. I'm not r-rich. I don't want to be. I don't want to come back to England."

"And your boy?" she flashed at him.

With an effort he said: "Simeon has his mother's money."

"So it's not incumbent on his father to make an effort for him! As he has that, you can let the

440

place that his grandfather bought, loved, dreamed in—go. Simeon will grow up in Italy, with no real place in the world, because he'll never be a real Italian—only one of those wretched international creatures who have no place in the world. My God, his mother must be delighted at the prospect! You're a coward, Emmanuel, a selfish coward!"

He leant back, his face very white, his eyes blazing with anger. "How dare you come here . . ." he burst out. Then with a violent effort he recovered himself and said smoothly: "I am afr-raid that I must ask you to go. I have a gr-reat deal of work to do. Will you excuse me?"

"Emmanuel, be reasonable, dine with Toby and me tonight and talk everything over. Don't let—"

He rang the bell which stood on his desk, and rose as Guido entered, saying: "Guido, will you take Mrs. Tatten down to the door and get her a taxi?" Then, bowing to Viva, he said: "Thank you for coming to see me, it was very kind of you. Good-bye."

She turned without looking at him again, and walked out with Guido. Emmanuel sank into his chair, covered his face with his hands, and remained so until the sound of Guido re-entering made him lift his head.

"What is it?" he asked, and Guido heard the utter weariness in his voice. "What is it?"

"The card—another card—of the Signora Tatten. She writes a message for you."

"Leave it. Leave me alone, Guido, there's a good fellow."

Guido laid down the card and crept from the room as if he feared to make the slightest noise. Emmanuel lifted the card and stared at it, his eyes blind with pain. The letters meant nothing, and it was only after some time that he made an effort to understand what Viva had written.

"Toby and I are going on to Rome. We shall be back in ten days. I'll come and see you. Don't be hurt, Emmanuel.—Viva".

He twisted the card in his fingers, his lips bitter, his eyes very sombre. How he hated to have everything touched, all the raw places in his soul laid open, made to ache and burn furiously! Why couldn't people let him alone? That was all he asked—to be let alone. He could go on, mechanically, even successfully. He could hide what he felt, and gradually people might believe that he had forgotten. Standing there, he raised his hands and pressed them against his heart, as if the pain was an actual physical thing, too terrible to be borne. The sweat stood on his forehead, and his eyes were bloodshot with the pain which he suffered. Once his lips moved, and he whispered with dreadful intensity: "God, if there is any mercy left in the world—let me go! I can't bear it any longer—it's living a long death."

"I'm going for today," he said to Guido, as he passed through the gallery. "Good-bye."

Guido started up and came after him. "Emmanuel," he said, "Emmanuel—"

"Yes, what is it?"

Guido's mouth quivered, his eyes filled. He stammered as he spoke: "I can't bear that you should be this way," he said, his voice shaking. "My friend, my master—is there not a little thing I can do?"

For one moment Emmanuel's face softened; then he said very gently: "Sorry, Guido, there isn't anything that anyone can do." He walked back to the flat, and as he entered, stopped and listened. Someone was playing—playing on the piano which had not been touched for nearly a year—playing a sad, wailing little tune which he knew—a tune Juliet had sung. He heard his breath come in a long, sobbing sigh, knew that he clenched his fists and started forward, ready to vent his anger on whoever should have dared to violate the silence. He opened the door and found the room in darkness except for one small light by the piano, which shone on the worn and undistinguished face of little Gilbert. As he heard the door open he started up and came to meet Emmanuel. His eyes were wet, and he blinked them very often behind his glasses.

"My dear young man," he said, in that thin,

precise voice which Emmanuel knew so well. "My dear young man. I ought not to have taken the liberty, but as I waited for you—I am only here for three days with Signora Toretti—I remembered how often I had played for—for Juliet in this room. You see, it was all I was ever able to do for her. I felt that she might be pleased that I went back to my work—I don't know if you understand me. It's very difficult to explain."

Emmanuel said: "I understand, Gilly. Go back and finish the song."

He stood by the fireplace and listened to the sounds which came from the piano. This was a song which she had sung in London, he had heard that one once at Ordingly, another his grand-father had loved—"Thank you, my dear Juliet." The room seemed to grow full of her presence, he felt that he could almost hear her voice saying as she had said before she began her last tour: "I don't want to be forgotten." The control which Emmanuel had imposed on himself for months was shivered, the misery which he had kept pent up in his heart burst the bonds which he had placed upon it, and he knew that the sobs which surged up in him, through the pain which they inflicted, brought a sense of relief. The music swept over him, healing, soothing, bringing him a sense of Juliet's closeness which he had not known since she died. He stood there, his head on his arm, crying like a lonely child who, having been lost and is found again, weeps with relief because its fears are over; who, though the recollection of them remains, is safe and realizes its safety.

He ceased to hear the music, and knew nothing except that his heart was freed from the iron bands which he had placed round it. He felt a touch on his shoulder, and started, turning to find Gilbert standing beside him.

"My dear young man," the little accompanist said softly, "I'm so glad that you can cry. Tears are very healing. I have cried as I play, I'm crying now. You see, very humbly, I loved her too. I am always proud that she called me 'My dear Gilly'. Perhaps sometimes you'd let me talk to you of her. I had known her so long, watched her so carefully—I think I understood her, that was why I was such a good accompanist."

Emmanuel, his sobs still shaking him, said: "Yes, Gilly. I'd like you to talk to me. I'd be very, very gr-rateful."

3

VIVA said: "That's so typical of Emmanuel. Bill tells him that he ought to go home, I go to a lot of trouble to say the same thing and get treated like someone canvassing for sewing-machines. Now he comes and announces quite calmly that he is going home, and taking the child! They are an unexpected lot, these Gollantz'!"

Toby Tatten tied the girdle of his brilliant dressing-gown very tightly, glanced at himself in the glass and said: "By Jove, I look frightfully like Hitler!" Then added: "Well, you don't know. I mean, perhaps some pal of his has put it to him in a new light. Y'know, supplied additional information, eh?"

"I know, I know"—eagerly. "That's where he's so funny. It's a little man with tow-coloured hair, glasses and blinking eyes, called Gilbert. He used to be Juliet Forbes' accompanist. Now, what the devil can that little thing have to say that neither Bill nor I thought of?"

Toby considered, gravely rumpling his hair in order to assist his thought. "I dunno," he said; "perhaps he didn't say so much, or said it differently. It's hard to say."

His wife made her way to the bathroom and,

leaving the door open between them, shouted back her remarks, the words issuing through a cloud of steam.

"No, they're just queer. They're unexpected. They always have been. You think that they're just ordinary—like you or me. They are, for three hundred and sixty-four days in the year, and on the three hundred and sixty-fifth they suddenly do something that puts you all wrong with your calculations. Something quixotic, or spectacular, or unbelievably cold. Y'know, Toby, I believe that's why we're all a bit frightened of Jews. We are, you know—"

Toby said: "Oh, hang it, I've never been frightened of a Jew in my life."

"You've never had any intimate dealings or relations with any of them," Viva retorted. "That's the only way to get to know them. You don't know Jews by meeting them at other people's houses, by playing cards with them, or going to Ascot with them. Then you only meet just as much as they want you to meet. Jews say, 'May I introduce myself? Myself is a very nice fellow and you'll like him.' And, by God, you do! Or he decides that 'Myself' will be a very hard-headed business man, and that's all you get to know. They are—what they want to be. But just once in a way they get taken off their guard, and something you never imagined shows itself in them. That's what's happened to Emmanuel. Something has smashed down that terribly cold

447

hardness which he must have assumed after his wife died, and he's going back to pull Gollantz and Son out of the fire. He'll do it, too, bless him!"

She emerged from the bathroom wrapped in a huge bath-wrap, her wet feet leaving marks on the carpet as she walked over to the fire. Toby watched her curiously, with concentrated attention. "I b'lieve you are still awfully fond of Gollantz," he said, making the remark as a statement, not as a question, and making it without the slightest trace of rancour.

"Of course I am! He's the nicest man, I think, I ever knew."

"Damn it!" Tatten said. "D'you really mean that? Where do I come in?"

"You come in as a remarkably nice husband to a remarkably nice wife," she returned. "Emmanuel never suited me as a husband, and you—unless you develop some horrible traits—always will."

As they talked in their hotel bedroom, Emmanuel sat with old Simeon Jaffe and discussed dissolving their partnership.

"I realize," Emmanuel said, "that I must go home. There isn't any other way out. I've no right to rob my son of his heritage, and that heritage, Simeon, means something more than the bricks, mortar, fields, trees and hothouses of Ordingly. He'll be the fourth Gollantz—and—

oh, there is something in one's pride in one's family and forbears, after all."

Simeon nodded. "Agreet. Hev I effer denied it? I em sorry dot you must go, but I belief dot you vill kom beck. For dot reason, if you agree, you vill remain as von of der partners of der firm, und Gollantz and Son vill edd anudder vord to their notices. Gollantz and Son, London und Milano."

"You've been a wonderful friend, Simeon."

"Dere is neffer no need to say—vonderful friend," Simeon said. "To be a friend—really und truthfully, is automatically to be a vonderful t'ing. I em gled dot you hev found me so."

"And you think that I am doing r-right to go?" Emmanuel smiled a little twisted smile. "You know, I don't want to go. Milan holds all my memories."

Simeon Jaffe heaved his huge bulk into a more comfortable position before he spoke.

"You are right to go," he said. "Because eider relationsheeps mean not'ing at all or dey mean somet'ing very important. Eider relations are component parts of der whole or dey are disintegratet atoms vot hev no connection mit each odder at all. Der is no helf-vay house. I t'ink dot mit Jews der sense of femily is very strong—so you must face secrifice, hard vork, exercising much patience. Only von more vord, for my heart aches bedly because you go, und it is dis: go beck mit courage, go beck ready to fight mit justice

449

for vot is right. Let no leetle t'ings like sentiment, veakness, regrets und so on, hemper you. Lay burdens on your shoulders eff you vill, but let dem be der burdens of people who ken no longer kerry them. Not der burdens of peoples who don't vant to kerry dem, and are only looking for a great demn' fool who vill sveat und toil for dem."

"And you think that Louis might come back and work with you?" Emmanuel changed the trend of the conversation abruptly, because he wanted to go home without prejudice, without preconceived ideas. When he arrived, then he might be in a position to judge. Up to the present his information had come only from Bill and Viva, who both disliked Julian extremely.

"Dere is just a chance. His Olympia is tired off Peris, und Louis wearies mit doing not'ing." He sighed heavily. "I should be gled if he kom."

Emmanuel thought of the long galleries, of the store-rooms, of the room where he had kept nothing but his old brocades, faded velvets and shimmering satins embroidered with flowers and birds. He thought of his rolls of papers, exquisite patterns which he had found here and there on his travels—papers covered with Chinese pagodas, papers covered with field flowers, with dragons, paper which looked like dull, beaten gold, and paper which felt like ancient parchment.

He had begun in the little shop in the insignificant street, where his purchases had been cheap

450

pieces picked up and stacked in the old car. Now there were perfect chairs, beautiful tables, bureaux of fine workmanship, and not a few admirable pictures. Crucifixes, vestments made originally for priests who had long since crumbled to dust, holy-water stoups, manuscripts illuminated by monks who were young when Milan, too, was in her glorious youth. Enamels, china, shawls, old ear-rings, bracelets—all arranged with care, tended and cleaned, numbered and their histories—so far as he could trace them—noted. It was his, he had made it—this splendid place, he had worked and won the trust and belief of the people who gave him work. He had lifted the gallery of Simeon Jaffe to a place which stood high among the traders of Milan—and he was leaving it. He might come back, Jaffe might insist that he was still a partner in the business, he might even send orders from time to time, and receive from them articles that he needed for his work in England; but the personal contact would be gone and if he came back it would be as a welcome visitor, nothing more.

It was not easy to say good-bye to Simeon Jaffe, but it was still harder to say it to Guido. Guido, who wept without restraint. Who clung to his hand and begged that he might come to England to do anything, the most menial tasks, so that he might catch sight, at least once a day, of his friend.

"Your place is here," Emmanuel said. "Jaffe

can't do without you. You know more about it all than anyone, except myself. You've got a future here, Guido, and you must think of yourself."

"What else do I think of but myself in wishing to come with you? Imagine life when you are not here! Will my heart be with contessas, with painted faces? Shall I be able to smile at the old trouts? Is it possible that I shall care when horrible old men come in with bad pictures to sell? Thirty times—no!"

Emmanuel said: "Look, old man, whatever you do, don't trust your judgment about pictures. Always consult Jaffe, won't you?"

Guido, the tears streaming down his face, answered: "That I swear, though one offer me the 'Ultima Cena' for five lire!" Then, with renewed energy: "You will die in London, my dear. Do I not know! Nebbia, nebbia, nebbia. Neve, neve, neve. Piógga, vento, it is one long dark night full of black soot. It will enter your lungs and you will die of suffocation. And the little boy, my adored bambino! What of him? They will send him to public schools where other boys will beat him, and he will get dirty, and smell of mice and rotten apples. He will come back when he is large and look at me and say, 'Dirty old dago, damn' well no good.' He will drink a great deal of beer, and smoke pipes with bulldog heads on them."

Then quite suddenly it was all over, and the furniture was packed and stored, and all the little foolish things which he loved because they had been Juliet's were ready to be shipped to England. Little Simeon and his nurse had gone. They were to stay the night in Paris, because Emmanuel was afraid that the long journey in one was too much for the boy. Guido stood by the window of the long room, crying—for Guido—almost silently. Emmanuel walked slowly from room to room, remembering and regretting.

He came back and laid his hand on Guido's shoulder.

"That's all," he said. "It's quite empty."

Guido's hand sought his and held it. "It's quite empty," Guido said.

"It's been rather wonderful," Emmanuel said softly. "Not all of it, but when she was here, and —oh, God, Guido, I hate to leave it. It's like leaving her, like shutting the door on her and giving the key to strangers."

The little Italian turned and faced him. His beautiful eyes were still wet, his mouth looked soft and tender, like the mouth of an unhappy child, his voice was not quite steady.

"No, no!" he said. "That is where she is more fortunate than I. She goes with you always. Only I am left here alone. Keys, railway trains, houses, locked doors, have nothing to do with her, only with poor people like yours always sincerely Guido. Let us go, Emmanuel, because I think in a very short time my heart will break. I am walking to the scaffold, but I am proud because

I walk there with you—for perhaps the last time." He lifted his face, and with the tears pouring down his cheeks, said: "I know that for English it is a contemptible thing to kiss men, but because I love you, and shall always love you, because my love for you has been very clean and smelt very sweet—you will kiss me good-bye, Emmanuel."

Emmanuel, without hesitation, bent down and kissed him on the cheek. His own throat ached and his eyes smarted.

"Good-bye, Guido," he said. "I shall never forget that—Juliet loved you very much—as I do."

Half an hour later Emmanuel Gollantz leant from the window of the trans-continental express as it slid out under the domed roof of Milan station. He saw the blue-bloused porters, the officials with their red velvet-topped caps, the grey–green uniforms of the military customs, and among them the figure of a little Italian wearing very baggy plus-fours, heavy brogue shoes, and a tweed coat of astonishing roughness, who, weeping without restraint or shame, gallantly waved a huge bandanna handkerchief.

He sat down in his corner, feeling weak and utterly tired. He was closing one of the books of his life, and the effort had been greater than he knew. Why was he leaving the only town in which he had known complete happiness? What was prompting him to begin again at thirty, leaving behind him a business which was his own achievement, friends who loved him, and the thousand and one memories which Milan held for him of the woman he had loved?

He was returning to work with his father, whose hostility towards him still persisted. Angela had written to him, Bill, and the rest, but no word beyond a rather conventionally worded telegram had come from Max when Juliet died. There would be difficulties, and he must face the fact that virtually every man's hand would be against him. He had told them that he was coming home. Angela had replied, saying that rooms would be prepared for him, the boy and his nurse at Ordingly. Her letter had been kind and affectionate, but even she seemed a little surprised at Emmanuel's sudden determination to return to England. Max had not written.

Emmanuel replied that he could not come to Ordingly because he expected to be too busy in London. He said nothing which indicated in any way his actual purpose in returning home. That should wait until he had discussed matters with his father.

He spent long hours making calculations on the backs of envelopes, jotting down notes as to what he wished to say, and staring out of the window at the landscapes which seemed to him to be retreating, leaving Milan farther and farther behind. His mind went back to the empty flat which he had left. He saw it again furnished, as it had been when he used to come back to Juliet after his work was done. He walked in fancy through the Galleria with her at his side, watched her bowing to this singer and that musician—people of little importance, but who knew her, and whom she did not forget. Still he heard the whisper as she passed: "Signorina Forbez!" Dimly he wondered if the pain would ever grow less, if some day he might be able to think of her without his heart aching so unbearably.

He saw her standing by the Fontana of Saint Francis, smiling as she watched, then, turning to him, saying, "The dearest of all Saints, surely! You may not care for Carlo Borromeo, I may not understand Saint Paul, but everyone loves Saint Francis."

The Briera, Santa Maria della Grazie, and the Last Supper, wonderful nights of opera at the Scala, supper afterwards at Salvini's—evenings when they went like two children to see some "movie" and Juliet laughed immoderately or cried whole-heartedly.

Emmanuel shivered and pulled his heavy coat more closely round him. It was over, finished and done, and he was beginning again—alone. It was like the awaking from a wonderful dream and finding the world colder and less friendly than one had believed possible. London looked cold, the pavements shone damply, and he pulled the boy's coat collar up and tucked a rug round his small legs. The child was excited, and kept

456

shouting with pleasure at the great scarlet buses, the motor-cars, and the flashing street signs. The nurse smiled, glad to be back in England.

"Lovely to see dear old London again, Mr. Gollantz."

Emmanuel said mechanically: "Very."

Little Simeon, for no particular reason, chanted: "No polenta, no polenta."

The nurse turned and cuddled her to him. "No polenta!" she said. "Simeon won't get polenta in London!"

"He's very forward for his age," she said with pride.

The hotel was warm; nurse praised the hot water, and decided that her room and Simeon's was "just what she wanted". Simeon yawned, rubbed his nose with his clenched fist and whimpered a little.

Nurse said: "Here's the dustman coming. I'll give him his bath and then he can have his supper and go bye-byes. I expect he's tired. Say good night to Daddy, Simeon."

Simeon kissed Emmanuel rather unwillingly, and murmured something which might have been "Good night", and which was probably nothing at all. Nurse carried him to the door, and when Emmanuel called "Good night" for the last time, Simeon replied, "Ciao, Ciao!"

Emmanuel telephoned to the Gallery and asked to speak to Max. His voice shocked Emmanuel;

it seemed so lacking in vitality, so dead and colourless.

"Yes—what? Emmanuel! We didn't expect you until tomorrow. I hope that you had a good journey."

"Very, thank you. Can I see you, or is it too late?"

"Too late! It's only just five. Where are you? I see." A little pause, then: "Emmanuel, I'll drive round to you now. No, no, I'll come to you. Yes, I can always drink tea." Emmanuel hung up the receiver, his heart beating very fast. There had been a little change of tone towards the end of their conversation. He thought: "He is glad to know that I'm back. He really wants to see me!"

He ordered tea and tried to rearrange the stiff hotel sitting-room so that it looked more homely. He rang for more coal and asked if they could get him some wood.

"I've just come from Italy—we don't use coal very much there, and wood is so cheerful."

The waiter said: "Indeed, sir! I'm afraid we don't supply wood for the fires. It's the best coal, sir."

Emmanuel went into his bedroom, bringing back the picture of Juliet, which he hated to have out of his sight. Holding the frame so that the light caught the photograph, he stared at it hungrily, as if he tried to read some new expression on the pictured face.

As Max entered, his son's first thought was:

"My God, he's an old man!" Max walked slowly, limping more than he had ever done. His hair was almost white, and there was a new stoop to his broad shoulders. He was as meticulously dressed as ever, and yet he gave Emmanuel the impression that he was shabby. His clothes were admirable, but he lacked that air of success, of assurance, which had stamped him previously.

"It was good of you to ring up, Emmanuel."

"Not a bit. I wanted to see you. I came home to see you."

Max stretched his lame leg into an easier position. "My leg bothers me a little," he said, as if explaining and excusing the movement. "I think I'm getting old!" He laughed, and Emmanuel felt that he tried to make a joke of what was in reality an unpleasant truth.

He spoke very little, sipped his tea in silence, and nibbled a piece of toast. Emmanuel watched him, wondering if he would begin presently to speak openly. Facing his father, he felt older, stabilized, more certain of himself. He had come to pull Gollantz and Son out of the fire, and he was going to do it—and do it on his own terms.

"Is your little boy with you?" Max asked.

"Yes. He stood the journey well and intimated to the best of his ability that he liked London."

"I must see him tomorrow. Angela is looking forward to meeting her grandson. Her second grandson," Max added quickly.

"Perhaps she'll come and lunch here."

Max shot him a quick, almost startled glance, and said: "You don't want to come to Ordingly, then?"

"No—at least, not at the moment, sir."

"Julian and Amanda are in Monte Carlo." Emmanuel knew that it had been an effort for Max to make the statement, and that having made it he forced himself to continue: "The poor chap can't stand English winters, they're too severe for him." Then with a sudden sigh, as if he was forced to confide in someone, Max added: "He's lost a good deal of money this week. Most unlucky!"

Emmanuel put down his cup, looked up quickly to where Juliet's photograph stood, as if the sight of her face gave him courage, then began to speak very rapidly.

"That is one of the r-reasons why I have come home. Julian is, I gather, losing a great deal too much money all r-round. If you wish to stand on his side, then I must r-return to Italy. But if you will give me a fr-ree hand, if you will help me, if you r-remember that Gollantz and Son includes not only Julian, but Bill, myself, and my own boy, then I'll work with you. I'll work hard, loyally, and between us we'll get things str-raight again. The decorating side is the side which pays today. People have very little money for antiques. The decorating, the furniture, was always my department. I've made a success of my own place

460

in Milan. Let me help you to make a new and gr-reater success with yours—and ours."

Max stared at him, then said: "Yes, it would be a great help. I should welcome your help, Emmanuel."

"And Julian will leave Ordingly and work, in so far as he is able."

"My dear fellow, Julian's a cripple! How can he work?"

"How far is he a cripple? We can find out from Meyer Bernstein. If he is in possession of his senses, free from pain, then he can work, and what is more—he shall work. Those are my terms, sir. I cannot and will not allow Julian to batten on the firm—the firm in which Bill and I, to say nothing of my mother, all have a share and on which we all have equal claims."

Max reached for his stick and rose stiffly.

"I have never allowed anyone to dictate to me, Emmanuel."

"Then there is no more to be said."

"Aren't you being very hard?"

"No, only just."

"Isn't justice a sufficiently hard thing?"

"Possibly. I have no more to say. There is my offer. Unless you wish to take it, I can r-return to Milan."

His father made a movement of impatience. "I'll bring your mother to lunch with you tomorrow, if I may? We'll discuss this then."

"I shall be delighted."

461

He walked to the door with his father, and as they made their way along the corridor Max stopped suddenly and laid his hand on Emmanuel's shoulder.

"Believe me," he said gently, "I am very glad to have you home again."

4

EMMANUEL slept badly and rose early, shivering a little, for the raw cold seemed to bite into his bones. Everyone was very attentive, very anxious to get all he wanted, but he missed the queer assumption of personal friendship on the part of the waiters to which he had become accustomed in Italy. He wandered about restlessly, and finally decided to walk down to Bond Street.

In the big outer office there were fewer clerks, and those who occupied the desks seemed to Emmanuel to be less immaculate, less well groomed, than the men he had known. Reuben Davis, stouter and more carelessly dressed, hurried forward and greeted him.

"Your father isn't coming down this morning," he said. "He might be in this afternoon. It's very nice to see you, very nice. I did hear a rumour" —he cocked his head on one side and looked knowing—"that you might be coming back to us."

"It is possible. I am talking it over with my father this afternoon,"

Reuben said: "I wish you would. No one has ever handled the decorating and new-furniture side as you did. I don't understand it, and your

463

father never cared for it. Always thought it just a little infra dig. for the House, I fancy." Then with a certain difficulty he added: "I was very sorry to hear of your loss. It must have been a terrible shock."

Emmanuel said, in that queer, expressionless voice, "Thank you."

He elected to walk through the galleries alone, noting this which must be changed, examining the lighting and deciding that their own system in Milan was more modern, cheaper, and gave a far better effect. The furniture was badly arranged, he decided; there was a great deal of wonderful stuff, but it wasn't shown well. Too crowded, indifferently kept. There were too many pictures. They were good, some of them were even masterpieces, but Emmanuel shook his head over them. Dead money, and the fashion in pictures—even in masterpieces—changed almost as often as the shape of women's hats. Jaffe's rooms in Milan contained goods not worth a tenth of those in the Gollantz galleries, but they were better shown, looked more attractive, and the majority of them were infinitely more saleable.

He walked back to Reuben's office and asked if he could see the orders for the decorating and manufacturing side. With something of a shock he realized that the little man hesitated, that his face flushed and his eyes were troubled.

"It's difficult, Emmanuel," Reuben said. "You see, I don't know how your father'd feel about it.

464

It's not as if I had his direct orders to work on—" Then with sudden desperation, "You do understand, don't you?"

It was the old Emmanuel Gollantz who replied: "My dear fellow, how right you are, and how stupid of me! My father ought to thank heaven every day of his life for you. Please forgive me, Reuben."

"Forgive! Emmanuel—only it's very difficult. Max doesn't like any interference. I tell you that for your ear alone. He keeps everything in his own hands." He paused, and added with a certain acidity in his voice, "Perhaps it's as well!"

Emmanuel agreed. "Perhaps, Reuben. I'll go and talk to Hannah, I think. See you later."

Hannah was stouter; her always heavy face had grown heavier, her chins were numerous, her great nose seemed to Emmanuel to look like the beak of an eagle. But her eyes, large, dark, and intelligent, were as kind as ever.

She seized his hands, looked into his face intently and pushed him into the most comfortable chair, pressing cigarettes on him.

"Oh, how good to see you!" she exclaimed. "It's so long since you were here. Dear Mr. Emmanuel . . ." Watching her, he saw that her eyes filled with tears, and he braced himself for what he knew must be impending. "I heard—I wanted to write to you—but I didn't like to. I saw her very often when she sang in London. She was a great artist—a great artist."

"Yes."

She twisted her hands together, trying to overcome her emotion, and for the first time since he came home Emmanuel felt that he wanted to listen to whatever she said of Juliet, felt that he wanted to talk of her freely and without constraint.

"It's difficult," Hannah Rosenfelt went on. "It's terribly difficult to learn to say 'The Lord has given and the Lord has taken away—'"

Emmanuel said bitterly, "Oh, believe me, I accept that!"

"Yes, yes!"—eagerly. "But the rest—'Blessed be the name of the Lord!' That's what you must learn to say, what you will learn to say."

He moved impatiently. "Tell me, for God's sake, how can I learn to bless where I cannot understand? How can I accept what seems to me wanton cruelty, and if not that, then inability to rule and govern events? How far will acceptance help me? How will blessing the name of a God I don't know content me? What is this acceptance, this humility, this belief that everything is a blessing in whatever disguise it comes? Less than a year, Hannah, and that must suffice me for the rest of my life!"

"Listen," she said, and stretched out her well-kept, plump hand and laid it on his. "We have a service—Sedar—when the mercies of God are told. The mercies as shown in the Exodus. As each mercy is recited, the family—for it

466

is a family service—responds, 'Dayenu'— 'Enough for us'. A year's complete happiness! And you cannot learn to say, 'Dayenu'!"

"No," he said. "Why should I try to learn? These things don't apply to me, Hannah I'm not a Jew!"

Her full lips smiled, tolerantly, as one might smile at a child who is defiant, but defiant with a certain gallantry. "Because you break the laws which your forefathers kept, because you never enter school, because—Shetus! You talk rubbish. Was your grandfather a Jew? You know that he was. Not froom perhaps, except in his mentality, not orthodox possibly. And so are you, and so you will always be. Oh, I'm not trying to convert you! It suits me to keep the Faith as my fathers kept it. Religion is a matter of diet. You must choose what suits your spiritual digestion, I suppose. But a Jew you certainly are, and always will be." She stopped short and laughed. "What's come over me, Mr. Emmanuel? I never talk like this. It's the pleasure of seeing you again. Look, it's eleven o'clock. Don't you think you'd like coffee? You always used to like coffee at eleven. I'll tell young Marks to run across the road and get some. It won't take a minute!"

It was pleasant to sit drinking black coffee and listening to Hannah Rosenfelt talking about the work of the firm. Emmanuel, listening, admired her because she gave nothing away. She talked, apparently, very frankly and freely, but when he came to examine her statements he found that there was no hint as to the profits or losses of the firm.

". . . a most wonderful thing. This complete dinner service in gold plate. It had to go to America. It nearly broke Sir Max's heart, but we can't afford gold dinner services in England today. We shall have to ship some of our expensive things to you in Milan to sell for us, I think. I've heard from several people what a splendid place you and Simeon Jaffe have there."

"Not now," Emmanuel said. "I've left Milano."

Her dark eyes widened. "Not for good? Just for a holiday?"

"No, no. For good—at least, I hope it may be for good. I've come back to work here with my father. I think he needs me."

"For good!" she repeated, as if she were trying to understand. "You've left Milan to work here, in London, with Sir Max. Oh, but why? What made you do that?"

"But I thought that you'd be delighted, that you'd think I'd done the right thing. Let's face it, Hannah. Things aren't going too well here. Neither my father nor Reuben knows much about the side of the business that was mine. My father's growing old, Julian's making hay while the sun shines—and from what I hear there won't be much more sunshine for Gollantz and Son at

468

this rate. Don't you think that my father needs me?"

She considered for a moment, her thick eyebrows drawn down, her heavy, intelligent face very grave. "He may need you," she said at length, "but I don't know that he really wants you. Emmanuel"—in her intensity she forgot the formal prefix which she had always accorded to him—"when you left us it was because you found your happiness lay away from this and you followed it. Do you remember how you hated the life here? Perhaps you've forgotten. D'you think that you won't hate it again? If you've come back now for the sake of your family, not for your own sake, make certain that they want what you can do for them. Elderly people don't like revolutions, even beneficent ones. They're too disturbing. Sir Max worries, not because of the —now I am speaking plainly, perhaps too plainly —inroads which your brother makes on his income. He worries because he realizes that Julian is doing nothing but waste what he has. If Julian would work at anything, Sir Max would gladly sink every penny he had in any scheme. He wants to be proud of Julian, he wants to prove that he is right in reinstating him, and Julian won't help him. This goes back further than the accident in Milan, believe me."

She stopped, breathing quickly and twisting her handkerchief in her hands. "Forgive me, Mr. Emmanuel—"

469

"There is nothing to forgive, Hannah. You may be right; but I have a son, and there is Ordingly, remember. My grandfather bought it, loved it—and so do I. Is my boy to get nothing?"

"Ordingly!" she cried with intense scorn. "What does Ordingly matter to you, or to your boy? Ordingly belongs to the past. Emmanuel Gollantz bought it to house the family which he had founded. It's served its purpose. It belongs to the time when this business was being built, founded, established. It, old Emmanuel, Max and Angela, belong to spacious times, when great houses housed great people—figures. When gardens and orchid-houses and horses and immense rooms were part of the life of those people. What do you care for living in the kind of state which was an actual part of their lives? What will your son care for that life? Why, by the time he's grown up that type of life will have ended. You're going to tie yourself, to bind yourself to this machine—which already is just a little out of date and cumbersome; you'll work and sweat and slave, you'll suffer through your brother because you've always suffered through him, and one day you will be able to say to your son: 'Look! That huge house, those trees, these rooms, are yours, and you've never had to work for any of them.' And d'you know what he'll say, Emmanuel? He'll say that he doesn't know what to do with it, and shall he let it, or sell it to someone for a cigarette factory!"

470

"You make me feel that I'm a stranger in a strange land."

"I wonder if that's not just what you are," she said quietly. "You tell me that the one perfect year of your life was spent in Italy. That's what you're going to remember all your life, Emmanuel. That one perfect year. Your people, however much they love you, and I know that your father and mother—especially your mother —do love you, know nothing of what was your life. They'll never know the time of your life which was real, actual, vivid. How can they?"

"I believe," Emmanuel said slowly, "that you're trying to make me afraid to stay. Trying to persuade me to go back."

"I'm trying to make you do nothing!" she returned with some emotion. "I'm trying to show you clearly what you won't allow yourself to see, because you have blinded yourself temporarily. I'm trying to arm you against pain, disappointment, and friction. God knows, I should welcome you back here; we all should. No, that's not true. Many of us would. I wish you Chayim, Emmanuel!"

He smiled. "I've told you that I am not a Jew—"

"Chayim!" she repeated impatiently. "Life, my dear. Life!"

Emmanuel rose and stood looking down at the Hebrew woman. He did not see at that moment her stout, heavy figure, on which middle-age had already laid its fingers; he saw her as Moses might have seen the prophetess Miriam. How many times had he listened to her advice upon a hundred matters? How well he remembered years ago, when he left London under the shadow of a shame which was not his, but Julian's, that it had been Hannah Rosenfelt who believed in him and tried to help him.

"I shall remember," Emmanuel said. "I may not act upon what you have said, but I shall remember that you had the courage to say it to me. I must go. My father and mother will be waiting for me. Perhaps one day you'll come and see my little boy, Hannah."

"I shall. I should like to see him. Mazal Tov, Emmanuel."

He drove back to his hotel, disturbed and thoughtful. Was she right? Perhaps he had come too late, had missed the tide which might have carried him back into Gollantz and Son. Instinctively he longed for Juliet, and felt his loneliness accentuated. He longed for her to talk with him, to advise him. He remembered how she had laughed once when he said that he was always grateful to her for the advice she gave him.

"But you don't often take it!" Juliet said.

"Perhaps not, but I am always ver-ry gr-rateful for it." And with that little recollection came a thousand others, each one carrying with it a stab and an aching because the future could hold no more such incidents.

They were waiting for him: Max, tall and dignified, his mother beautiful, with the tender beauty of the evening. She came towards him, her hands outstretched, crying: "Emmanuel, Emmanuel, my dear! How good to see you again! Oh, Max, isn't it good?" Then very gently with her finger-tips she touched the temples where his hair was silvered, saying softly: "My darling, my poor boy. I always loved her too. I'm so ashamed now of the mess I made of everything. Just pride, my dearest. Just—'That wild lie—'"

They stood together, her arm through his, drawing him very close to her, neither of them anxious or able to speak. Max came to where they stood, and laid his hand on Emmanuel's shoulder. For that brief moment the three of them were very close, very tender towards each other, filled with a love which wiped away all the mistakes of the years which were past.

Making a great effort, Emmanuel said, "You've seen the boy?"

"Not yet—bring him quickly."

He went for the child, and carried him back to them. He had never been shy, never afraid, and now he smiled and offered his cheek to be kissed, opening and shutting his small fist and saying, "Ciao, ciao!"

"What does he mean?" Angela said. "Chow, baby, chow."

Emmanuel smiled. "It means very much what

you want it to mean. Good morning, good-bye, saluti—anything."

The child continued to repeat "Ciao, ciao" at intervals. Max held out his arms and held him for a moment, then said: "He's not older than Julian's boy? No, of course he isn't. What's his name? What is your name?"

Simeon smiled radiantly. "Thimeon E-mannoil Gollanth."

Angela, watching him, touching the light bright hair and his small soft cheek, said: "How like her he is!"

Max nodded: "Yes, indeed. A very beautiful little fellow. Now, little Max is a Gollantz through and through—more like you, Emmanuel, than Julian."

As if she felt the sudden sense of strain, Angela said quickly: "Where have you been this morning?"

"Down to Bond Street," Emmanuel said. "I thought that you might be there, sir. So I stayed and talked to Reuben and Hannah."

Max's eyebrows were raised a fraction, his voice lost a little of its former warmth. "Indeed. I hope that you were interested."

Emmanuel thought: "My God, he thinks that I went down to pry into affairs which didn't concern me."

Over the luncheon table Max returned to the question of Emmanuel's return. He spoke without either great enthusiasm or actual disapproval. He made his statement calmly and clearly. He would welcome Emmanuel back with all his heart. He would be only too happy for Emmanuel to take over entirely the running of the decorating side, the furniture-making and the repairs. He wished to keep "my own special line"—the antiques, pictures and so forth entirely in his hands.

"That was what I suggested," Emmanuel agreed. "My only point is this. I want to come back—if you wish without a salary—as partner with a share in the profits. I have been in that position in Milano and I could scarcely come back on any other terms to London. I'm sure that you see that, sir."

Max leant back in his chair and laid his finger-tips together.

"I don't like partnerships," he said. "I admit that my father insisted that my name—only as 'Son' remember—should be included in the firm's, but I was never a partner, and though he allowed me to draw a magnificent salary, I had no voice in the actual spending of the profits. That he kept entirely in his own hands."

Emmanuel's lips closed tightly. When he spoke his voice was very cold: "Quite!" he said. "I understand. My only feeling is that if I come back I must have a free hand. It is apparent to me that the firm is not—well, not making what it was three years ago."

"No business of our type is."

475

"I am prepared to see that it does. I submit, with all respect, that the firm cannot afford to carry passengers at this juncture. My mother, yourself—the money invested in the firm is yours, and you must of necessity have first claim on it. I have no wish to draw any tremendous sum. I only want enough to live on simply and look after Simeon Emmanuel. But—I say this very seriously —no business today can afford to carry passengers."

"Meaning, of course," Max said with dangerous suavity, "your brother Julian?"

"You have my meaning, sir."

"I told you last night that I allowed no one to dictate to me, Emmanuel."

"Except my brother Julian."

Angela said softly, "Emmanuel, my dear, be careful."

"I have told you that your brother Julian is a cripple," Max said patiently. "It is impossible for him to work, and now let me tell you something else, which you have apparently forgotten: that he is a cripple today because of an attack made upon him by your Italian friend on the day when he came to see you, to try and make friends with you. It seems to me that this fact alone ought to force you to look more kindly on any act of Julian's which might appear, to anyone less cognizant of the facts, a little self-indulgent."

Angela sat with her hand pressed against her lips. It was terrible to her to listen to the two

476

men she loved, her husband and her son, growing every moment colder and more formal. Dreadful to know that with each word they spoke the breach between them was growing wider and wider.

"Guido's—attack—was made because Julian chose to insult me, and—what is in my eyes unforgivable—my wife. I know the truth, you evidently know what Julian has told you. With regard to Julian's illness, it's over, and there are people who can testify that he could work if he wished to. Meyer Bernstein admits it, and I have not the slightest doubt that other doctors will bear out his opinion."

Angela stretched out her hand and laid it on her husband's.

"Max dear, you're allowing yourself to become antagonistic. You'll never either of you under-stand the other if you do that. Can't you both try to understand? Don't just listen only to words. Listen to something below the words. I beg you, both of you, don't assume the worst of each other. You can't, you mustn't. It's unthinkable."

"I understand," Max said slowly, "that Emmanuel wants to run my business for me, he wishes to reduce the allowance which I make to his brother—who is, I repeat, an invalid. He would like me to turn Julian out of his home, with his wife and child. I can't and won't do it!"

"It is Emmanuel's home too," she said.

"He is welcome to come there whenever he wishes. He knows that."

"To provide amusement for Julian's tongue, wit and general tendency to offer insults! It's impossible," Emmanuel interjected.

Angela turned to him, appealing: "My dear, you don't know. I think he's kinder, more gentle. He does little kindnesses—"

"The last time I saw him," Emmanuel said, "I struck him over the face for saying something unforgivable about Juliet. I couldn't forget. One doesn't forget these things. I tell you that it's impossible for me to live under the same roof as Julian. More, I cannot work, put the best of myself into my work, and know that all one's efforts are nullified because Julian wants to gamble, keep horses, and—"

Max got up from the table and turned to Angela.

"It's useless," he said. "We might go on discussing this for ever. This is what Emmanuel calls justice. I call it something almost approaching inhumanity. It is impossible for me to allow him to dictate to me. He must see that. I am going down to Bond Street. Will you telephone what time you want the car?"

5

THEY sat for some time in silence.
Emmanuel hurt and angry, Angela
suffering acutely because, though she
understood them both, it seemed impossible that
they could understand each other. Emmanuel
came over to where she sat and stood looking
down at her, his face very tender.

"Poor darling!" he said. "I think it's more
difficult for you than for any of us. Perhaps,
despite the fact that we really love each other and
have a real respect for each other, my father and
I have never—walked along together easily."

"But, my dear," she protested, "he is so good.
His kindness is limitless."

"To you, to Julian, perhaps to Bill, never to
me. I can think back to the first time Julian
shouldered something on to me. Nothing that
mattered much, and at the time it would have
made a great difference to him. Max believed
instantly that I was to blame. Oh, I don't grumble
at that! It was what I intended him to do. Only
it was just the sort of thing I never should have
done; any more than I could have done—that
other thing for which I left England. Don't think
that I am tr-rying to make a hard-luck story out

479

of it. Only it shows so plainly that he can't know me very well."

"And the fact—if it is a fact—that he cannot understand you makes you blind to all his real goodness. My poor Max! It's more than that, Emmanuel. It goes deeper than that. I sensed it when you were home last time—you've grown away from us."

He lifted her hand to his lips, "Never from you, my dearest."

"Yes," she persisted, "from me too. You love me, you'll always love me, but I'm not the biggest thing in your life any longer. I don't regret it, dearest, I never could. When you were little, I was quite literally the centre of your world. It used to worry me sometimes. Meyer Bernstein used to tell me that I mustn't let you love me so desperately. Even when you fell in love with Viva, I was still first. Then Juliet came, and in her you found everything. In me you had only found maternity. Her love for you, yours for her, was a very complete thing. You fulfilled yourself through her. Through her you spent the most— perhaps the only—perfect time of your life. If you had lived in England during that time, then you might have turned back to us now—to me and Max. But you spent it in Italy, and that's where your eyes will always turn. You still have belief in happiness there, for you, for your boy —you have none in finding happiness here.

"Perhaps Max senses that. He's more sensitive

480

than you suppose. Perhaps I sense it too. And perhaps, Emmanuel, I don't want you to come back to work with Max; perhaps I would rather that you went back—to where you have been happy."

"You're sending me away from you again," he said; but she could catch no note of regret in his voice, only a great tenderness and understanding. "You don't want me here."

"No," Angela said firmly, "I don't think I want you here. I think that I love you too much, that I've seen you suffer too often. I can't bear any more—and there would be more, Emmanuel. Julian and you, Max and you, your boy and Julian's—I should be torn in pieces. I've lived too long to face suffering with any great fortitude now. Let me come and see you, and together we'll recapture little bits of happiness that we two —you and I—have known together. Some day you shall come back and see us here—but not yet. You've been too unhappy, you've been too hurt, you can't bear any more."

"Do you think that I shall be wildly happy in Milano?"

She laughed softly. "What a child you are! Do I think that wild happiness is found like brambles on every roadside? I know that you won't be wildly happy—but there you will, as I told you, still believe that happiness at least existed once upon a time."

He slipped down at the side of her chair,

481

resting his arms on her knee as he had done so often. She let her finger-tips touch his hair, and as she stroked it softly it came to her with a certainty that was almost overwhelming that this was the best loved of all her children—and perhaps for that very reason she must send him away.

"You see, if you stay, you, your presence, will throw everything out of gear, Emmanuel. Now I can manage to keep everything smooth for me—I have always been a selfish woman, remember. I love Max devotedly. I love Bill. Bill is so nice and dependable and solid and untroubled by speculations. I love Julian because he is my son, and possibly because he has done nothing that I once hoped he would do. It's as if Julian expended all his energy in the first years when he began to make a career. He was too clever, too brilliant, too good-looking. It wasn't real energy, it wasn't real love of his Party and its politics, and so it fizzled out, and he finds that he likes amusing himself much better than he ever liked work. But, oh, poor Julian!—he'll get so utterly sick of it one day, he'll want to get back, and by that time he'll have forgotten how to work and everyone will have forgotten him. Things move fairly smoothly as they are. Max gets angry sometimes when Julian asks for an unusually large cheque, but that doesn't happen every day, after all! If you came back there'd be two camps, my dear. Julian and Max in one, you and me in another, with Bill as a sort of umpire, who'd always give his decision in our favour.

"I've got to the age when I want peace—even if it's peace with a certain amount of dishonour. My fighting days are over. I couldn't even fight for you very long or very fiercely, Emmanuel. Julian won't ruin Max. He may make things less easy than they were ten years ago, there may be very little left when Max and I have finished with it all. Does that matter a lot, d'you think? The third generation will have been started, and the fourth—well, they must work a little harder, that's all."

Emmanuel took the hand which stroked his hair and held it pressed against his cheek. He knew that he was virtually accepting banishment, virtually being told that he must let Ordingly go. Hannah Rosenfelt might say what she pleased, Ordingly might never mean anything to Simeon, but it still meant something to him. It was his home, he had loved it, been proud of it, and the thought that it might never be his, that he might never look upon its beauties again except in an impersonal fashion, hurt him.

"Yes, I see," he said softly. "Only I have loved Ordingly. It's been—it's been part of my dreams for years."

"Dreams!" Angela repeated. "Dreams! Haven't I had dreams too? My dreams never held you in Milan, Julian wasting his life, and Bill hard-working, rather stolid, and utterly unromantic. I never saw Max old in my dreams. I never saw myself as a woman with grey hair and lines round my mouth. But we've had our dreams, my dear, you and I. Now we're waking, and all we can be thankful for is that we can say, 'Still my dreams are mine.' Only let's face it that they are dreams. You dreamed of Ordingly peopled with men and women you loved, and if you had it tomorrow, at least one of the rooms would be empty, Emmanuel. Do you really want Ordingly—without her?"

He did not reply, but she felt his whole body stiffen with the effort he was making to control himself, and knew that the hand which he still held against his cheek was wet.

"My dearest," Angela said softly. "My dear Emmanuel."

"No," he said, rather loudly and very firmly, as if the effort he made to render his voice unshaken changed it. "No, I couldn't dream of Juliet there. You're right. I can take my dreams with me down the noise of the Galleria, in the big square in front of the Duomo when the moon shines on it and makes it look like a great Christmas cake. My dreams belong to blue skies, to silver olive trees and rather theatrical cypresses. To pink-washed villas, baroque churches, little narrow streets in lake-side towns, and queer boats with three-cornered sails. They're wrapped up in apple-green brocade embroidered with small pink flowers—embroidered three hundred years ago for a priest by someone who wanted to make a thanksgiving. You're right—I think that you almost always have been right, darling—they'd die here. Here it's difficult to speak of the dead without a terrible solemnity. There—you can talk of them fr-reely and even laugh. Here, if people spoke of her they'd scarcely know what to call her—there, they still call her La For-rbez, and discuss which were her best songs. She said to me, 'I don't want to be forgotten,' and it would be less easy to remember—here. Nothing happened here except things which made us both wr-retched. Nothing happened there except things which made us happy—for that last year, at least."

"Your Wonderful Year! I'm so glad that you had, at least, that."

Emmanuel went on almost as if he spoke to himself. "And Simeon, he shall grow up one of the modern little democrats. How I dislike democracy! He'll want to be a little Fascist, and believe that he'd like to die for Italy. It's going to be a devil of a job to convince him that he'd better live for her! He'll go to a gymnasium, and wear strange cloaks and a pseudo-military cap. But he'll have sunshine, and people round him who laugh very easily, and he'll pr-robably alternate between fr-ree-thinking and intense religious convictions. I shall get ver-ry muddled about him, and Juliet will be ver-ry much amused! Guido will idolize him, Jaffe will scold him, and

485

then press ten-lire pieces into his hand. We shall plan that he will one day carr-ry on the business —Jaffe and Gollantz, and one day he will come and tell me that he has a voice and wants to be a singer, or that he would like to be a pr-riest, or an engineer or an airman."

His voice died away, and again there was silence between them. To Angela the moment was one of intense suffering. She wanted so much to beg him to stay, because she wanted him; she knew that she must tell him to go, because he no longer needed her and what she could give him.

He moved, rose, and stood beside her. "Yes, I'll go back," he said.

"When?"

For the first time he smiled. "Tomorrow. I must catch my dr-reams again. If I don't hurr-ry I may lose them in the crowd in the Galleria. Will you let me drive you down to Bond Street, so that I can say good-bye to Max?"

"Shan't I see you again?" Angela asked breathlessly.

"Of course. You will come to Milano—I don't even need to remember to call it Milan any longer!—and stay with me. You shall be treated like a queen, and given indigestible foods, and hear a gr-reat deal of music, and drink any number of rather indifferent wines. Simeon will call you Nonna Mia, and be expansive about his toys, and school and books. And we'll talk, my dear, as we've always been able to talk when we were together, and you'll find that I've r-remembered how to laugh again. You will come, say that you will!"

His eyes were shining; it seemed that years had dropped from him. She felt that he was like some lover returning to his mistress after a long separation. He was talking of things she did not know, of a life which she did not understand, and yet the closeness, the nearness, still persisted, and they were both happy in that companionship which had meant so much to them both.

"I shall come," she said unsteadily. "You make me want to come—now, for always, Emmanuel. Perhaps one day—I shall—oh, my dear, it would be—would be—"

"Tr-remendous fun!" he said, and thought the words were trivial. It seemed to Angela Gollantz that she had never heard any phrase which held promise of so much happiness.

They entered Max's office and found him immersed in his letters. Hannah Rosenfelt sat near him with her pad and the beautifully sharpened pencil—which Emmanuel always connected with her—in her fingers. Max looked up, took off his glasses, rose, and said: "My dear, this is very pleasant. I didn't expect you."

"Emmanuel brought me," Angela said. "He has something to tell you."

"Yes?" Hannah had risen and he nodded to her. She slipped away, moving softly as she always did, in spite of her heavy figure.

"Yes?" Max said again.

Emmanuel stood by the big desk—the desk which had belonged to a great Jewish statesman and later to the first Emmanuel Gollantz—and rested the tips of his fingers on the smooth top.

"I have decided that I was too precipitous," he said. "I came here without sufficient thought, I judged everything from my own standpoint, and did not try to understand yours. If I have upset or worr-ried you, will you please forgive me? Perhaps in extenuation I might say that I have been r-running my own business, and, having r-run it with some small success, I fancied that I could r-run this business of yours. I was wr-rong. I r-realize fully—because my mother has talked to me—that I have not the smallest r-right to interfere. It was a gr-reat impertinence. I hope that sometimes you will let us do business together. That if there is any small thing we can do for you in Milano—in Milan—that you will call on us, and that if we ask for your help or advice at any time, you will be so gener-rous as to give it."

Max said: "The generosity comes from you, my dear Emmanuel. It's very good of you to speak as you have done. Will you assure me that you mean, from your heart, all that you have said?"

"Ever-ry word!" He met his father's eyes and smiled back at him.

"You're a queer fellow!" Max stretched out

his hand and Emmanuel took it. "Remember, however things may appear, Emmanuel, whatever you may think, that I love you very dearly, and always shall. I may not understand you, but—you are the firstborn, you know."

"I shan't forget. I came to say good-bye. I'm leaving tomorrow."

"So soon! But why not stay? We want to see you, see the boy—"

"No!" Angela said. "He can't stay. He has to find something in—where was it, Emmanuel?—the Galleria."

Max said, "Is it necessary?"

Emmanuel, still smiling gravely, answered, "I think it is—very."

"Very well. If you can wait a moment, I should like to send back a little present to Simeon Jaffe, with my affectionate regards."

They were left alone, and Angela drew him to her as she sat in old Emmanuel's big carved chair.

"Let me say good-bye to you here," she whispered. "Good-bye, my dearest, and remember how to laugh again, and God bless you."

He bent and kissed her. "Good-bye, until you come to Italy. You will come, you promise?"

"I promise—one day. There, go quickly, you know how I hate to be made to cry. My dear—"

As he passed the door of Hannah's office, he opened it and looked in.

"Hannah," he whispered, "I'm going back. You were r-right." She looked up from her typewriter, massive, sallow, marred by the excessive marks of her race, but calm and very serene.

"I'm very happy," she said. "Mazal Tov."

"What was that word you told me this morning? Say it again."

"You told me that you were not a Jew," she said, her full lips smiling a little. "Learn to say it in English—'Enough for us'."

"I will," he assured her. "I pr-romise that I will."

Max came to the door of the taxi, spoke kindly, affectionately, insisting that he should take a little roll of notes to be spent on little Simeon. He was the father Emmanuel had always known, but added to his obvious concern that his son should remember that there was always a home for him at Ordingly, always a place for him in Gollantz and Son, was a strange little note of relief that a difficult situation had been put behind them both.

As he drove away, a gold snuff-box which had belonged to a king making a hard little bulge in his pocket, Emmanuel smiled.

"Dear Max!" he said softly. "He'll be a much happier man tonight than he was last night!"

Bill, wearing an impossibly thick and solid-looking overcoat, was waiting on Victoria platform. He grumbled because Emmanuel was going.

"Rushing away, leaving everything to come to Julian. You're throwing away more than you

490

know, going back to live in a foreign country, among people who don't speak your own language!"

"But that's just what they do speak," Emmanuel said.

"Nonsense! And Charles is as angry as I am! I can tell you that if I were in your shoes, if I had been the eldest son, this would have ended very differently. It's not fair to yourself, it's not fair to this little feller! I'm damned if it is! I saw Viva this morning lunching at the Savoy. She feels exactly the same."

"You and Viva are two tremendously nice people, Bill. Tell her I said so when you see her again."

"Reconsider it," Bill urged. "Think it over. Come back with me, and you and Charles and I can talk it over from every angle. It's too big a thing to throw away."

Emmanuel's smile widened. "That's so exactly what I feel, Bill."

"We're talking at cross purposes, or you're wilfully misunderstanding me—"

"I'm not. No good getting angr-ry, old chap. I've had sufficient difficulty with nurse. She thinks that I ought to stay in England in order to give her time to visit her aunt in Buxton! I've made up my mind. Angela is pleased, Max is pleased, Hannah Rosenfelt is pleased—"

"What the deuce has it got to do with Hannah Rosenfelt?"

"And young Simeon—look at him!"

Bill's fresh, stolid face cleared suddenly. He liked children and he found Simeon very attractive. He snapped his fingers at him and made noises which he believed to be acceptable to infant ears.

"Nice little beggar. That's what I feel, it's so damned hard on him. To go—"

Emmanuel said: "We're off. Don't lose any sleep over this business, Bill. I shan't! Come and see us next year."

"Good-bye, Emmanuel—you're a fool! But a nice fool. Good-bye, Simeon!"

Simeon gravely opened and shut a small fist, saying as he did so, "Ciao, ciao!"

"Which means?" Bill asked.

"Almost anything you want it to mean, Bill. Good-bye, good morning, good luck—Mazal Tov—anything! Ciao, Bill."

The train drew slowly out of Victoria Station, on through the dingy suburbs, through the empty hopfields of Kent on its way to Dover.

Sermione,
Lago di Garda,
   Italy.

SWEETHEARTS AND WIVES
by C. L. Skelton

This sequel to *The Maclarens* tells the story of a new generation of the famous Highland clan—its regiment, its wars, its loves, its honour. *Sweethearts and Wives* follows the Maclarens through the Egyptian Campaign to the Boer War. A credible tale of battle and bravery, and of what men call cowardice: a tale of officers and men, and of the women they love. For Donald Bruce it begins when he is unable to give the order to kill one of his own men. For Ian Maclaren, eldest son of the Laird, it begins with his passionate love for Naomi— a half-caste, a bastard and forbidden. This is their story and that of their fathers—proud men with their strong memories of the past.

MAN ON FIRE
by A. J. Quinnell

Creasy and Guido had served together in the French Foreign Legion. They knew all about discipline, guns and grenades, and were first-class soldiers. Now Creasy had no purpose in life and was fast becoming an alcoholic, until Guido finds him a job as a bodyguard to the daughter of a rich Italian family. A close and happy relationship develops and Creasy enjoys life once more. But then something terrible happens, and Creasy sets out to exact a fearful revenge.

I KNOW MY LOVE
by Catherine Gaskin

Ballarat, Australia, 1854 . . . a bleak encampment of tents in a valley. Here 30,000 men scramble for the gold under their feet by day—and every night drink it, gamble it away, or spend it on their women. Strange circumstances at Ballarat bring two of these women together. Rose Maguire, ravishing and flamboyant, who meets life with open arms and a calculating brain . . . Emma Brown, lonely, shy and gentle—who has killed two men. Their lives are inextricably tangled when they fall in love with the same man.

BREAD UPON THE WATERS
by Irwin Shaw

Allen Strand and his family were ready for dinner, except for his teenage daughter who had not returned from a tennis match. When she finally did, it was in the company of a very bloody stranger whom she had rescued from muggers in Central Park. The stranger, an eminent lawyer—and a lonely man—was strongly attracted by the harmony of the Strand family. As his involvement with the family increased, so did his desire to use his influence and wealth on their behalf. For Allen Strand it becomes a struggle for the survival of his family against the overwhelming efforts of their would-be benefactor.

TESS OF THE D'URBERVILLES
by Thomas Hardy

This age-old tale of the maid who goes to the greenwood and returns a maiden no more becomes in Hardy's hands an indictment of all the crimes and hypocrisies of 19th century England. Of all of the author's heroines, the milkmaid Tess is, by common consent, the most touching, and of all his novels this is the one with the most universal scope.

THE KEY TO REBECCA
by Ken Follett

"Our spy in Cairo is the greatest hero of them all", said Rommel in 1942. The man referred to was Alex Wolff, who presented as great a danger to British hopes of containing the German army as Rommel himself. This story of the Second World War is woven around Wolff, who arrived out of the desert, armed with a radio set, a copy of Daphne du Maurier's *Rebecca*, and his own conviction that he would triumph. Only Major William Vandam could stop Wolff's infiltration of British troop movements and strategic plans. A dramatic novel of a subtle, intricate relationship between spy and spy-catcher, between pursuer and his prey. The stakes are the survival of the British in North Africa . . . or the collapse of the resistance to the Axis powers.

XPD
by Len Deighton

On the morning of June 11th, 1940, Winston Churchill, Prime Minister of Great Britain, met in secret with the would-be conqueror of Europe: Adolph Hitler. Forty years later, the truth about that meeting remains Britain's most closely guarded secret—a secret still so dangerous that anyone who might reveal it is marked down for "expedient demise": XPD . . . Set in the summer of 1979 this novel of intrigue and suspense moves from the mansions of Hollywood, to the back streets of London, from Lake Geneva to the Baltic Sea, until it reaches a climax on a film set of the Fuhrer's study under the shadow of a Nazi eagle.

LOVING
by Danielle Steel

Bettina Daniels had everything: youth, beauty, a glamorous life that circled the globe—everything her father's love, fame and money could buy. Then, without warning, Justin Daniels was gone. Bettina stood alone before a mountain of debts and a world full of strangers—men who promised her many things, who tempted her with their words of love. Bettina had to live her own life, take her own chance, but could she pay the bittersweet price of . . . loving.

SEASON OF PASSION
by Danielle Steel

Kate and Tom were the original star-crossed lovers. Kate, a beautiful model, Tom, a successful American football star at the peak of his career. It almost seemed they were made to share their lives together. Then one day the bubble bursts. A gunshot ends Tom's career and puts him in a sanitorium—forever. Kate is left alone in a world with nothing to live for. And the fear that she will never love again.

NO LOVE LOST
by Helen Van Slyke

Pauline and Howard Tresher live in a twelve room apartment on Fifth Avenue. They have two children, a son called James and a daughter Lindsay. A quarrel between her parents—sparked off by Howard's many infidelities—is overheard by Lindsay who, at ten years old, is not quite sure what it is about but realises that something is radically wrong. Much was wrong at that time because it was 1930, the time of the Depression, and Adele, one of Lindsay's friends, was left fatherless by suicide. The story of Lindsay and Adele, James, Geoff the man Lindsay marries, their loves and fortunes through World War II and the strange twists that emotions and fate take, makes this an unusual and absorbingly readable narrative.

BLOODLINE
by Sidney Sheldon

Elizabeth Roffe was the only daughter of one of the world's richest and most powerful men. When, without warning, he died mysteriously while mountain climbing in the French Alps, she had to take command of the family-owned drug company, a giant international pharmaceutical manufacturer. As Roffe and Sons' new president, she discovers that someone unknown in the highest echelon of the firm is not only out to destroy the company, but is determined to kill her.

WOMEN IN LOVE
by D. H. Lawrence

This novel, which Lawrence himself considered his best, is the story of the lives and emotional conflicts of two sisters. Gudrun and Ursula Brangwen, who also appeared in *The Rainbow*, live in a Midlands colliery town. Ursula falls in love with Birkin (a self-portrait of Lawrence) and Gudrun has a tragic affair with Gerald, the son of the local colliery owner. These four, and such well-drawn characters as Hermione, the sensuous and intellectual hostess and Loerke the sculptor, clash in thought, passion and belief. The tale reaches its tragic conclusion in the Alps as the reader is gripped by the deeply held convictions about love and modern society.

THE MACLARENS
by C. L. Skelton

The first volume of the author's projected "Regiment Quartet", a saga which will take one family through nearly a hundred years of history, is a story of love, war and honour, spanning three continents. The Maclarens are a famous Highland clan. Andrew Maclaren, young, sensitive, is serving with his regiment, the 148th Foot, in India when the Mutiny of 1857 breaks out. After the shocking carnage, he discovers Maud, raped and homeless, who becomes inextricably involved in his life. But the good of the Regiment would be damaged by his marrying a sullied woman.

THE OSTERMAN WEEKEND
by Robert Ludlum

John Tanner, network news director, is looking forward to a weekend party with his closest friends—the Ostermans, the Tremaynes, and the Cardones. But then the CIA tells him that they are all suspected Soviet agents: fanatical, traitorous killers working for Omega, a massive Communist conspiracy. From this moment Tanner and his family are caught up in a nightmare whirlpool of terror, helpless isolation, violence and slaughter. Until the shattering climax, Tanner cannot know who are his friends, who are his implacable, deadly enemies . . .

ROUGH DIAMOND
by James Broom Lynne

Born two hundred million years ago, the 8-carat diamond was to mark the beginning of a long journey into fear and intrigue. Its discovery was destined to play the catalyst in the lives of many people. The reader is taken along the unique corridors of the diamond monopolies and into Central Africa; to Sierra Leone and across the Atlantic to Brazil and the murderous Quaqueros of Colombia, and to the urbane, but no less dangerous cities of London, New York and Geneva. A strong cast of characters tells the story of diamonds, from the mines to the glittering showcases of Tiffany's. But, between discovery and final polishing lies double-dealing, theft and murder.

THE FOXES OF HARROW
by Frank Yerby

Set in New Orleans and Louisiana State in the troubled days between 1825 and the Civil War, *The Foxes of Harrow* has a broad sweep and is charged with colour and action, with white-hot animosities, with strife and warfare and the clash of races. Dominating this fast-moving story is the figure of Stephen Fox, who is loved by three women, who has the face of an angel and a mind which can conjure visions of both beauty and evil.

KENILWORTH
by Sir Walter Scott

The story is based on the tradition of the tragic fate, in the reign of Queen Elizabeth, of the beautiful Amy Robsart, daughter of Sir Hugh Robsart of Devon. Beguiled by her charms, the Earl of Leicester, the Queen's favourite, has secretly married her and established her at Cumnor Place. Caught in a net of ambition and intrigue Leicester is forced to acknowledge that Amy is his wife, thereby calling down on himself the furious anger of the jealous Queen. A sycophant, Richard Varney, convinces Leicester that Amy is guilty of infidelity, and in a passion Leicester orders her death.

CAPTAINS COURAGEOUS
by Rudyard Kipling

The story of how an accident changes the character of a rich, spoilt boy called Harvey Cheyne. Swept overboard from a liner bound for Europe, he is picked up by a trawler and forced to work hard to earn his keep. The skipper, Disko Troop, refuses to turn his boat around and land Harvey, so it is nearly a year later when he is reunited with his parents. His father, an American millionaire, is pleased to find that this "unsatisfied dough-faced youth" has become a respectful, and healthy young man.

WINTER KILLS
by Richard Condon

Fourteen years after the assassination of Tim Kegan, late President of the United States, his extraordinarily wealthy and powerful family learns, at a death-bed confession, that their beloved brother and son had not been murdered by a lone, psychopathic killer but had been the victim of a conspiracy. Satirically it is a revelation of a people who had been able to accept the death of their leader as an entertainment event; as something to be accepted and forgotten. Tim Kegan's family were no different—but they were forced against their wills to follow the chains of actual and false evidence.

THE JUDAS TREE
by A. J. Cronin

The story of a man who ruins his own life, and the lives of the four women who have the misfortune to come under the spell of his charm, by his selfishness, weakness, and capacity for self-deception. David Moray begins his professional life as a medical student, and it is then that he falls in love with Mary Douglas. They agree to marry; but Moray is persuaded to throw Mary over for the sake of a tempting business partnership, with marriage to another woman as part of the bargain.

FOLLOW THE DRUM
by James Leasor

India, in the mid-nineteenth century, was virtually run by a British commercial concern, the Honourable East India Company, whose directors would pay tribute to one Indian ruler and then depose another in their efforts to maintain their balance sheet of power and profit. But great changes were already casting shadows across the land, and when a stupid order was given to Indian troops to use cartridges greased with cow fat and pig lard (one animal sacred to the Hindus and the other abhorrent to Moslems) there was mutiny, changing the lives of millions for ever.

THE MATLOCK PAPER
by Robert Ludlum

James Matlock, Professor of English at Carlyle University, is assigned by the United States government to investigate what seems to be a large-scale dope and prostitution business. Matlock has a motive for accepting the assignment, his younger brother had died from an overdose of heroin. But would he have accepted if he knew the mental and physical agony it would bring his beloved Patricia? Would he have accepted if he knew the terror and violence it would bring to his own life and to the people around him?